COMPOSITE MATHEMATICS

FOR CLASS – V

Enriched with *Math Lab Activities*
and *Multiple Choice Questions*

Dr. R.S. AGGARWAL
M.Sc., Ph.D.
VIKAS AGGARWAL

S. CHAND & COMPANY LTD.

(AN ISO 9001 : 2000 COMPANY)

RAM NAGAR, NEW DELHI - 110 055

S. CHAND & COMPANY LTD.

(An ISO 9001 : 2000 Company)
Head Office: 7361, RAM NAGAR, NEW DELHI - 110 055
Phone: 23672080-81-82, 9899107446, 9911310888
Fax: 91-11-23677446

Shop at: schandgroup.com; e-mail: info@schandgroup.com

Branches :

AHMEDABAD : 1st Floor, Heritage, Near Gujarat Vidhyapeeth, Ashram Road, **Ahmedabad** - 380 014,
Ph: 27541965, 27542369, ahmedabad@schandgroup.com

BENGALURU : No. 6, Ahuja Chambers, 1st Cross, Kumara Krupa Road, **Bengaluru** - 560 001,
Ph: 22268048, 22354008, bangalore@schandgroup.com

BHOPAL : Bajaj Tower, Plot No. 243, Lala Lajpat Rai Colony, Raisen Road, **Bhopal** - 462 011,
Ph: 4274723. bhopal@schandgroup.com

CHANDIGARH : S.C.O. 2419-20, First Floor, Sector - 22-C (Near Aroma Hotel), **Chandigarh** -160 022,
Ph: 2725443, 2725446, chandigarh@schandgroup.com

CHENNAI : 152, Anna Salai, **Chennai** - 600 002, Ph:28460026, 28460027, chennai@schandgroup.com

COIMBATORE : No. 5, 30 Feet Road, Krishnasamy Nagar, Ramanathapuram, **Coimbatore** -641 004, Ph. 0422-2323620,
coimbatore@schandgroup.com **(Marketing Office)**

CUTTACK : 1st Floor, Bhartia Tower, Badambadi, **Cuttack** - 753 009, Ph: 2332580; 2332581, cuttack@schandgroup.com

DEHRADUN : 1st Floor, 20, New Road, Near Dwarka Store, **Dehradun** - 248 001,
Ph: 2711101, 2710861, dehradun@schandgroup.com

GUWAHATI : Pan Bazar, **Guwahati** - 781 001, Ph: 2738811, 2735640 guwahati@schandgroup.com

HYDERABAD : Padma Plaza, H.No. 3-4-630, Opp. Ratna College, Narayanaguda, **Hyderabad** - 500 029,
Ph: 24651135, 24744815, hyderabad@schandgroup.com

JAIPUR : A-14, Janta Store Shopping Complex, University Marg, Bapu Nagar, **Jaipur** - 302 015,
Ph: 2719126, jaipur@schandgroup.com

JALANDHAR : Mai Hiran Gate, **Jalandhar** - 144 008, Ph: 2401630, 5000630, jalandhar@schandgroup.com

JAMMU : 67/B, B-Block, Gandhi Nagar, **Jammu** - 180 004, (M) 09878651464 **(Marketing Office)**

KOCHI : Kachapilly Square, Mullassery Canal Road, Ernakulam, **Kochi** - 682 011, Ph: 2378207, cochin@schandgroup.com

KOLKATA : 285/J, Bipin Bihari Ganguli Street, **Kolkata** - 700 012, Ph: 22367459, 22373914, kolkata@schandgroup.com

LUCKNOW : Mahabeer Market, 25 Gwynne Road, Aminabad, **Lucknow** - 226 018, Ph: 2626801, 2284815, lucknow@schandgroup.com

MUMBAI : Blackie House, 103/5, Walchand Hirachand Marg, Opp. G.P.O., **Mumbai** - 400 001,
Ph: 22690881, 22610885, mumbai@schandgroup.com

NAGPUR : Karnal Bag, Model Mill Chowk, Umrer Road, **Nagpur** - 440 032, Ph: 2723901, 2777666 nagpur@schandgroup.com

PATNA : 104, Citicentre Ashok, Govind Mitra Road, **Patna** - 800 004, Ph: 2300489, 2302100, patna@schandgroup.com

PUNE : 291/1, Ganesh Gayatri Complex, 1st Floor, Somwarpeth, Near Jain Mandir,
Pune - 411 011, Ph: 64017298, pune@schandgroup.com **(Marketing Office)**

RAIPUR : Kailash Residency, Plot No. 4B, Bottle House Road, Shankar Nagar, **Raipur** - 492 007,
Ph: 09981200834, raipur@schandgroup.com **(Marketing Office)**

RANCHI : Flat No. 104, Sri Draupadi Smriti Apartments, East of Jaipal Singh Stadium, Neel Ratan Street, Upper Bazar,
Ranchi - 834 001, Ph: 2208761,
ranchi@schandgroup.com **(Marketing Office)**

SILIGURI : 122, Raja Ram Mohan Roy Road, East Vivekanandapally, P.O., **Siliguri**-734001,
Dist., Jalpaiguri, (W.B.) Ph. 0353-2520750 **(Marketing Office)**

VISAKHAPATNAM : Plot No. 7, 1st Floor, Allipuram Extension, Opp. Radhakrishna Towers, Seethammadhara North Extn.,
Visakhapatnam - 530 013, (M) 09347580841, visakhapatnam@schandgroup.com **(Marketing Office)**

First Edition 1999
Sebsequent Editions and Reprints 2000, 2001, 2002, 2003, 2004, 2005,
2006 (Twice), 2007, 2008, 2009 (Twice), 2010
Revised Edition 2011

ISBN : 81-219-2728-5   **Code :** 14C 526

PRINTED IN INDIA
By Rajendra Ravindra Printers Pvt. Ltd., 7361, Ram Nagar, New Delhi -110 055
and published by S. Chand & Company Ltd., 7361, Ram Nagar, New Delhi -110 055.

Preface

In response to the tremendous response and numerous feedbacks received from teachers and our readers, we hereby feel great pleasure to bring out the new **multicoloured** edition of this book.

As you are well aware, the primary classes form the foundation of a student's knowledge. It is at this very level that a child grasps the most fundamental concepts of mathematics, which he goes on to apply to all sorts of fields in higher classes. So, it becomes quite essential to make him understand these concepts very clearly.

The latest syllabus prescribed by NCERT stresses on practical approach to studies, so that the child can learn the basic concepts from things around him. Further, the concept of CCE (Continuous and Comprehensive Evaluation) introduced by CBSE seeks to test the knowledge of basic concepts of a child through objective-type, very-short answer and short-answer questions supported by Fill in the blanks and True-False type of questions.

This new edition of the book is fully in accordance with the principles of CCE.

The salient features of the book are:

1. The theory is presented in a very simple language and supported with examples from everyday life.

2. A new section called **'ACTIVITY-TIME'** has been added to each chapter containing the relevant Maths-Lab activities which the child can easily practice to understand the concept well.

3. A new section called **'CCE DRILL'** has been added to each chapter. This consists of two parts:

   (a) Question Bag-1 consisting of multiple-choice questions based on the content of the chapter.

   (b) Question Bag-2 consisting of a self-assessment test in which short-answer questions, True-False questions and Fill in the blanks have been given

4. More questions for practice have been added to enable the child to have enough practice on each topic.

We extend our grateful thanks to the entire management and editorial staff of S.Chand and Co. Ltd. who took great pains to get the book published in such a nice form.

Suggestions for the improvement of the book are always welcome.

Authors

Contents

1 REVISION

1. Write the Roman numeral for each of the following Hindu-Arabic numerals:
   (a) 18   (b) 26   (c) 33   (d) 39   (e) 44
   (f) 65   (g) 77   (h) 82   (i) 91   (j) 99

2. Write the Hindu-Arabic numerals corresponding to each of the following:
   (a) LXVI   (b) XXXI   (c) XLV   (d) LXVIII   (e) XC
   (f) XCVII   (g) LXXIII   (h) LXXXI   (i) LXXIX   (j) XCV

3. Observe the periods and write the number names:
   (a) 5,37,412   (b) 88,088   (c) 636,905   (d) 1,01,001
   (e) 49,06,090   (f) 14,00,140   (g) 9,536,087   (h) 8,080,080

4. Express the following numbers in figures, placing the commas at the right places:
   (a) Twenty thousand twenty two
   (b) Five lakh five thousand five hundred five
   (c) Four lakh forty thousand forty
   (d) Ten lakh thirty
   (e) Two hundred six thousand five hundred one
   (f) One million three hundred fifty-four thousand fifteen
   (g) Two million thirty-two thousand one hundred eight
   (h) Five million eight

5. (a) How many thousands make a lakh?
   (b) How many lakhs make a million?

6. Find the place value of each of the digits in the following numerals:
   (a) 28,967   (b) 5,30,194   (c) 52,67,908

7. (a) Find the difference between the place value and face value of 9 in 3,09,812.
   (b) Find the difference between the place values of 1 and 6 in the numeral 17,68,905.
   (c) Find the difference between the place values of 7 in the numeral 72,08,763.

8. Write each of the following numbers in expanded form:
   (a) 80,656   (b) 4,05,077   (c) 18,65,540

9. Write in short form:
   (a) 2,00,000 + 8,000 + 6 = ...
   (b) 10,00,000 + 10,000 + 500 + 50 = ...
   (c) 20,00,000 + 3,00,000 + 4,000 + 4 = ...

10. *Compare the numbers and put the correct symbol >, < or = in the placeholder:*
    (a) 10,056 ☐ 10,506   (b) 72,070 ☐ 70,270
    (c) 5,50,505 ☐ 5,55,050   (d) 2,31,031 ☐ 2,31,310
    (e) 90,999 ☐ 99,099   (f) 28,31,467 ☐ 28,34,167

11. (a) Write the smallest number of different digits formed by using the digits 5, 9, 3,1 and 0.
    (b) Write the greatest number of different digits formed by using the digits 2, 0, 8, 7 and 5.

12. (a) Write the smallest 4-digit number using the digits 6, 0, 5, repeating 5 twice.
    (b) Write the greatest 4-digit number using the digits 3, 6 and 9, using 6 twice.

13. *Add:*
    (a)
```
   37548
   20976
+ 116394
```
    (b)
```
  205968
  346593
+  54876
```
    (c)
```
  1650784
   439567
+   86249
```
    (d)
```
   283967
  3032188
+    9793
```

14. The cost of a refrigerator is Rs 48748 and the cost of a motorcycle is Rs 29657 more than that of a refrigerator. What is the total cost of both the refrigerator and the motorcycle?

15. In an election, 498656 votes were found valid, 6768 votes were found invalid and 83865 persons did not cast their votes. How many votes were registered in all?

16. *Subtract:*
    (a)
```
  510324
- 274569
```
    (b)
```
  801605
- 534578
```
    (c)
```
  3240202
- 1785696
```

17. The sum of two numbers is 102003. If one of them is 64597, find the other.

18. The difference between two numbers is 78489. If the larger number is 350102, find the smaller number.

19. *Fill in the placeholders:*
    (a) 168574 × 10 = ☐   (b) 39623 × 100 = ☐
    (c) 9785 × 1000 = ☐   (d) 207 × 300 = ☐
    (e) 725 × 6000 = ☐   (f) 585 × 9000 = ☐

20. *Find the following products:*
    (a)
```
  23719
  ×  87
```
    (b)
```
  9647
 × 238
```
    (c)
```
  8765
 × 306
```

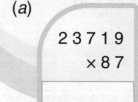
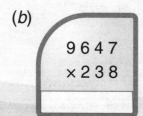
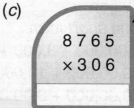

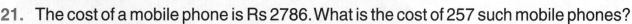

21. The cost of a mobile phone is Rs 2786. What is the cost of 257 such mobile phones?

22. *In each of the following division sums, find the quotient and remainder:*

(*a*) 66863 ÷ 76   (*b*) 431035 ÷ 49   (*c*) 850658 ÷ 97

(*d*) 132507 ÷ 10   (*e*) 1046549 ÷ 100   (*f*) 235174 ÷ 1000

23. An aeroplane takes 17 hours to fly a distance of 15419 km. How far does it fly in one hour?

24. The cost of a fluorescent tube is Rs 57. How many such tubes can be bought for Rs 19893?

25. List all the factors of: (*a*) 48   (*b*) 120

26. (*a*) Write first five multiples of 7.

    (*b*) Write first four multiples of 18.

27. (*a*) Write down the first 20 odd numbers.

    (*b*) Write down all even numbers between 70 and 90.

28. *Circle the prime numbers:*

2	5	9	13	17	21	27	31	37	43	49	54
63	68	69	71	73	75	77	83	85	87	91	93
95	97	99									

29. *Find the H.C.F. of:*

(*a*) 32 and 56   (*b*) 90 and 105

30. *Find the L.C.M. of:*

(*a*) 6 and 8   (*b*) 15, 20 and 30

31. *Fill in the missing numerals:*

(a) $\dfrac{9}{16} = \dfrac{27}{\boxed{}}$ (b) $\dfrac{5}{13} = \dfrac{\boxed{}}{78}$ (c) $\dfrac{11}{17} = \dfrac{\boxed{}}{51}$

32. Find an equivalent fraction of $\dfrac{75}{90}$ with

(*a*) numerator 15   (*b*) denominator 36

(*c*) numerator 35   (*d*) denominator 60

33. *Put the correct symbol > or < in the place holder:*

(a) $\dfrac{5}{9} \ \boxed{} \ \dfrac{8}{9}$ (b) $\dfrac{19}{20} \ \boxed{} \ \dfrac{17}{20}$ (c) $\dfrac{3}{8} \ \boxed{} \ \dfrac{7}{8}$

(d) $\dfrac{7}{11} \ \boxed{} \ \dfrac{7}{15}$ (e) $\dfrac{15}{23} \ \boxed{} \ \dfrac{15}{19}$ (f) $\dfrac{21}{20} \ \boxed{} \ \dfrac{21}{29}$

34. *Arrange the following fractions in ascending order:*

(a) $\dfrac{2}{7}, \dfrac{3}{7}, \dfrac{6}{7}, \dfrac{5}{7}$ (b) $\dfrac{13}{19}, \dfrac{15}{19}, \dfrac{2}{19}, \dfrac{10}{19}$

(c) $\dfrac{1}{7}, \dfrac{1}{4}, \dfrac{1}{2}, \dfrac{1}{5}, \dfrac{1}{3}$ (d) $\dfrac{5}{6}, \dfrac{5}{10}, \dfrac{5}{8}, \dfrac{5}{11}, \dfrac{5}{9}$

35. *Add:*

(a) $\dfrac{3}{7} + \dfrac{2}{7}$ (b) $\dfrac{2}{9} + \dfrac{5}{9}$ (c) $\dfrac{3}{8} + \dfrac{4}{8}$ (d) $\dfrac{3}{11} + \dfrac{4}{11} + \dfrac{2}{11}$

36. *Find the difference:*

(a) $\dfrac{4}{5} - \dfrac{2}{5}$ (b) $\dfrac{5}{7} - \dfrac{2}{7}$ (c) $\dfrac{9}{13} - \dfrac{7}{13}$ (d) $\dfrac{11}{15} - \dfrac{7}{15}$

37. *Convert each of the following mixed numerals into an improper fraction:*

(a) $6\dfrac{5}{7}$ (b) $9\dfrac{3}{8}$ (c) $5\dfrac{11}{17}$

38. *Convert the following improper fractions into mixed numerals:*

(a) $\dfrac{107}{9}$ (b) $\dfrac{189}{11}$ (c) $\dfrac{212}{15}$

39. *Express each of the following fractions as a decimal:*

(a) $\dfrac{3}{10}$ (b) $\dfrac{7}{100}$ (c) $\dfrac{23}{100}$ (d) $\dfrac{9}{1000}$ (e) $\dfrac{79}{1000}$

40. *Express each of the following as a fraction:*

(a) 0.6   (b) 0.75   (c) 32.5   (d) 0.064   (e) 65.189

41. *Write each of the following decimals in an expanded form:*

(a) 18.956   (b) 402.05   (c) 59.003

42. *Add the following amounts:*

(a)
```
  Rs 256.83
  Rs 308.75
+ Rs  98.06
_____
```

(b)
```
  Rs  80.96
  Rs 119.18
+ Rs 763.38
_____
```

(c)
```
  Rs 100.28
  Rs   9.96
+ Rs  75.87
_____
```

43. *Subtract:*

(a)
```
  Rs 787.85
- Rs  94.92
_____
```

(b)
```
  Rs 436.56
- Rs 378.64
_____
```

(c)
```
  Rs 926.39
- Rs 834.68
_____
```

44. Sarita went to a confectionery store. She purchased biscuits worth Rs 105.60, bread worth Rs 19.75, juice tins worth Rs 228.65 and toffees worth Rs 8.80. She gave a five-hundred rupee note to the shopkeeper. What amount did she get back?

45. A cricket bat costs Rs 376.65. What is the cost of 35 such bats?

46. Rahul bought 7 chocolates for Rs 68.25. What is the cost of 1 chocolate?

47. *Change:*

(a) 2 hm 3 dam into metres

(b) 8 m 56 mm into mm

(c) 3 quintals 65 kg into kg

(d) 2 *kl* 5 *l* into *l*

(e) 15 *l* 730 *ml* into *ml*

(f) 12 kg 220 g into g

48. *Change:*

(a) 5530 mm into m and cm

(b) 2685 *ml* into *l* and *ml*

(c) 565 kg into quintals and kg

(d) 8760 g into kg and g

49. *Add:*

(a) 68 kg 756 g and 86 kg 968 g

(b) 57 m 68 cm and 75 m 86 cm

(c) 26 km 774 m and 84 km 668 m

(d) 54 *l* 565 *ml* and 79 *l* 785 *ml*

50. *Find the difference between:*

(a) 21 m 12 cm and 7 m 84 cm

(b) 105 km 413 m and 39 km 788 m

(c) 467 kg 205 g and 278 kg 457 g

(d) 92 *l* 142 *ml* and 65 *l* 566 *ml*

51. An electrician bought 500 metres of wire. He sold 43 m 75 cm of the wire to one customer and 158 m 50 cm of it to another customer. What length of wire is now left with him?

52. A tin full of pulses weighs 15 kg 200 g. If the empty tin weighs 1 kg 375 g, what is the net weight of the pulses contained in the tin?

53. An oil tanker has a capacity of 100 litres. If it contains 76 *l* 275 *ml* of oil, how much more oil it can have?

54. *Which of the following figures are polygons?*

(a)

(b)

(c)

(d)

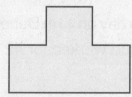

(e)

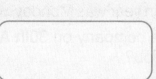

(f)

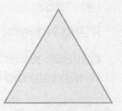

55. *Fill in the blanks:*

(a) A .... has no length, breadth or thickness.

(b) A .... has only one end-point.

(c) A curve which does not intersect itself is called a ....

(d) A polygon is formed of .... or more line segments.

(e) The diagonals of a .... are always equal.

(f) .... is the longest chord of a circle.

(g) The perimeter of a circle is called its ....

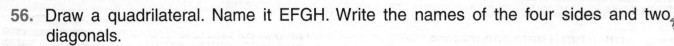

56. Draw a quadrilateral. Name it EFGH. Write the names of the four sides and two diagonals.

57. A circle has a radius of 12 cm. How long is its diameter?

58. A circle has a diameter of 16 cm. How long is its radius?

59. *Find the perimeter of each of the following figures:*

(*a*)
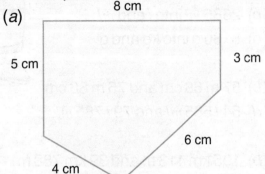

(*b*)
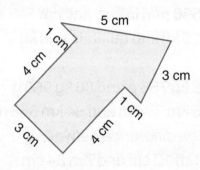

60. *Find the perimeter of:*

   (*a*) a rectangle of length = 9 m 35 cm and breadth = 6 m 45 cm

   (*b*) a square of each side = 8 m 35 cm

61. *What time will it be:*

   (*a*) 2 hours 30 minutes after 10 : 40 p.m?   (*b*) 30 minutes before 12 noon?

   (*c*) 1 hour 50 minutes after 11 : 20 a.m?   (*d*) 10 hours after 3 a.m?

62. Ashish started writing a letter at 9 : 25 a.m. He finished writing at 11 : 05 a.m. How much time did he take to write the letter?

63. A seminar started at 10 : 10 a.m. and it lasted for 3 hours 35 minutes. At what time was the seminar concluded?

64. *Which of the following are leap years?*

   (*a*) 1982   (*b*) 1992   (*c*) 2002   (*d*) 2100

65. If 2nd November in a certain year was Monday, what was the day on 11th December?

66. Kailash joined service in a company on 30th April, 2010 and worked for 42 days. On what date did he leave the job?

In class IV, we have learnt reading and writing of Roman numerals upto 100. In this section, we shall extend learning of reading and writing of these numerals upto 500.

We already know that there are seven basic symbols to write any Roman numeral.

These symbols with their corresponding Hindu-Arabic numerals are given below:

Roman Numeral	I	V	X	L	C	D	M
Hindu-Arabic Numeral	1	5	10	50	100	500	1000

In Roman system, there is no symbol for zero.

This system is also not a place value system.

RULES FOR FORMING ROMAN NUMERALS

Rule 1.	*Repetition of a Roman numeral means addition.*
Caution:	(1) Only I, X, C, M can be repeated.
	(2) V, L and D cannot be repeated.
	(3) No numeral can be repeated more than 3 times.
Examples:	II = 1 + 1 = 2, III = 1 + 1 + 1 = 3,
	XX = 10 + 10 = 20, XXX = 10 + 10 + 10 = 30,
	CC = 100 + 100 = 200, CCC = 100 + 100 + 100 = 300.
Rule 2.	*A smaller numeral written to the right of a larger numeral is always added to the larger numeral.*
Examples:	VI = 5 + 1 = 6, VII = 5 + 1 + 1 = 7, VIII = 5 + 1 + 1 + 1 = 8,
	XI = 10 + 1 = 11, XII = 10 + 1 + 1 = 12, XIII = 10 + 1 + 1 + 1 = 13, XV = 10 + 5 = 15,
	LX = 50 + 10 = 60, LXX = 50 + 10 + 10 = 70, LXXX = 50 + 10 + 10 + 10 = 80,
	CX = 100 + 10 = 110, CXX = 100 + 10 + 10 = 120,
	CXXX = 100 + 10 + 10 + 10 = 130, CL = 100 + 50 = 150.
Rule 3.	*A smaller numeral written to the left of a larger numeral is always subtracted from the larger numeral.*

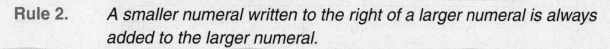

Caution : (1) V, L and D are never subtracted.

(2) I can be subtracted from V and X only.

Examples : IV = 5 − 1 = 4, IX = 10 − 1 = 9

(3) X can be subtracted from L and C only.

Examples : XL = 50 − 10 = 40, XC = 100 − 10 = 90.

(4) C can be subtracted from D and M only.

Example : CD = 500 − 100 = 400.

Rule 4. *When a smaller numeral is placed between two larger numerals, then it is always subtracted from the larger numeral immediately following it.*

Examples : XIV = 10 + (5 − 1) = 14, XIX = 10 + (10 − 1) = 19,

CXIV = 100 + 10 + (5 − 1) = 114,

CXC = 100 + (100 − 10) = 190.

WRITING ROMAN NUMERALS FOR HINDU-ARABIC NUMERALS UPTO 500

The numerals 1 to 9; 10, 20, 30, 40,............, 90 and 100, 200, ..., 500 can be written in Roman numerals using the above rules as shown below:

Hindu-Arabic Numeral	Roman Numeral	Hindu-Arabic Numeral	Roman Numeral	Hindu-Arabic Numeral	Roman Numeral
1	I	10	X	100	C
2	II	20	XX	200	CC
3	III	30	XXX	300	CCC
4	IV	40	XL	400	CD
5	V	50	L	500	D
6	VI	60	LX		
7	VII	70	LXX		
8	VIII	80	LXXX		
9	IX	90	XC		

When we write any number in Roman numeral, we write it in expanded form first and then write the Roman numeral for the hundreds first, followed by the Roman numeral for the tens and then for the ones to the right of it.

Thus, we have:

(a) 89 = 80 + 9 = LXXX + IX = LXXXIX	(b) 97 = 90 + 7 = XC + VII = XCVII	(c) 146 = 100 + 40 + 6 = C + XL + VI = CXLVI
(d) 199 = 100 + 90 + 9 = C + XC + IX = CXCIX	(e) 258 = 200 + 50 + 8 = CC + L + VIII = CCLVIII	(f) 335 = 300 + 30 + 5 = CCC + XXX +V = CCCXXXV

(g) 410 = 400 + 10 = CD + X = CDX	(h) 444 = 400 + 40 + 4 = CD + XL + IV = CDXLIV

Similarly, we have:

(a) CIX = C + IX = 100 + 9 = 109	(b) CLXIX = C + L + X + IX = 100 + 50 + 10 + 9 = 169	(c) CXCIV= C + XC + IV = 100 + 90 + 4 = 194

(d) CCXLVII = CC + XL + VII = 200 + 40 + 7 = 247	(e) CDXXXVIII = CD + XXX + VIII = 400 + 30 + 8 = 438

EXERCISE 2

1. Write the Roman numeral for each of the following Hindu-Arabic numerals:

   (a) 78   (b) 189   (c) 247   (d) 196   (e) 365
   (f) 399   (g) 449   (h) 495   (i) 344   (j) 466

2. Write the Hindu-Arabic numerals corresponding to each of the following:

   (a) LXIX   (b) XCI   (c) CXLVI   (d) CXCII
   (e) CCCLXXXV   (f) CCLIX   (g) CCXCVI   (h) CXCVI
   (i) CCLXVI   (j) CCCXIII

3. Which of the following are meaningless?

   (a) IC   (b) CI   (c) IL   (d) LI   (e) VC
   (f) CV   (g) CXXXXVI   (h) CCCCXVI   (i) LLIV   (j) CCV

4. Compare and put the correct symbol >, < or = in the placeholder:

   (a) XCIII ◯ CXIII   (b) CD ◯ CCCXC

   (c) CCLIX ◯ CCXLI   (d) CDXL ◯ CDLX

   (e) CXLIX ◯ CLXXXIX   (f) CCXXVI ◯ CCXXIX

C.C.E. DRILL - 1

QUESTION BAG-1

(OBJECTIVE-TYPE QUESTIONS)

Tick (✓) the correct answer:

1. In Roman numerals, there are only .... basic symbols.

   (*a*) 7   (*b*) 8   (*c*) 9   (*d*) 10

2. Roman numeral for the smallest four-digit number is

   (*a*) X   (*b*) C   (*c*) M   (*d*) D

3. Which of the following numerals cannot be repeated?

   (*a*) I   (*b*) V   (*c*) X   (*d*) C

4. IX + XV + XX =?

   (*a*) 35   (*b*) 40   (*c*) 44   (*d*) 45

5. I can be subtracted from

   (*a*) V   (*b*) V and X   (*c*) X and C   (*d*) V, X and C

6. Compare : CDXLIX ◯ CDLX

   (*a*) >   (*b*) <   (*c*) =   (*d*) None of these

7. XIX + XXIX = ?

   (*a*) XXXVIII   (*b*) XLVII   (*c*) XXXIX   (*d*) XLVIII

8. CC – CXXV = ?

   (*a*) LXV   (*b*) LXXV   (*c*) LXXXV   (*d*) XCV

1. *Complete the following table :*

	Hindu-Arabic Numeral	Roman Numeral		Hindu-Arabic Numeral	Roman Numeral
(a)	198	....	(b)	....	CCXCVI
(c)	229	....	(d)	350	....
(e)	....	CCCXLIX	(f)	389	....
(g)	430	....	(h)	....	CDIV
(i)	495	....	(j)	....	CDXCIX

2. *Fill in the blanks:*

 (a) Symbols ...., ... and .... are never subtracted or repeated.

 (b) X can be subtracted from .... and ....

 (c) C can be subtracted from .... and ....

3. *Cross the Roman numerals which are not written correctly:*

 (a) XD (b) VX (c) CDXL (d) CVX (e) CVV

 (f) ICC (g) XLIX (h) LC (i) CCCXC

4. *Write the following Roman numerals in ascending order:*

 (a) CXIX, XCIX, CXXI, CIX, CXX

 (b) CCLX, CCXC, CCXX, CXC, CCXL

 (c) CDLXIX, CDLXV, CDLXIII, CDXLV, CDLVIII

5. *Solve and write the answer in Roman numerals:*

 (a) XCII − XV =

 (b) XLIX + XXXIX =

 (c) LVII − XXIX =

 (d) LIV × VI =

 (e) CVIII + CXLVI =

 (f) LXIX × VII =

LARGE NUMBERS
(UPTO TEN CRORES)

INTRODUCTION

In class IV, we have studied upto 7-digit numbers.

We know that the largest 7-digit number is 9999999.

Putting its digits in Indian Place-Value Chart, we have :

T-L	L	T-Th	Th	H	T	O
9	9	9	9	9	9	9

So, we can read it easily as :

'*Ninety-nine lakh ninety-nine thousand nine hundred ninety-nine*'.

On adding 1 to 9999999, we get :

$$\begin{array}{r} 9999999 \\ + 1 \\ \hline 10000000 \end{array}$$

Thus, 9999999 + 1 = 10000000.

We read 10000000 as **one-crore.**

This is the smallest 8-digit number.

The eighth place is called the **Crores place.**

We may now extend the place-value chart to 8 places.

Thus, 20000000 is read as 'two crores';

30000000 is read as 'three crores';

70000000 is read as 'seven crores';

90000000 is read as ' nine crores'.

The largest 8-digit number is 99999999.

Putting its digits in Indian Place-Value Chart having 8 places, we have :

C	T-L	L	T-Th	Th	H	T	O
9	9	9	9	9	9	9	9

Thus, we can read it as :

'*Nine crore ninety-nine lakh ninety-nine thousand nine hundred ninety-nine.*'

On adding 1 to 99999999, we get :

$$
\begin{array}{r}
99999999 \\
+\ 1 \\
\hline
100000000 \\
\end{array}
$$

We read 100000000 as **ten-crores.**

This is the smallest 9-digit number.

The ninth place is called the **Ten-Crores place.**

Thus, we may now extend the Indian Place-Value Chart to 9 places.

Periods in a Place-Value Chart:

In an Indian Place-Value Chart, the nine places are grouped into four periods.

These periods from right to left are : **Ones, Thousands, Lakhs, Crores.**

Given below is the place-value chart showing the first nine places.

INDIAN PLACE VALUE CHART

Periods →	Crores		Lakhs		Thousands		Ones		
Places →	Ten Crores 100000000	Crores 10000000	Ten Lakhs 1000000	Lakhs 100000	Ten Thousands 10000	Thousands 1000	Hundreds 100	Tens 10	Ones 1
	T-C	C	T-L	L	T-Th	Th	H	T	O

In a given numeral, starting from right, the first three places make the **ones period,** *the next two places make the* **thousands period,** *the next two places make the* **lakhs period** *and the next two places make the* **crores period.**

HOW TO WRITE A NUMERAL?

In a given numeral, we separate the periods by using commas (,).

The following examples will make the ideas more clear.

Example 1. *Write the numeral 183672123 by separating the periods.*

Solution : Starting from the right we make bunches of 3 digits, 2 digits, 2 digits and 2 digits respectively and separating the bunches by commas, we may write 183672123 as

T-C	C	T-L	L	T-Th	Th	H	T	O
1	8	3	6	7	2	1	2	3

So, we write it as 18,36,72,123.

Example 2. *Arrange the digits of each of the following numerals in the place-value chart and write it by separating the periods :*

(*a*) 29574   (*b*) 136095   (*c*) 3705160

(*d*) 18256479   (*e*) 20703584   (*f*) 240800218

Solution : Starting from the right, we make entries of the digits of each numeral in the place value chart as shown below.

Now, separating the periods, we may write the given numerals as under.

	\multicolumn{9}{c}{Given Numeral}	
	\multicolumn{2}{c}{Crores}	\multicolumn{2}{c}{Lakhs}	\multicolumn{2}{c}{Thousands}		\multicolumn{2}{c}{Ones}	Using Commas
	T-C	C	T-L	L	T-Th	Th	H	T	O	
(*a*)					2	9	5	7	4	29,574
(*b*)				1	3	6	0	9	5	1,36,095
(*c*)			3	7	0	5	1	6	0	37,05,160
(*d*)		1	8	2	5	6	4	7	9	1,82,56,479
(*e*)		2	0	7	0	3	5	8	4	2,07,03,584
(*f*)	2	4	0	8	0	0	2	1	8	24,08,00,218

How to Read a Numeral ?

While reading a numeral all the digits in the same period are read together and the name of the period, except the ones, is read along with them.

Example 3. *Write the following numerals in words :*

(*a*) 295708   (*b*) 1407319   (*c*) 12043056

(*d*) 50834570   (*e*) 230305211   (*f*) 920517068

Solution : Separating the periods of ones, thousands, lakhs and crores from the right in each numeral, we may write the given numerals as under :

	\multicolumn{9}{c}{Given Numeral}	
	\multicolumn{2}{c}{Crores}	\multicolumn{2}{c}{Lakhs}	\multicolumn{2}{c}{Thousands}		\multicolumn{2}{c}{Ones}	Number Names
	T-C	C	T-L	L	T-Th	Th	H	T	O	
(*a*)				2	9	5	7	0	8	Two lakh ninety-five thousand seven hundred eight
(*b*)			1	4	0	7	3	1	9	Fourteen lakh seven thousand three hundred nineteen
(*c*)		1	2	0	4	3	0	5	6	One crore twenty lakh forty-three thousand fifty-six

	T-C	C	T-L	L	T-Th	Th	H	T	O	Number Names
(d)		5	0	8	3	4	5	7	0	Five crore eight lakh thirty-four thousand five hundred seventy
(e)	2	3	0	3	0	5	2	1	1	Twenty-three crore three lakh five thousand two hundred eleven
(f)	9	2	0	5	1	7	0	6	8	Ninety-two crore five lakh seventeen thousand sixty-eight

Example 4. *Find the place-value of each of the digits in the numeral* 367405281.

Solution: We may write the given numeral as :

T-C	C	T-L	L	T-Th	Th	H	T	O
3	6	7	4	0	5	2	8	1

Place-value of 1 $= 1$ one $= 1 \times 1 = 1$

Place-value of 8 $= 8$ tens $= 8 \times 10 = 80$

Place-value of 2 $= 2$ hundreds $= 2 \times 100 = 200$

Place-value of 5 $= 5$ thousands $= 5 \times 1000 = 5000$

Place-value of 0 $= 0$ ten-thousand $= 0 \times 10000 = 0$

Place-value of 4 $= 4$ lakhs $= 4 \times 100000 = 400000$

Place-value of 7 $= 7$ ten-lakhs $= 7 \times 1000000 = 7000000$

Place-value of 6 $= 6$ crores $= 6 \times 10000000 = 60000000$

Place-value of 3 $= 3$ ten-crores $= 3 \times 100000000 = 300000000$

Example 5. *Write* 490570316 *in the expanded from.*

Solution : The given numeral may be written as :

T-C	C	T-L	L	T-Th	Th	H	T	O
4	9	0	5	7	0	3	1	6

Thus, we have :

490570316

$= 4$ ten-crores $+ 9$ crores $+ 0$ ten-lakhs $+ 5$ lakhs $+ 7$ ten-thousands
$+ 0$ thousand $+ 3$ hundreds $+ 1$ ten $+ 6$ ones

$= 4 \times 100000000 + 9 \times 10000000 + 0 \times 1000000 + 5 \times 100000$
$+ 7 \times 10000 + 0 \times 1000 + 3 \times 100 + 1 \times 10 + 6 \times 1$

$= 400000000 + 90000000 + 0 + 500000 + 70000 + 0 + 300 + 10 + 6$

$= 400000000 + 90000000 + 500000 + 70000 + 300 + 10 + 6.$

1. Rewrite the following numerals using commas to separate the periods according to the Indian Place-Value Chart :

    (a) 623974   (b) 3768954   (c) 52673894

    (d) 430615029   (e) 681008546   (f) 705000038

    (g) 800808088   (h) 900000100   (i) 303100001

2. Write the following numerals in words :

    (a) 74,10,507   (b) 39,00,302   (c) 2,41,05,063

    (d) 10,00,53,109   (e) 22,07,08,518   (f) 36,10,06,284

    (g) 50,19,00,006   (h) 10,01,01,100   (i) 4,04,04,004

3. Write the following numbers in figures :

    (a) Ninety-two lakh five thousand fifty-five

    (b) Six crore sixty-five lakh twenty thousand seven hundred sixteen

    (c) Nine crore nineteen lakh nine thousand nine hundred ninety

    (d) Twelve crore ten lakh three hundred sixty-five

    (e) Five crore forty-two thousand one hundred nine

    (f) Twenty-three crore five lakh seven thousand one hundred eight

    (g) Thirty crore fifteen thousand eighteen

    (h) Fifty-two crore one lakh thirty-one

    (i) Thirteen crore five hundred seventy

    (j) Ten crore ten thousand eleven

    (k) One crore one thousand one

4. Using Indian Place-value system, write the place-value of each of the digits in the numeral 64,19,70,528.

5. Using Indian system of numeration, find the place-value of the underlined digits in each of the following :

    (a) 5<u>9</u>0713568   (b) 635<u>7</u>09412   (c) <u>8</u>20307514

    (d) 813<u>3</u>605247   (e) 246<u>0</u>53819   (f) 913<u>5</u>46007

6. Write the following numbers in an expanded form :

    (a) 5,29,347   (b) 23,09,519   (c) 9,72,34,026

    (d) 13,06,19,804   (e) 37,24,09,578   (f) 89,30,16,870

7. Write the following in standard form :

    (a) 3000000 + 700000 + 60000 + 9000 + 70 + 6

    (b) 60000000 + 8000000 + 30000 + 400 + 80 + 4

(c) $20000000 + 200000 + 2000 + 200 + 2$

(d) $700000000 + 30000000 + 200000 + 80000 + 4000 + 60 + 9$

(e) $500000000 + 5000 + 50 + 5$

(f) $900000000 + 900000 + 900 + 9$

(g) $40000000 + 10 + 7$

8. Counting in thousands, write the numbers from 2906754 to 2911754.

9. Counting in lakhs, write the numbers from 52736109 to 53236109.

10. Counting in crores, write the numbers from 163057500 to 223057500.

11. *Look at the pattern and write next three numbers :*

   (a) 3140624, 3140724, 3140824, ..., ..., ...

   (b) 3256419, 3257419, 3258419, ..., ..., ...

   (c) 70809010, 70909010, 71009010, ..., ..., ...

   (d) 191817600, 201817600, 211817600, ..., ..., ...

   (e) 302010400, 292010400, 282010400, ..., ..., ...

12. Write the smallest number of 9 digits and the largest number of 8 digits.

13. *Answer the following :*

   (a) What comes just after 9536999?   (b) What comes just before 9900000?

   (c) What comes just after 13700899?   (d) What comes just before 10000000?

ORDER RELATION

In order to compare two numbers, we adopt the following rules :

Rule 1. *The number with less digits is less than the number with more digits.*

Rule 2. *Suppose we have to compare two numbers with the same number of digits.*

Step 1. *First compare the digits at the leftmost place in both the numbers.*

Step 2. *If they are equal in value, then compare the second digits from the left.*

Step 3. *If the second digits from the left are equal, compare the third digits from the left.*

Step 4. *Continue until you come across unequal digits at the corresponding places. Now, the number with greater such digit is the greater of the two.*

The following examples will make the ideas clear.

Example 1.   *Which is greater 25476801 or 6789968 ?*

Solution :   Here we have to compare 25476801 and 6789968.

   Clearly, 25476801 consists of 8 digits while 6789968 contains 7 digits.

   $\therefore$ $25476801 > 6789968$.

Example 2. *Which is greater* 96580734 *or* 96721643 ?

Solution : Let us arrange the given numbers in a place-value chart.

C	T-L	L	T-Th	Th	H	T	O
9	6	5	8	0	7	3	4
9	6	7	2	1	6	4	3

Both the numbers have 8 digits.

At the crores place both have the same digit, namely 9.

At the ten-lakhs place both have the same digit, namely 6.

But, at the lakhs place, the first number has 5 while the second has 7.

Clearly, $5 < 7$.

$\therefore$ $96580734 < 96721643$.

> **Numbers in Ascending Order** *means the numbers from smaller to greater.*
>
> **Numbers in Descending Order** *means the numbers from greater to smaller.*

Example 3. *Arrange the following numbers in an ascending order :*

3751234, 15267302, 143605217, 15458314, 4062341

Solution : Let us arrange the given numbers in a place-value chart.

T-C	C	T-L	L	T-Th	Th	H	T	O
		3	7	5	1	2	3	4
	1	5	2	6	7	3	0	2
1	4	3	6	0	5	2	1	7
	1	5	4	5	8	3	1	4
		4	0	6	2	3	4	1

Out of the given numbers two are 7-digit numbers, two are 8-digit numbers and one is a 9-digit number.

In 7-digit numbers, clearly $3751234 < 4062341$ (since 3 T-L < 4 T-L)

In 8-digit numbers, clearly $15267302 < 15458314$ (since 2 L < 4 L)

Clearly, the 9-digit number is the largest.

$\therefore$ $3751234 < 4062341 < 15267302 < 15458314 < 143605217$

Hence, the given numbers in ascending order are :

3751234, 4062341, 15267302, 15458314, 143605217

Example 4. *Arrange the following numbers in descending order :*

483672906, 74635618, 483910257, 9876879, 74613898

Solution :   Let us arrange the given numbers in a place-value chart :

T-C	C	T-L	L	T-Th	Th	H	T	O
4	8	3	6	7	2	9	0	6
	7	4	6	3	5	6	1	8
4	8	3	9	1	0	2	5	7
		9	8	7	6	8	7	9
	7	4	6	1	3	8	9	8

Out of the given numbers two are 9-digit numbers, two are 8-digit numbers and one is a 7-digit number.

In 9-digit numbers, clearly 483910257 > 483672906 (*Since 9 L > 6 L*)

In 8-digit numbers, clearly 74635618 > 74613898 (*Since* 3 T-Th > 1 T-Th)

Clearly, the 7-digit number is the smallest.

∴ 483910257 > 483672906 > 74635618 > 74613898 > 9876879

Hence, the given numbers in descending order are :

483910257 , 483672906 , 74635618 , 74613898 , 9876879

EXERCISE 4

1. Fill in each of the following boxes with appropriate symbol > or < :

(a) 1002456 ☐ 987896   (b) 23507104 ☐ 14536523

(c) 54836903 ☐ 103213102   (d) 203645817 ☐ 164786938

(e) 35672416 ☐ 35670590   (f) 478907506 ☐ 478913401

(g) 613054901 ☐ 613045989   (h) 750890315 ☐ 750890410

(i) 89276584 ☐ 101625302   (j) 917263954 ☐ 917260954

2. Arrange the following numbers in descending order :

(a) 12965784, 3076897, 129654503, 2789988, 21345603

(b) 245368009, 45639918, 93216723, 53791325, 245370119

(c) 62790568, 627905480, 62791023, 627905623, 62790931

(d) 63082318, 30728510, 27169237, 50643701, 7987689

(e) 7546890, 23150014, 998765, 23149925, 7546785

3. Arrange the following numbers in ascending order :

(a) 14865710, 20507106, 30008215, 2786789, 2876879

(b) 9368516, 10540603, 91032401, 9367839, 10541201

(c) 2537928, 101002301, 20547946, 100515602, 14035710

(d) 38715206, 129405817, 73678314, 7876589, 69721656

(e) 743162109, 304288713, 561945107, 89590788, 602357100

4. *Encircle the largest number in each of the following :*

(a) 31650829, 307482134, 4536794, 41035106, 238590746

(b) 102234102, 93645753, 27810591, 102240003, 93646800

(c) 9037848, 12345716, 101010706, 91537964, 100718967

(d) 9000009, 90000001, 9935469, 87590909, 88888888

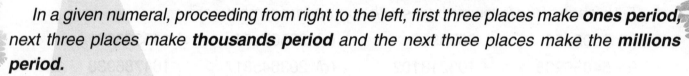

INTERNATIONAL (OR WESTERN) PLACE-VALUE SYSTEM

This system is followed by a large number of countries in the world. In this system, we write :

1 lakh = 100 thousands

10 lakhs = 1 million

1 crore = 10 millions

10 crores = 100 millions

In this system, *we have periods of **ones, thousands** and **millions.***

In a given numeral, proceeding from right to the left, first three places make **ones period**, next three places make **thousands period** and the next three places make the **millions period.**

Given below is the international place-value chart.

INTERNATIONAL PLACE- VALUE CHART

Millions			Thousands			Ones		
Hundred-Millions 100000000	Ten-Millions 10000000	Millions 1000000	Hundred-Thousands 100000	Ten-Thousands 10000	Thousands 1000	Hundreds 100	Tens 10	Ones 1
HM	TM	M	H-Th	T-Th	Th	H	T	O

Example 1. *Rewrite the following numerals with proper commas, using International system of numeration:*

(a) 94536708   (b) 765049813   (c) 400835029

Solution : Arranging the given numerals in an International Place-Value Chart and then separating the periods, we may write them as shown.

Given Numeral									Notation
Millions			Thousands			Ones			
HM	TM	M	H-Th	T-Th	Th	H	T	O	
(a)		9	4	5	3	6	7	0	8	94,536,708
(b)	7	6	5	0	4	9	8	1	3	765,049,813
(c)	4	0	0	8	3	5	0	2	9	400,835,029

Example 2. Write the number names of the following :

(a) 56,472,083   (b) 120,907,406   (c) 374,006,035

(d) 30,805,107   (e) 10,001,001   (f) 450,000,045

Solution : We know that in each numeral, starting from the right, we have periods of ones, thousands and millions. So, we may write the given numbers as under.

Numeral	Number Name
(a) 56, 472, 083	Fifty-six million four hundred seventy-two thousand eighty-three
(b) 120, 907, 406	One hundred twenty million nine hundred seven thousand four hundred six
(c) 374, 006, 035	Three hundred seventy-four million six thousand thirty-five
(d) 30, 805, 107	Thirty million eight hundred five thousand one hundred seven
(e) 10, 001, 001	Ten million one thousand one
(f) 450, 000, 045	Four hundred fifty million forty-five

EXERCISE 5

1. Rewrite the following numerals with proper commas, using international-system:

(a) 35684129   (b) 50968302   (c) 103854179

(d) 42560247   (e) 491560543   (f) 793654182

(g) 300700006   (h) 100006001   (i) 90007010

2. Write the number names of the following :

(a) 25,863,475   (b) 30,807,541   (c) 81,923,054

(d) 140,905,319   (e) 231,600,148   (f) 490,300,007

(g) 101,010,001   (h) 23,006,100   (i) 560,001,010

3. Write the following in figures :

(a) Sixty-four million one hundred nineteen thousand eighteen

(b) Two hundred eighty-nine million sixty-nine thousand forty-eight

(c) One hundred five million one hundred eight thousand seven

(d) Seven hundred sixteen million six hundred five

(e) Three hundred one million two thousand thirty-one

(f) Ten million three thousand thirty-six

(g) Nineteen million nineteen

(h) Sixty million forty-four thousand sixty-four

(i) Two hundred million two thousand twenty

THINGS TO REMEMBER

1. In Indian Place-Value chart, the nine places are grouped into four periods, namely *Ones, Thousands, Lakhs and Crores.*

2. Given below is the place-value chart, showing the first nine places.

Periods →	Crores		Lakhs		Thousands		Ones		
Places →	Ten Crores	Crores	Ten Lakhs	Lakhs	Ten Thousands	Thousands	Hundreds	Tens	Ones
Short Form	T-C	C	T-L	L	T-Th	Th	H	T	O

3. Starting from right, the first three places make the ones period, the next two places make the thousands period, the next two places make the lakhs period and the next two places make the crores period.

4. In a given numeral, we separate the periods by using commas.

5. In International Place-Value system, we have periods of *ones, thousands and millions*, as shown below :

Millions			Thousands			Ones		
Hundred-Millions	Ten-Millions	Millions	Hundred Thousands	Ten-Thousands	Thousands	Hundreds	Tens	Ones
HM	TM	M	H-Th	T-Th	Th	H	T	O

6. We have :

(a) 1 lakh = 100 thousands

(b) 10 lakhs = 1 million

(c) 1 crore = 10 millions

(d) 10 crores = 100 millions

C.C.E. DRILL - 2

QUESTION BAG - 1

(OBJECTIVE - TYPE QUESTIONS)

Tick (✓) the correct order:

1. Commas are inserted in a number after each
   (a) digit   (b) place   (c) period   (d) group

2. A 7-digit number starts with .... place in the Indian system.
   (a) lakhs   (b) ten thousands   (c) ten lakhs   (d) crores

3. An 8-digit number starts with .... place in the international system.
   (a) hundred thousands   (b) millions
   (c) ten millions   (d) crores

4. The place value of 9 in the numeral 90521367 is
   (a) nine million   (b) ninety million
   (c) ninety lakh   (d) nine hundred thousand

5. The numeral 4, 39, 65, 817 will be written in the International system as
   (a) 43, 965, 817   (b) 43, 96, 58, 17
   (c) 4, 396, 581, 7   (d) 439, 658, 17

6. The sum of the greatest 6-digit number and the greatest 7-digit number is
   (a) 1099998   (b) 10999998   (c) 1009998   (d) 10099998

7. The place value and face value of a digit are always equal at
   (a) ones place   (b) tens place
   (c) hundreds place   (d) Never

8. The number of zeros in 100 million are
   (a) 7   (b) 8   (c) 9   (d) None of these

9. The numeral for 'Ninety crore nine thousand' is
   (a) 909000   (b) 90009000   (c) 900009000   (d) 90090000

10. The numeral for 'Ninety million ninety thousand ninety' is
    (a) 909090   (b) 9090090   (c) 90900090   (d) 90090090

QUESTION BAG - 2

1. *Fill in the blanks:*
   (a) The Indian and the international system of numeration follow the same pattern upto the .... place.
   (b) 100 million = ... crore
   (c) 1 million = ... lakh

(d) 1 crore = ... million

(e) The place value of .... is always the same as its face value.

(f) There are .... zeros in 30 million.

(g) There are .... zeros in 8 crore.

(h) When 1 is added to a given number we get the .... of the given number.

(i) The predecessor of 86, 30, 000 is ....

(j) The successor of 6, 09, 99, 999 is ....

(k) The predecessor of 1,41,000 is ....

(l) The successor of 79, 98, 999 is ....

(m) In 2,67,48,903; 2 is in the .... place and 7 is in the .... place.

(n) In 178,563,910; 7 is in the .... place and 5 is in the .... place.

2. *State whether each of the following statements is true or false:*

(a) The place value of 8 in 856, 321 is 8 lakh. ....

(b) The place value of 9 in 9,60,58,324 is 9 crore. ....

(c) There are 2 places in the millions period. ....

(d) There are 3 places in the lakhs period. ....

3. *Rewrite each of the following numbers in the Indian system:*

(a) 636,821   (b) 6,954,128   (c) 87,198,362

(d) 10,101,010   (e) 843,034,467

4. *Rewrite each of the following numbers in the Indian as well as International system of numeration, in both figures and words:*

(a) 846379   (b) 6309903   (c) 81818818

(d) 101036365

5. *Write the period, the place, face value and place value of the underlined digits:*

(a) 60, 187, 549   (b) 84,16,25,903

6. *Compare and put the correct symbol >, < or = in the placeholder:*

(a) 9339393 [   ] 939993   (b) 9989889 [   ] 9989988

(c) 10101010 [   ] 10100101   (d) 609960069 [   ] 609906069

7. *Arrange in ascending order:*

45454545, 5454545, 45545455, 4554454, 5454554

8. *Write the smallest and the greatest number, using each of the following digits only once:*

(a) 2, 7, 8, 5, 0, 6   (b) 9, 0, 5, 1, 3, 2, 6

9. (a) Write the smallest 6-digit number having all different digits.

(b) Write the greatest 6-digit number having all different digits.

10. (a) Write the smallest 8-digit number having three different digits.

(b) Write the greatest 8-digit number having three different digits.

11. *Make the smallest possible 7-digit number using the digits:*

(a) 6, 9, 3, 5, 1   (b) 4, 7, 1, 8, 0

OPERATIONS ON LARGE NUMBERS

4

You are already familiar with four basic mathematical operations- Addition, Subtraction, Multiplication & Division. Now we shall perform the same operations on large numbers.

ADDITION

We know that in a problem on addition, each one of the numbers to be added is called an **addend** and the result of addition is called their **sum.**

In class IV we have learnt the addition of 6-digit numbers. In the same way we add numbers having 7 or more digits.

The following examples will make the ideas more clear.

Example 1. *Add 5436289 and 2578657 and write the sum in words.*

Solution : Arranging the digits of the given numbers in column form and adding columnwise, we get :

T-L	L	T-Th	Th	H	T	O	
①	①	①		①	①		← carry
5	4	3	6	2	8	9	
+ 2	5	7	8	6	5	7	
8	0	1	4	9	4	6	

∴ The sum of the given numbers = 8014946.

The sum in words is 'eighty lakh fourteen thousand nine hundred forty- six.'

Explanation:

Adding Ones : 9 ones + 7 ones = 16 ones
= 10 ones + 6 ones = 1 ten + 6 ones.

Write 6 under ones column and carry over 1 to tens column.

Adding Tens : 1 ten (carried over) + 8 tens + 5 tens = 14 tens
= 10 tens + 4 tens = 1 hundred + 4 tens.

Write 4 under tens column and carry over 1 to hundreds column.

Adding Hundreds :

1 hundred (carried over) + 2 hundreds + 6 hundreds = 9 hundreds.

Write 9 under hundreds column.

Adding Thousands :

6 thousands + 8 thousands = 14 thousands

= 10 thousands + 4 thousands

= 1 ten-thousand + 4 thousands.

Write 4 under thousands column and carry over 1 to ten-thousands column.

Adding Ten-Thousands :

1 ten-thousand (carried over) + 3 ten-thousands + 7 ten-thousands

= 11 ten-thousands

= 10 ten-thousands + 1 ten-thousand

= 1 lakh + 1 ten-thousand.

Write 1 under ten-thousands column and carry over 1 to lakhs column.

Adding Lakhs :

1 lakh (carried over) + 4 lakhs + 5 lakhs = 10 lakhs

= 1 ten-lakh + 0 lakh.

Write 0 under lakhs column and carry over 1 to ten-lakhs column.

Adding Ten-Lakhs :

1 ten-lakh (carried over) + 5 ten-lakhs + 2 ten-lakhs = 8 ten-lakhs.

Write 8 under ten-lakhs column.

Example 2. *Add* 57085639 *and* 34768596 *and write the sum in words.*

Solution : Arranging the digits of the given numbers in column form and adding columnwise, we get :

C	T-L	L	T-Th	Th	H	T	O	
①		①	①	①	①		①	← carry
5	7	0	8	5	6	3	9	
3	4	7	6	8	5	9	6	
9	1	8	5	4	2	3	5	

∴ The sum of the given numbers is :

'Nine crore eighteen lakh fifty-four thousand two hundred thirty-five'.

Example 3. *Find the sum :* 367285109 + 481827825 + 2368789.

Solution : Arranging the digits of the given numbers in column form and adding columnwise, we get :

T-C	C	T-L	L	T-Th	Th	H	T	O	
①	①	①	①	②	①	①	②		← carry
3	6	7	2	8	5	1	0	9	
4	8	1	8	2	7	8	2	5	
		2	3	6	8	7	8	9	
8	5	1	4	8	1	7	2	3	+

Hence, the sum of the given numbers is 851481723.

EXERCISE 6

Add:

1.
```
  3 6 7 5 2 1 8
+ 2 5 1 7 6 7 3
```

2.
```
  7 4 5 3 6 1 9
+ 1 8 7 6 9 8 4
```

3.
```
  7 5 4 3 6 9 4 8
+   2 7 8 4 2 3 6
```

4.
```
  3 8 2 5 6 7 1 4
+   3 9 6 7 4 8 9
```

5.
```
  4 3 2 6 8 9 7 4
  6 7 9 4 3 4 7
+   3 1 6 5 5 4
```

6.
```
  1 6 8 7 5 3 0 9
  2 3 4 2 6 7 9 3
+   4 2 3 1 5 1 8
```

7.
```
  1 3 4 5 2 6 7 2 9
  2 4 3 6 4 7 3 9 4
+   6 9 3 1 8 4 5 3
```

8.
```
  2 4 5 7 1 9 5 6 3
  4 6 3 2 6 7 4 7 8
+   7 1 9 3 2 3 4 5
```

9.
```
    5 7 6 4 2 3 9
    4 3 0 7 5 7 8 6
  1 3 9 6 0 8 9 4 5
+       9 6 5 7 8
```

10.
```
  5 4 6 2 7 1 2 8 5
  1 7 3 8 2 7 4 9 3
    1 0 3 7 4 6 7 8
+     2 9 9 2 7 8 9
```

Find the sum of the following :

11. 13256978 + 6975684 + 23679

12. 343851728 + 166452675 + 3672563 + 935

13. 474361279 + 236554385 + 53168837 + 20716314

WORD PROBLEMS ON ADDITION

Example 1.   *A company earned Rs 14632739 in the year 2009. Next year the earning of the company increased by Rs 3974687. How much did the company earn in the year 2010 ?*

Solution :   Earning of the company in the year 2009   = Rs 14632739.

Increase in the earning during next year   = Rs 3974687.

∴ Earning of the company in the year 2010   = Rs (14632739 + 3974687).

C	T-L	L	T-Th	Th	H	T	O	
	①	①		①	①	①		← carry
1	4	6	3	2	7	3	9	
+	3	9	7	4	6	8	7	
1	8	6	0	7	4	2	6	

Hence, in 2010, the company earned Rs 18607426.

Example 2 .   *A survey shows that the population of Andhra Pradesh is 96304854, Karnataka 84617398 and Kerala 45038237. What is the total population of these three states?*

Solution :   Population of Andhra Pradesh = 96304854.

Population of Karnataka = 84617398.

Population of Kerala = 45038237.

T-C	C	T-L	L	T-Th	Th	H	T	O	
②	①			②	①	①	①		← carry
	9	6	3	0	4	8	5	4	
	8	4	6	1	7	3	9	8	
+	4	5	0	3	8	2	3	7	
2	2	5	9	6	0	4	8	9	

Hence, the total population of the three states is 225960489.

Example 3. *The difference between two numbers is 8974568. If the smaller number is 6468457, find the greater number.*

Solution :

Difference between the two numbers   = 8974568.

Smaller number   = 6468457.

∴   Greater number   = 8974568 + 6468457.

C	T-L	L	T-Th	Th	H	T	O	
①	①	①	①	①	①	①		← carry
	8	9	7	4	5	6	8	
+	6	4	6	8	4	5	7	
1	5	4	4	3	0	2	5	

Hence, the greater number is 15443025.

EXERCISE 7

1. The number of persons who visited the holy shrine of Mata Vaishno Devi during last two consecutive years was 6378907 and 7865089 respectively. How many persons visited the shrine during these two years?

2. Last year, three sugar factories in a town produced 23807575 bags, 19728686 bags and 8962347 bags respectively. How many bags in all were produced by all the three factories during last year?

3. In a city, there are 5726439 men, 4439675 women and 2016348 children. What is the total population of the city?

4. In a particular year, the male population of a city was 2359324 more than the female population. The number of females was 6813675. What was the male population? What was the total population of the city during that year ?

5. The sales-receipt of a company during the year 2009 was Rs 13047546. Next year it increased by Rs 7973674. What was the sales-receipt of the company in the year 2010? What was the total sales-receipt of the company during these two years?

6. In a particular year an industry produced 6736265 bicycles. Next year, the number of bicycles produced was 1374589 more than those produced in the preceding year. How many bicycles were produced during these two years?

7. There were three candidates in an election. They received 678509 votes, 462397 votes and 97685 votes respectively. The number of invalid votes was 16489 and 45716 persons did not vote. How many votes were registered?

8. A survey conducted on an Indian State shows that 1623540 people have only primary education; 9768678 people have secondary education; 6437945 people have higher education and 2682635 people are illiterates. If the number of children below the age of school admission be 698781, find the population of that State.

9. A number exceeds 35637844 by 7674156. What is that number?

SUBTRACTION

We know that in a problem on subtraction, *the larger number from which we subtract the other number is called the* **minuend** *and the number which is subtracted is called the* **subtrahend.**

The result of subtraction is called the **difference** between the given numbers.

So far we have learnt the subtraction with borrowings for numbers consisting of 6 or less digits. In the same way we subtract larger numbers.

SOLVED EXAMPLES

Example 1. *Subtract 2736879 from 5342568.*

Solution : Here minuend = 5342568 and subtrahend = 2736879.

Arranging the digits of the given numbers in column form and subtracting columnwise, we get:

T-L	L	T-Th	Th	H	T	O
④	⑬	③	⑪	⑭	⑮	⑱	← After borrowing
⁴5̸	3̸	³4̸	¹2̸	⁴5̸	⁵6̸	8̸
− 2	7	3	6	8	7	9
2	6	0	5	6	8	9

Hence, 5342568 − 2736879 = 2605689.

Explanation :

Subtracting Ones :

We cannot subtract 9 ones from 8 ones.

So, we borrow 1 ten, leaving behind 5 tens.

Now, 1 ten + 8 ones = 10 ones + 8 ones = 18 ones.

And, 18 ones − 9 ones = 9 ones.

Write 9 under ones column.

Subtracting Tens :

We cannot subtract 7 tens from 5 tens.

So, we borrow 1 hundred, leaving behind 4 hundreds.

Now, 1 hundred + 5 tens = 10 tens + 5 tens = 15 tens.

And, 15 tens − 7 tens = 8 tens.

Write 8 under tens column.

Subtracting Hundreds :

We cannot subtract 8 hundreds from 4 hundreds.

So, we borrow 1 thousand, leaving behind 1 thousand.

Now, 1 thousand + 4 hundreds = 10 hundreds + 4 hundreds
                              = 14 hundreds.

And, 14 hundreds − 8 hundreds = 6 hundreds.

Write 6 under hundreds column.

Subtracting Thousands :

We cannot subtract 6 thousands from 1 thousand.

So, we borrow 1 ten-thousand, leaving behind 3 ten-thousands.

Now, 1 ten-thousand + 1 thousand = 10 thousands + 1 thousand
                                 = 11 thousands.

And, 11 thousands − 6 thousands = 5 thousands.

Write 5 under thousands column.

Subtracting Ten-thousands :

3 ten-thousands − 3 ten-thousands = 0 ten-thousand.

Write 0 under ten-thousands column.

Subtracting Lakhs :

We cannot subtract 7 lakhs from 3 lakhs.

So, we borrow 1 ten-lakh, leaving behind 4 ten-lakhs.

Now, 1 ten-lakh + 3 lakh = 10 lakhs + 3 lakhs = 13 lakhs.

And, 13 lakhs − 7 lakhs = 6 lakhs.

Write 6 under lakhs column.

Subtracting Ten-Lakhs :

4 ten-lakhs − 2 ten-lakhs = 2 ten-lakhs.

Write 2 under ten-lakhs column.

Hence, the difference between the given numbers = 2605689.

Example 2 .   *Find the difference between 26879354 and 63457148.*

Solution :   Here both the given numbers are 8-digit numbers.

Comparing their leftmost digits, we find that 2 < 6.

∴ 26879354 < 63457148.

So, minuend = 63457148 and subtrahend = 26879354.

Arranging the digits of the given numbers in column form and subtracting columnwise, we get :

C	T-L	L	T-Th	Th	H	T	O	
⑤	⑫	⑬	⑭	⑯	⑩	⑭		← After borrowing
^{5}6	^{2}3	^{3}4	^{4}5	^{6}7	^{0}1	4	8	
− 2	6	8	7	9	3	5	4	
3	6	5	7	7	7	9	4	

Hence, the difference between the given numbers = 36577794.

EXERCISE 8

Subtract :

1.
```
  5 6 4 7 8 1 2
− 2 7 8 5 7 4 5
```

2.
```
  7 8 5 6 4 2 9
− 3 6 9 8 3 6 7
```

3.
```
  9 3 4 2 5 1 7
− 7 4 5 6 7 8 9
```

4.
```
  6 3 5 4 7 2 4
−   9 6 8 8 3 6
```

5.
```
  3 4 2 7 5 0 6 3
−   9 7 8 9 1 7 4
```

6.
```
  5 0 3 0 4 6 0 1
−   8 7 3 6 7 2 4
```

7.
```
  2 3 1 6 2 9 5 4 7
− 1 9 2 7 3 9 7 8 9
```

8.
```
  7 1 3 0 5 0 0 4
− 2 4 6 1 7 0 5 8
```

9.

```
  9 0 4 0 0 0 1 3
− 6 0 5 0 2 4 1 7
```

10.

```
  3 0 2 4 1 5 2 0 6
− 2 0 3 5 1 6 4 3 8
```

Find the difference :

11. 5826704 − 3927815

12. 8134205 − 5146307

13. 6010036 − 5419947

14. 12034504 − 8075698

WORD PROBLEMS ON SUBTRACTION

Example 1. The sum of two numbers is 3148654. If one of the numbers is 1952789, find the other number.

Solution :

The sum of two numbers = 3148654.

One number = 1952789.

The other number = 3148654 − 1952789.

```
  ②  ⑩  ⑭  ⑦  ⑮  ⑭  ⑭      ← After borrowing
  ²3̶  ⁰1̶  4̶  ⁷8̶  ⁵6̶  ⁴5̶  4̶
− 1   9   5   2   7   8   9
  1   1   9   5   8   6   5
```

Hence, the other number is 1195865.

Example 2. The population of a city in the year 2009 was 8793675. In the following year, the population became 11005200. Find the increase in the population.

Solution :

The population of the city in the year 2010 = 11005200.

The population of the city in the year 2009 = 8793675.

∴ Increase in population = 11005200 − 8793675

```
  ⓪  ⑩  ⑨  ⑩  ④  ⑪  ⑨  ⑩      ← After borrowing
  ¹1̶  ⁰1̶  ⁹0̶  0̶  ⁴5̶  ¹2̶  ⁹0̶  0̶
−     8   7   9   3   6   7   5
      2   2   1   1   5   2   5
```

Hence, the increase in population of the city is 2211525.

Example 3. *There was a stock of 3567123 quintals of wheat in a godown of the Food Corporation of India. Out of this stock, 956341 quintals of wheat was sent to Haryana and 823658 quintals to Punjab. How much is the balance stock now?*

Solution : Total stock of wheat = 3567123 quintals.

Quantity of wheat sent to Haryana = 956341 quintals.

Quantity of wheat sent to Punjab = 823658 quintals.

Total quantity of wheat taken out of the godown

= (956341 + 823658) quintals

= 1779999 quintals.

∴ Balance stock of wheat in the godown

= (3567123 – 1779999) quintals

= 1787124 quintals.

Working

```
    9 5 6 3 4 1
 +    8 2 3 6 5 8
    1 7 7 9 9 9 9
```

```
    3 5 6 7 1 2 3
 –  1 7 7 9 9 9 9
    1 7 8 7 1 2 4
```

EXERCISE 9

1. By how much is 6437859 less than 7016418 ?

2. By how much does 7102340 exceed 6824572 ?

3. What must be added to 5678469 to make 6164324 ?

4. What must be subtracted from 9005413 to get 7906547 ?

5. The sum of two numbers is 13604050. If one of the numbers is 7824361, find the other number.

6. In an examination conducted by a board of secondary education, 1008314 candidates appeared. Out of these 789425 candidates passed. How many failed ?

7. A factory produced 5365129 switches in a particular year and 6010016 switches in the following year. Find the increase in the production of switches.

8. An election was contested by two candidates. The winning candidate received 6872403 votes and won by a margin of 983516 votes. How many votes did the other candidate receive?

9. In an Indian state, a survey shows that there are in all 7651234 students in all the secondary schools. Out of these, there are 2963459 girl-students. How many boys are there in these schools ?

10. The total population of a city is 15207635. There are 6751574 men and 6036425 women and the remaining are children. How many children are there in the city?

11. In an examination, 506212 candidates could get through. Out of these, 197538 passed in first division, 238604 passed in second division. How many passed in third division?

MULTIPLICATION

We know that in a multiplication sum, *the number to be multiplied is called* **multiplicand** and the number by which we multiply is called **multiplier.**

And, the result of multiplication is called ***product.***

Example :   In $125 \times 3 = 375$, we have :

multiplicand = 125, multiplier = 3 and product = 375.

Now, we recall the various properties of multiplication.

PROPERTIES OF MULTIPLICATION

I. Order Property of Multiplication :

The product of two numbers does not change when the order of the numbers is changed.

Thus, $63 \times 27 = 27 \times 63$; $137 \times 125 = 125 \times 137$ etc.

II. Grouping Property of Multiplication :

The product of three numbers does not change when the grouping of the numbers is changed.

Thus, $15 \times (16 \times 17) = (15 \times 16) \times 17$;
$125 \times (240 \times 265) = (125 \times 240) \times 265$ etc.

III. Distributive Property of Multiplication over Addition :

We have : $23 \times (100 + 25) = (23 \times 100) + (23 \times 25)$;
$130 \times (145 + 245) = (130 \times 145) + (130 \times 245)$ etc.

IV. Multiplicative Property of 1 :

(Any number) $\times 1 =$ *the number itself.*

Thus, $536 \times 1 = 536$, $10641 \times 1 = 10641$ etc.

V. Multiplicative Property of 0 :

(Any number) $\times 0 = 0$.

MULTIPLICATION BY 10, 100, 1000

Multiplication of a Number by 10 :

Rule : *To multiply a given number by 10, insert one zero on the right of the given number.*

Thus, $27 \times 10 = 270$, $147 \times 10 = 1470$, $2485 \times 10 = 24850$ etc.

Multiplication of a Number by 100 :

Rule : *To multiply a given number by 100, insert two zeros on the right of the given number.*

Thus, $76 \times 100 = 7600$, $382 \times 100 = 38200$ and $2895 \times 100 = 289500$ etc.

Multiplication of a Number by 1000 :

Rule : *To multiply a given number by 1000, insert three zeros on the right of the given number.*

Thus, $87 \times 1000 = 87000$; $435 \times 1000 = 435000$; $4967 \times 1000 = 4967000$ etc.

MULTIPLICATION OF A NUMBER BY A MULTIPLE OF 10, 100, 1000 ETC.

The following examples will make the ideas clear.

Example 1. *Find the products :*

(a) 589×20 (b) 1356×90

Solution : We have :

(a) 589×20 (b) 356×90
$= 589 \times 2 \times 10$ $= 1356 \times 9 \times 10$
$= (589 \times 2) \times 10$ $= (1356 \times 9) \times 10$
$= 1178 \times 10 = 11780.$ $= 12204 \times 10 = 122040.$

Example 2. *Find the products :*

(a) 294×300 (b) 4567×500

Solution : We have :

(a) 294×300 (b) 4567×500
$= 294 \times 3 \times 100$ $= 4567 \times 5 \times 100$
$= (294 \times 3) \times 100$ $= (4567 \times 5) \times 100$
$= 882 \times 100 = 88200.$ $= 22835 \times 100 = 2283500.$

Example 3. *Find the products :*

(a) 378×4000 (b) 2503×7000

Solution : We have :

(a) 378×4000 (b) 2503×7000
$= 378 \times 4 \times 1000$ $= 2503 \times 7 \times 1000$
$= (378 \times 4) \times 1000$ $= (2503 \times 7) \times 1000$
$= 1512 \times 1000 = 1512000.$ $= 17521 \times 1000 = 17521000.$

Example 4. *Using suitable grouping, find the following products :*

(a) $4 \times 237 \times 25$ (b) $8 \times 1047 \times 125$

Solution : We have :

(a) $4 \times 237 \times 25$ (b) $8 \times 1047 \times 125$
$= (4 \times 25) \times 237$ $= (8 \times 125) \times 1047$
$= 100 \times 237 = 23700.$ $= 1000 \times 1047 = 1047000.$

EXERCISE 10

1. Fill in the blanks :

   (a) $1485 \times \boxed{} = 2346 \times 1485$ (b) $2947 \times 4508 = 4508 \times \boxed{}$

   (c) $2772 \times \boxed{} = 2772$ (d) $4358 \times \boxed{} = 0$

   (e) $35 \times (100 + 37) = (35 \times 100) + (35 \times \boxed{})$

   (f) $146 \times (1000 + 48) = (146 \times \boxed{}) + (146 \times \boxed{})$

   (g) $375 \times (147 \times 903) = (375 \times 147) \times \boxed{}$

   (h) $\boxed{} \times (1030 \times 975) = (2460 \times 1030) \times 975$

2. Fill in the blanks :

   (a) $2718 \times 10 = \boxed{}$ (b) $16875 \times 10 = \boxed{}$ (c) $3875 \times 100 = \boxed{}$

   (d) $29272 \times 100 = \boxed{}$ (e) $6087 \times 1000 = \boxed{}$ (f) $47385 \times 1000 = \boxed{}$

Find the following products :

3. 6540×50
4. 9784×60
5. 15235×70
6. 7892×300
7. 8986×700
8. 26305×800
9. 2981×4000
10. 7897×6000
11. 99999×2000

By using suitable grouping, find the following products :

12. $2 \times 467 \times 5$
13. $5 \times 1986 \times 20$
14. $4 \times 829 \times 25$
15. $4 \times 248 \times 125$
16. $8 \times 3472 \times 125$
17. $2 \times 5726 \times 500$

MULTIPLICATION OF LARGER NUMBERS

We have already learnt the multiplication of a number by a two-digit or three-digit number. In the same way we multiply with larger numbers.

SOLVED EXAMPLES

Example 1. Multiply 5347 by 486.

Solution : We have : $486 = 400 + 80 + 6$.

$\therefore 5347 \times 486 = 5347 \times (400 + 80 + 6)$
$= 5347 \times 400 + 5347 \times 80 + 5347 \times 6$
$= 2138800 + 427760 + 32082 = 2598642.$

Shorter Form :

$$
\begin{array}{r}
5\ 3\ 4\ 7 \\
\times\ 4\ 8\ 6 \\
\hline
3\ 2\ 0\ 8\ 2 \quad \leftarrow (5347 \times 6) \\
4\ 2\ 7\ 7\ 6\ 0 \quad \leftarrow (5347 \times 80) \\
2\ 1\ 3\ 8\ 8\ 0\ 0 \quad \leftarrow (5347 \times 400) \\
\hline
2\ 5\ 9\ 8\ 6\ 4\ 2 \quad \leftarrow (5347 \times 486) \\
\end{array}
$$

Example 2. Multiply 9896 by 2347.

Solution : We have :

```
        9 8 9 6
      × 2 3 4 7
      ─────────
        6 9 2 7 2    ← ( 9896 × 7 )
      3 9 5 8 4 0    ← ( 9896 × 40 )
    2 9 6 8 8 0 0    ← ( 9896 × 300 )
  1 9 7 9 2 0 0 0    ← ( 9896 × 2000 )
  ─────────────────
  2 3 2 2 5 9 1 2    ← ( 9896 × 2347 )
```

EXERCISE 11

Find the following products :

1.
```
    6 8 5 4
  ×     8 9
```

2.
```
  2 6 8 5 7
  ×     6 8
```

3.
```
    9 6 7 5
  ×   9 2 5
```

4.
```
  2 3 6 8 9
  ×   1 3 7
```

5.
```
  1 2 4 5 6
  ×     7 8 4
```

6.
```
  1 9 8 4 7
  ×     3 5 4
```

7.
```
    2 4 6 7
  × 1 3 5 9
```

8.
```
    4 8 7 3
  × 1 7 0 8
```

9.
```
    3 9 4 3
  × 2 3 5 6
```

10.
```
    9 3 5 6
  × 2 4 3 1
```

11.
```
    3 2 6 5
  × 2 7 8 4
```

12.
```
  1 2 8 7 4
  ×   1 3 8 6
```

Multiply :

13. 10654 by 875

14. 14567 by 1065

15. 8985 by 1789

16. 10023 by 1034

17. 20185 by 1648

18. 15487 by 1526

WORD PROBLEMS ON MULTIPLICATION

Example 1. *The cost of a steel almirah is Rs 5975. What is the cost of 864 such almirahs?*

Solution : Cost of 1 almirah = Rs 5975.

Cost of 864 almirahs = Rs (5975 × 864).

```
      5 9 7 5
  ×     8 6 4
  _____
      2 3 9 0 0
    3 5 8 5 0 0
  4 7 8 0 0 0 0
  _____
  5 1 6 2 4 0 0
```

Hence, the cost of 864 almirahs = Rs 5162400.

Example 2. *4912 screws can be packed in one carton. How many screws can be packed in 1475 such cartons?*

Solution : Number of screws in 1 carton = 4912.

Number of screws in 1475 cartons = 4912 × 1475.

```
      4 9 1 2
  ×   1 4 7 5
  _____
      2 4 5 6 0
    3 4 3 8 4 0
  1 9 6 4 8 0 0
  4 9 1 2 0 0 0
  _____
  7 2 4 5 2 0 0
```

Hence, the number of screws to be packed in 1475 cartons is 7245200.

EXERCISE 12

1. The cost of a scooter is Rs 36453. Find the cost of 270 scooters.

2. The cost of a bicycle is Rs 2895. Find the cost of 1486 bicycles.

3. A truck can carry 6785 kg of goods. How much can 759 trucks carry?

4. There are 1483 bags of wheat in a godown. If each bag weighs 108 kg, find the total weight of these bags.

5. A cloth mill produces 3746 metres of cloth in a day. How much cloth will it produce in 286 days ?

6. A box contains 2748 pencils. How many pencils are there in 1674 such boxes ?

7. A bundle of rope measures 548 metres. How much rope will be there in 2367 such bundles ?

8. There are 1869 students on the rolls of a school. If each student pays Rs 27650 as fees annually, how much money is collected in a year ?

9. A newspaper contains 124 colums. Each column contains 136 lines. Each line has 36 letters. How many letters are there in the newspaper ?

Find the continued product :

10. $628 \times 537 \times 96$

11. $2356 \times 126 \times 103$

DIVISION

In class IV, we have learnt how to divide a 4-digit number by a 2-digit number. In the same way, we can divide larger numbers by a two-digit or a three-digit number.

SOLVED EXAMPLES

Example 1. *Divide* 2950682 *by* 35.

Solution :

```
              84305
        35)2950682(2
            280
            150
            140
            106
            105
             182
             175
               7
```

∴ Quotient = 84305, Remainder = 7.

Explanation :

Step 1. Here the divisor is a 2-digit number.

So, consider the number formed by 2 extreme left digits of the dividend.

It is 29. But, 29 < 35.

So, take the number formed by 3 leftmost digits of the dividend.

It is 295.

Let us see how many times 35 is contained in 295.

Now, $35 \times 8 = 280$ and $35 \times 9 = 315$.

$280 < 295$ while $315 > 295$.

$\therefore$ 35 is contained in 295 eight times.

Write 8 in the quotient just above 5 as shown in the solution.

Write 280 below 295 and subtract.

$295 - 280 = 15$.

Step 2. Bring down the next digit, i.e., 0 from the dividend to make 150.

Now, $35 \times 4 = 140$ and $35 \times 5 = 175$.

Clearly, $140 < 150$ and $175 > 150$.

$\therefore$ 35 is contained in 150 four times.

Write 4 in the quotient just next to 8 as shown in the solution.

Write 140 below 150 and subtract.

$150 - 140 = 10$.

Step 3. Bring down the next digit, i.e., 6 from the dividend to make 106.

Now, $35 \times 3 = 105$ and $35 \times 4 = 140$.

Clearly, $105 < 106$ and $140 > 106$.

$\therefore$ 35 is contained in 106 three times.

Write 3 in the quotient just next to 4 as shown in the solution.

Write 105 below 106 and subtract.

$106 - 105 = 1$.

Step 4. Bring down the next digit, i.e., 8 to make 18.

Now, $18 < 35$.

So, 35 goes into 18 zero times.

Write 0 in the quotient just next to 3 as shown in the solution.

$18 - 0 = 18$.

Step 5. Bring down the next digit, i.e., 2 to make 182.

Now, $35 \times 5 = 175$ and $35 \times 6 = 210$.

Clearly, $175 < 182$ and $210 > 182$.

So, 35 goes into 182 five times.

Write 5 in the quotient just next to 0 as shown in the solution.

$182 - 175 = 7$.

Thus, 7 is the remainder.

Hence, Quotient = 84305, Remainder = 7.

Example 2 . *Divide* 2017908 *by* 569.

Solution :

```
                    3 5 4 6
        569 ) 2 0 1 7 9 0 8 (
              1 7 0 7
              ─────────
                3 1 0 9
                2 8 4 5
                ─────────
                  2 6 4 0
                  2 2 7 6
                  ─────────
                    3 6 4 8
                    3 4 1 4
                    ─────────
                      2 3 4
```

∴   Quotient = 3546, Remainder = 234.

Explanation :

Step 1.   The divisor is a 3-digit number.

So, consider the number formed by the 3 leftmost digits of the dividend.

It is 201, which is less than 569.

Thus, we cannot divide 201 by 569.

So, consider the number formed by the 4 leftmost digits of the dividend.

It is 2017.

Let us see how many times 569 goes into 2017.

Now, $569 \times 3 = 1707$ and $569 \times 4 = 2276$.

Clearly, 1707 < 2017 and 2276 > 2017.

Thus, 569 goes into 2017 three times.

Write 3 in the quotient above 7 as shown in the solution.

Write 1707 below 2017 and subtract.

$2017 - 1707 = 310$.

Step 2.   Bring down the next digit, i.e., 9 to make 3109.

Now, $569 \times 5 = 2845$ and $569 \times 6 = 3414$.

Clearly, 2845 < 3109 and 3414 > 3109.

So, 569 goes into 3109 five times.

Write 5 next to 3 in the quotient as shown in the solution.

Write 2845 below 3109 and subtract.

$3109 - 2845 = 264$.

Step 3. Bring down the next digit, i.e., 0 to make 2640.

Now, $569 \times 4 = 2276$ and $569 \times 5 = 2845$.

And, $2276 < 2640$ while $2845 > 2640$.

∴ 569 goes into 2640 four times.

Write 4 next to 5 in the quotient as shown in the solution.

Write 2276 below 2640 and subtract.

$2640 - 2276 = 364$.

Step 4. Bring down the next digit, i.e., 8 to make 3648.

Now, $569 \times 6 = 3414$ and $569 \times 7 = 3983$.

And, $3414 < 3648$ while $3983 > 3648$.

So, 569 goes into 3648 six times.

Write 6 next to 4 in the quotient as shown in the solution.

Write 3414 below 3648 and subtract.

$3648 - 3414 = 234$, which is the remainder.

Thus, Quotient = 3546, Remainder = 234.

Example 3. *Divide 7521000 by 763.*

Solution : We may perform the division as under.

```
                9 8 5 7
   763 ) 7 5 2 1 0 0 0 (
         6 8 6 7
         ─────────
           6 5 4 0
           6 1 0 4
           ─────────
             4 3 6 0
             3 8 1 5
             ─────────
               5 4 5 0
               5 3 4 1
               ─────────
                 1 0 9
```

∴ Quotient = 9857, Remainder = 109.

EXERCISE 13

Divide and find the quotient and remainder :

1. $83254 \div 58$
2. $547802 \div 97$
3. $673900 \div 86$

4. $333624 \div 137$ 5. $598613 \div 243$ 6. $1808016 \div 359$

7. $2265737 \div 479$ 8. $5419307 \div 396$ 9. $8670863 \div 561$

10. $9362596 \div 594$ 11. $6932570 \div 642$ 12. $9736215 \div 937$

13. $8203015 \div 798$ 14. $11911100 \div 697$ 15. $12340560 \div 971$

Find the dividend when :

16. Divisor = 187, Quotient = 3078, Remainder = 96

17. Divisor = 429, Quotient = 5237, Remainder = 248

18. Find the quotient and the remainder when the largest 7-digit number is divided by the largest 3-digit number.

19. Find the quotient and the remainder when the smallest 8-digit number is divided by the largest 2-digit number.

WORD PROBLEMS ON DIVISION

Example 1.   A packet can hold 144 pens. How many packets are required to pack 3845952 pens?

Solution :   Total number of pens = 3845952.

Number of pens that can be packed in 1 packet = 144.

Number of packets required to pack 3845952 pens = $3845952 \div 144$.

```
            2 6 7 0 8
144 ) 3 8 4 5 9 5 2 (
      2 8 8
        9 6 5
        8 6 4
        1 0 1 9
        1 0 0 8
          1 1 5 2
          1 1 5 2
                0
```

Hence, the number of packets required to pack 3845952 pens = 26708.

Example 2.   The cost of 125 refrigerators is Rs 6710625. What is the cost of one refrigerator?

Solution :   The cost of 125 refrigerators = Rs 6710625.

∴ The cost of 1 refrigerator = Rs $(6710625 \div 125)$

```
                    5 3 6 8 5
        125 ) 6 7 1 0 6 2 5 (
              6 2 5
                4 6 0
                3 7 5
                  8 5 6
                  7 5 0
                  1 0 6 2
                  1 0 0 0
                        6 2 5
                        6 2 5
                            0
```

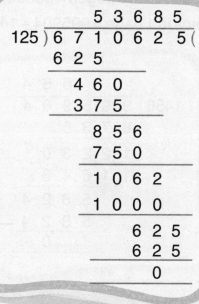

Hence, the cost of one refrigerator is Rs 53685.

Example 3 .   *An industrial organisation collected Rs 7568825 from its shareholders. If the value of each share is Rs 425, what is the total number of shares issued by the organisation?*

Solution :   Total amount collected = Rs 7568825.

Value of each share = Rs 425.

Number of shares issued = 7568825 ÷ 425.

```
                    1 7 8 0 9
        425 ) 7 5 6 8 8 2 5 (
              4 2 5
              3 3 1 8
              2 9 7 5
                3 4 3 8
                3 4 0 0
                    3 8 2 5
                    3 8 2 5
                        0
```

Hence, the number of shares issued by the organisation = 17809.

Example 4 .   *A book of 1456 pages has 995904 words in it. How many words are there in each page? If each page consists of 38 lines, how many words are there in each line?*

Solution :   Number of words in 1456 pages = 995904.

Number of words in 1 page = 995904 ÷ 1456.

```
              6 8 4
1456 ) 9 9 5 9 0 4 (
       8 7 3 6
       1 2 2 3 0
       1 1 6 4 8
           5 8 2 4
           5 8 2 4
                 0
```

∴ The number of words in 1 page = 684.

But, each page has 38 lines.

∴ The number of words in 38 lines = 684.

The number of words in 1 line = 684 ÷ 38

```
          1 8
38 ) 6 8 4 (
     3 8
     3 0 4
     3 0 4
         0
```

Hence, the number of words in each line = 18.

EXERCISE 14

1. A carton can hold 275 screws. How many cartons are required to pack 4426125 screws ?

2. 7359105 pencils are packed equally in 845 boxes. How many pencils are packed in one box ?

3. The cost of 347 radios is Rs 1664212. What is the cost of one radio ?

4. The cost of 736 quintals of wheat is Rs 1214400. Find the cost of one quintal of wheat.

5. 249 trucks can carry 1711875 kg weight. How much weight can be carried by one truck ?

6. 187 water tanks of the same capacity can hold 1323025 litres of water. What is the capacity of each tank ?

7. A calculator costs Rs 845. A shopkeeper collected Rs 742755 by selling the calculators in one month. How many transistors did he sell in one month ?

8. 669375 books are to be arranged equally in shelves. If 375 books are arranged in each shelf, how many shelves will be needed ?

9. 950589 persons visited Appu Ghar in 327 days. How many persons on an average visited Appu Ghar in one day ?

10. 1633500 metres of wire is to be packed in bundles. If each bundle contains 182 metres of wire, how many bundles will be made and how much wire will remain unpacked ?

11. The product of two numbers is 1785483. If one of the numbers is 987, what is the other number ?

THINGS TO REMEMBER

1. In an addition sum, each one of the numbers to be added is called an *addend* & the result of addition is called their *sum*.

2. In a subtraction sum, the larger number is called the *minuend*, the smaller number is called the *subtrahend* and the result of subtraction is called the *difference* between the given numbers.

3. In a multiplication sum, the number to be multiplied is called *multiplicand*, the number by which we multiply is called *multiplier* and the result of multiplication is called *product*.

4. (*a*) The product of two numbers does not change when their order is changed.

   (*b*) The product of three or more numbers does not change when their grouping is changed.

   (*c*) (any number) × 1 = the number itself.   (*d*) (any number) × 0 = 0.

   (*e*) 347 × 568 = 347 × (500 + 60 + 8) = 347 × 500 + 347 × 60 + 347 × 8

5. (*a*) To multiply a given number by 10, insert one zero on the right of the given number.

   (*b*) To multiply a given number by 100, insert two zeros on the right of the given number.

   (*c*) To multiply a given number by 1000, insert three zeros on the right of the given number.

6. In a division sum : *Dividend = (Divisor × Quotient) + Remainder*.

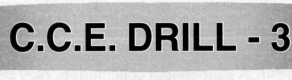

C.C.E. DRILL - 3

(OBJECTIVE-TYPE QUESTIONS)

Tick (✓) the correct answer:

1. In $a - b = c$, a is called
   (*a*) minuend
   (*b*) subtrahend
   (*c*) difference
   (*d*) addend

2. What should be added to 68965 to get 87013?
   (*a*) Rs 17668
   (*b*) Rs 17848
   (*c*) Rs 18048
   (*d*) Rs 18068

3. $3535 \times 101 = ?$
   (*a*) 350035
   (*b*) 353035
   (*c*) 355035
   (*d*) 357035

4. $5749 \times 5 \times 10 \times 0 \times 8 = ?$
   (*a*) 229960
   (*b*) 459920
   (*c*) 2299600
   (*d*) 0

5. Kamal saved Rs 485 every month. How much did he save in 5 years?
   (*a*) Rs 24250
   (*b*) Rs 26675
   (*c*) Rs 28560
   (*d*) Rs 29100

6. $4000 \times 5000 = ?$
   (*a*) 2 lakh
   (*b*) 20 lakh
   (*c*) 2 crore
   (*d*) 2 million

7. A sack holds 560 onions. How many onions can fit in 148 sacks?
   (*a*) 54880
   (*b*) 71680
   (*c*) 77280
   (*d*) 82880

8. $765765 \div 765 = ?$
   (*a*) 11
   (*b*) 101
   (*c*) 1001
   (*d*) not possible

9. Pick out the correct statement:
   (a) When we divide a number by 0, we obtain 0 as the quotient.
   (b) The sum is always greater than each of the addends.
   (c) Dividend is always greater than the divisor.
   (d) $a \times (b + c) = (a \times b) + (a \times c)$.

10. Divide 77664 by 56. Then,
    (a) Q = 1386, R = 46
    (b) Q = 1386, R = 48
    (c) Q = 1387, R = 46
    (d) Q = 1387, R = 48

1. *Find the missing digits:*

   (*a*)
   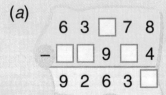
   ```
     6 3 □ 7 8
   - □ □ 9 □ 4
     9 2 6 3 □
   ```

   (*b*)
   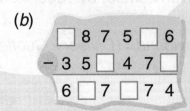
   ```
   □ 8 7 5 □ 6
   - 3 5 □ 4 7 □
     6 □ 7 □ 7 4
   ```

(c)

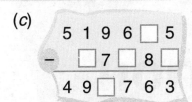

```
  5 1 9 6 □ 5
−   □ 7 □ 8 □
  4 9 □ 7 6 3
```

(d)

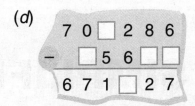

```
  7 0 □ 2 8 6
−   □ 5 6 □ □
  6 7 1 □ 2 7
```

2. Subtract:
(a) 656789 from 2001005
(b) 2635845 from 10101010

3. Fill in the missing numbers:
(a) $635 \times 100 =$ ⬜
(b) $1000 \times 10 =$ ⬜
(c) $8500 \times 100 =$ ⬜
(d) $650 \times 1000 =$ ⬜
(e) $50 \times 40 =$ ⬜
(f) $80 \times 900 =$ ⬜
(g) $6000 \times 200 =$ ⬜
(h) $1674 \times$ ⬜ $= 0$
(i) $2358 \times$ ⬜ $= 2358$
(j) $13 \times 4000 =$ ⬜
(k) $1500 \times 8000 =$ ⬜
(l) $639 \div$ ⬜ $= 639$
(m) $0 \div 289 =$ ⬜
(n) $2657 \div$ ⬜ $= 1$

4. Multiply 9999 by 999.

5. The difference of two numbers is 8, 67, 089. If the smaller number is 25, 76, 977, find the larger one.

6. What must be added to 57, 89, 535 to make it equal to 75 lakh?

7. What number should be subtracted from the sum of 8,93,645 and 6,35,489 to get 10,00,000?

8. A stadium has a capacity of 64070 persons. How many persons should be seated in one row if there are 86 rows?

9. The product of two numbers is 68306. If one of the numbers is 287, find the other.

10. In the year 2010, a ration shop sold 97090 kg of wheat. If equal quantity of wheat was distributed everyday, find the quantity of wheat sold per day. Also, find the quantity of wheat sold altogether in the months of February and March.

11. A state has 1,76,67,314 male voters and 1,48,75,699 female voters. In an election 7,85,195 voters did not vote. How many people cast their vote in the election?

12. To buy a plot of land, Mr. Gupta paid Rs 68650 every month for 8 years. How much did he pay in all?

13. Find the greatest number of five digits that is divisible by 25.

14. Toffees are packed in fancy packs of 256 toffees each. How many packs will be needed to pack 68900 toffees? How many toffees will be left?

15. In a factory, 493056 clips were packed in 384 boxes. How many clips will be packed in 495 boxes?

16. Find the product of the greatest and the smallest three-digit numbers formed with the digits 6, 3 and 8.

SIMPLIFICATION

NUMERICAL EXPRESSIONS

A combination of numbers connected by one or more of the symbols +, −, ×, ÷ and of, is called a **numerical expression.**

Thus, (*i*) $15 + 8 \div 4 - 6$ (*ii*) $16 - 4 \times 3 + 8 \div 2$

are examples of numerical expressions.

On performing the operations involved in an expression, we obtain a value of the expression.

Performing these operations is called the **simplification** *of the expression.*

In order to get a unique value of a given expression, we have to perform the operations strictly in a definite order given below:

     (*i*) **Division**   (*ii*) **Multiplication**   (*iii*) **Addition**   (*iv*) **Subtraction**

Be careful, we cannot change the order of these operations.

Remember the word '**DMAS**', Where

      D stands for **Division**;   **M** stands for **Multiplication**;

      A stands for **Addition**;   **S** stands for **Subtraction**.

SOLVED EXAMPLES

Example 1. *Simplify:* $60 - 48 \div 6 \times 4 + 8$.

Solution: We have

$$60 - 48 \div 6 \times 4 + 8 = 60 - 8 \times 4 + 8 \quad [\div \text{ simplified}]$$
$$= 60 - 32 + 8 \quad [\times \text{ simplified}]$$
$$= 68 - 32 \quad [+ \text{ simplified}]$$
$$= 36.$$

Example 2. *Simplify:* $39 - 16 + 18 \times 9 \div 3$.

Solution: We have

$$39 - 16 + 18 \times 9 \div 3 = 39 - 16 + 18 \times 3 \quad [\div \text{ simplified}]$$
$$= 39 - 16 + 54 \quad [\times \text{ simplified}]$$
$$= 39 + 54 - 16$$
$$= 93 - 16 \quad [+ \text{ simplified}]$$
$$= 77.$$

Example 3. *Simplify:* $100 - 56 \div 7 + 15 \times 2$.

Solution: We have

$$100 - 56 \div 7 + 15 \times 2 = 100 - 8 + 15 \times 2 \quad [\div \text{ simplified}]$$
$$= 100 - 8 + 30 \quad [\times \text{ simplified}]$$
$$= 100 + 30 - 8$$
$$= 130 - 8 \quad [+ \text{ simplified}]$$
$$= 122.$$

EXERCISE 15

Simplify:

1. $12 + 9 \div 3$
2. $16 \times 8 \div 4$
3. $23 - 8 \times 2$
4. $32 \div 8 + 4 \times 6 - 2$
5. $100 - 72 \div 8 + 4 \times 3$
6. $30 + 75 \div 15 \times 4 - 18$
7. $8 \times 6 + 24 \div 6 - 18$
8. $56 - 36 \div 4 \times 2 + 7$
9. $56 \div 14 \times 3 - 10 \div 5 + 1$
10. $98 - 42 \times 15 \div 5 + 6$
11. $105 \times 14 \div 7 + 6 - 1$
12. $17 + 34 \div 17 \times 5 - 20$

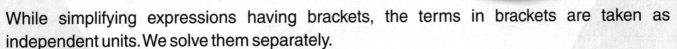
USE OF BRACKETS

We know that the **grouping symbols** called **brackets** are used to separate various parts of an expression.

There are four kinds of brackets:

(i)	**Bar** or **Vinculum**	—
(ii)	**Round Brackets** or **Small brackets**	( )
(iii)	**Curly Brackets** or **Braces**	{ }
(iv)	**Square Brackets** or **Big brackets**	[ ]

While simplifying expressions having brackets, the terms in brackets are taken as independent units. We solve them separately.

The order of working with brackets is given below:

(*i*) Bar   (*ii*) Small brackets
(*iii*) Curly brackets   (*iv*) Big brackets

To simplify expressions involving brackets we must proceed in the order of the letters of the word, '**BODMAS**'.

Here **B, O, D, M, A, S** stand for *Bracket, of, Division, Multiplication, Addition* and *Subtraction* respectively.

Note: In the absence of any sign before a bracket, we take the sign as multiplication.

SOLVED EXAMPLES

Example 1. *Simplify:* $12 - [20 \div \{8 - 2(9 - 5 - 2)\}]$

Solution: We have

$12 - [20 \div \{8 - 2(9 - 5 - 2)\}]$

$\quad = 12 - [20 \div \{8 - 2 \times 2\}]$ [*Removing small brackets*]

$\quad = 12 - [20 \div \{8 - 4\}]$

$\quad = 12 - [20 \div 4]$ [*Removing braces*]

$\quad = 12 - 5$ [*Removing big brackets*]

$\quad = 7.$

Example 2. *Simplify:* $[24 \div \{10 - (8 - \overline{6 - 2})\}]$

Solution: We have

$[24 \div \{10 - (8 - \overline{6 - 2})\}] = [24 \div \{10 - (8 - 4)\}]$ [*Removing bar*]

$\quad\quad\quad\quad\quad\quad\quad\quad\quad = [24 \div \{10 - 4\}]$ [*Removing small brackets*]

$\quad\quad\quad\quad\quad\quad\quad\quad\quad = 24 \div 6$ [*Removing braces*]

$\quad\quad\quad\quad\quad\quad\quad\quad\quad = 4.$ [*Removing big brackets*]

EXERCISE 16

Simplify:

1. $20 - \{18 \div (7 - 2 + 1)\}$ 2. $23 - [6 + \{8 - (9 - 6)\}]$

3. $2[19 - \{7 + (12 \div 4)\}]$ 4. $40 - [12 + \{16 - (12 \div 3)\}]$

5. $[\{(30 - \overline{9 - 6}) \div 3\} \times 6 + 6]$ 6. $12 - [6 \div 3 + \{8 \div 2(8 - 6)\}]$

7. $[40 \div \{19 - 3(6 - \overline{4 - 1})\}]$ 8. $[105 \div \{23 + 2(9 - \overline{5 - 2})\}]$

THINGS TO REMEMBER

1. For simplifying an expression, the order of performing the various operations should be strictly in the following order :

   (*i*) *Brackets*   (*ii*) *of*   (*iii*) *Division*   (*iv*) *Multiplication*
   (*v*) *Addition*   (*vi*) *Subtraction*

2. Remember the word '**BODMAS**', where the letters **B, O, D, M, A, S** stand for *Brackets, Of, Division, Multiplication, Addition* and *Subtraction* respectively.

C.C.E. DRILL - 4

QUESTION BAG - 1

(OBJECTIVE-TYPE QUESTIONS)

Tick (✓) the correct answer:

1. Which of the following operations is performed first in simplifying a numerical expression?
   (*a*) +   (*b*) −   (*c*) ×   (*d*) ÷

2. $8 \times 8 - 8 = ?$
   (*a*) 0   (*b*) 1   (*c*) 56   (*d*) 64

3. $100 \div 10 + 10 \times 10 = ?$
   (*a*) 1   (*b*) 50   (*c*) 110   (*d*) 200

4. Which of the following types of brackets is simplified first?
   (*a*) Bar   (*b*) Round bracket   (*c*) Curly bracket   (*d*) Square bracket

5. $49 \div 7 \times 7 + 5 \times 3 - 2 = ?$
   (*a*) 6   (*b*) 14   (*c*) 54   (*d*) 62

6. $63 \div 9 + 12 \times 4 - 5 = ?$
   (*a*) 7   (*b*) 23   (*c*) 50   (*d*) 71

7. $100 \times 10 - 100 + 2000 \div 100 = ?$
   (*a*) 29   (*b*) 780   (*c*) 920   (*d*) 979

8. $5751 \times \{45 - (90 \div 2)\} = 0$
   (*a*) 0   (*b*) 639   (*c*) 5751   (*d*) None of these

QUESTION BAG - 2

1. *Fill in the blanks :*
   (*a*) $5 - 6 + 3 =$ (*b*) $3 \times 8 \div 4 =$
   (*c*) $6 + 6 - 6 \div 6 \times 6 =$ (*d*) $4 + 4 + 4 + 4 \div 4 =$
   (*e*) $100 + 50 \times 2 =$ (*f*) $80 + 800 \div 8 =$
   (*g*) $15 \times 5 - 60 \div 15 =$ (*h*) $16 + 8 \div 4 - 2 \times 3 =$
   (*i*) $21 \div 7 + 16 - 5 \times 3 =$ (*j*) $5 \times 50 + 57 - 57 \div 57 =$

2. *Simplify :*
   (*a*) $289 + 153 \div 17 - 8 \times 19$ (*b*) $7614 + 832 \times 48 \div 16 - 8$
   (*c*) $7823 - 128 \div 16 \text{ of } 4 - 3973$ (*d*) $80 + [20 \times \{20 - (10 \div 5)\}]$
   (*e*) $[\{64 - (12 + 13)\} \div 3] + 15$ (*f*) $10 \times 10 + [400 \div \{100 - (50 - \overline{3 \times 10})\}]$

3. *State whether each of the following statements is true or false:*
   (*a*) $8 \times 9 \div 9 = (8 \times 9) \div 9$ ....
   (*b*) In simplification, we simplify 'of' before multiplication.   ....
   (*c*) $15 \times 2 + 120 \div 20 - 8 < 15 \times 2 + 120 \div (20 - 8)$ ....
   (*d*) $45 \div 3 \times 5 = 45 \div (3 \times 5)$ ....
   (*e*) $26 - 3 \times 8 \div 4 = 26 - (3 \times 8) \div 4$ ....

6

FACTORS AND MULTIPLES

In class IV, we studied the concept of factors and multiples. Let us review these definitions.

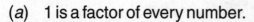

FACTORS AND MULTIPLES

*When a number divides another number exactly, then the divisor is called a **factor** of the dividend.*

*And, the dividend is called a **multiple** of the divisor.*

Example 1. We know that 5 divides 15 exactly.

∴ 5 is a factor of 15. And, 15 is a multiple of 5.

Example 2. (*a*) All factors of 4 are 1, 2, 4.   (*b*) All factors of 6 are 1, 2, 3, 6.

(*c*) All factors of 12 are 1, 2, 3 ,4, 6, 12.

Example 3. (*a*) First five multiples of 4 are 4, 8, 12, 16, 20.

(*b*) First five multiples of 5 are 5, 10, 15, 20, 25.

(*c*) First five multiples of 6 are 6, 12, 18, 24, 30.

PROPERTIES OF FACTORS

(*a*) 1 is a factor of every number.

(*b*) Every non-zero number is a factor of itself.

(*c*) A factor of a non-zero number is less than or equal to the number.

(*d*) 1 is the only number having one factor, namely itself.

(*e*) Every non-zero number other than 1 has at least two factors, namely 1 and itself.

(*f*) Every non-zero number is a factor of 0.

PROPERTIES OF MULTIPLES

(*a*) *Every number is a multiple of 1.*

   Examples : $2 = 1 \times 2, 3 = 1 \times 3, 4 = 1 \times 4$ etc.

(*b*) *Every number is a multiple of itself.*

   Examples : $2 = 2 \times 1, 3 = 3 \times 1, 4 = 4 \times 1$ etc.

(*c*) *Every non-zero multiple of a non-zero number is greater than or equal to the number.*

   Examples: Multiples of 2 are 2, 4, 6, 8,........etc. and clearly, each one of them is ≥ 2.

(d)   We can find as many multiples of a non-zero number as we want.

   Example: Multiples of 2 are 2, 4, 6, 8, 10, ..., which are infinitely many.

(e)   *0 is a multiple of every number.*

EVEN AND ODD NUMBERS

EVEN NUMBERS: *Counting numbers which are exactly divisible by 2 are called* **even numbers.**

Thus, every even number has 0, 2, 4, 6 or 8 as its unit digit.

Examples: 162, 374, 906 and 618 are all even numbers.

ODD NUMBERS: *Counting numbers which are not exactly divisible by 2 are called* **odd numbers.**

Thus, every odd number has 1, 3, 5, 7 or 9 as its unit digit.

Examples: 231, 543, 915, 167, 489 are all odd numbers.

TESTS OF DIVISIBILITY

1.   **Test of Divisibility By 2:**

   A number is divisible by 2 if its unit digit is any one of 0, 2, 4, 6 and 8.

   Examples: (a)   Each of the numbers 612, 354, 576, 938 and 730 is divisible by 2.

   (b)   None of 351, 423, 605, 867 and 219 is divisible by 2.

2.   **Test of Divisibility by 3:**

   A number is divisible by 3 if the sum of its digits is divisible by 3.

   Examples : (a)   Consider the number 16701.

   Sum of its digits = $(1 + 6 + 7 + 0 + 1)$ = 15, which is divisible by 3.

   $\therefore$ 16701 is divisible by 3.

   (b)   Consider the number 78421.

   Sum of its digits = $(7 + 8 + 4 + 2 + 1)$ = 22, which is not divisible by 3.

   $\therefore$ 78421 is not divisible by 3.

3.   **Test of Divisiblity By 4:**

   A number is divisible by 4 if the number formed by its last two digits on its extreme right is divisible by 4.

   Examples : (a)   Consider the number 58236.

   The number formed by its last two digits is 36, which is divisible by 4.

   $\therefore$ 58236 is divisible by 4.

   (b)   Consider the number 459106.

   The number formed by its last two digits is 06, which is not divisible by 4.

   $\therefore$ 459106 is not divisible by 4.

4. Test of Divisibility By 5:

A number is divisible by 5 if its unit digit is 0 or 5.

Examples : (a) Each of the numbers 5790, 7300, 2345 and 1085 has unit digit as 0 or 5. So, each one is divisible by 5.

(b) Look at the numbers 1643, 3952, 4721, 5087. None of them has 0 or 5 as the unit digit. So, none of them is divisible by 5.

5. Test of Divisibility By 6:

A number is divisible by 6 if it is divisible by each one of 2 and 3.

Examples : (a) Consider the number 75864.

Its unit digit is 4. So, it is divisible by 2.

Sum of its digits = (7 + 5 + 8 + 6 + 4) = 30, which is divisible by 3.

So, the given number is divisible by 3.

Thus, it is divisible by each one of 2 and 3.

Hence, 75864 is divisible by 6.

(b) Consider the number 27568.

Its unit digit is 8. So, it is divisible by 2.

Sum of its digits = (2 + 7 + 5 + 6 + 8) = 28, which is not divisible by 3.

So, the given number is not divisible by 3.

Hence, 27568 is not divisible by 6.

6. Test of Divisibililty By 7:

Step 1. *Double the digit at ones place.*

Step 2. *Find the difference between the number obtained in step 1 and the number formed by rest of its digits.*

Step 3. *If the number so obtained is divisible by 7, then the given number is divisible by 7.*

Examples : (a) Consider the number 6895.

Now, 689 − (2 × 5) = (689 − 10) = 679, which is divisible by 7.

∴ 6895 is divisible by 7.

(b) Consider the number 727.

Now, 72 − (2 × 7) = (72 − 14) = 58, which is not divisible by 7.

∴ 727 is not divisible by 7.

7. Test of Divisibility By 8:

A number is divisible by 8 if the number formed by its last 3 digits on its extreme right is divisible by 8.

Examples : (a) Consider the number 6753104.

The number formed by its last three digits is 104, which is divisible by 8.

· 6753104 is divisible by 8.

(*b*) Consider the number 5978164.

The number formed by its last three digits is 164, which is not divisible by 8.

∴ 5978164 is not divisible by 8.

8. Test of Divisibility By 9:

A number is divisible by 9 if the sum of its digits is divisible by 9.

Examples : (*a*) Consider the number 867105.

Sum of its digits = (8 + 6 + 7 + 1 + 0 + 5) = 27, which is divisible by 9.

∴ 867105 is divisible by 9.

(*b*) Consider the number 5632104.

Sum of its digits = (5 + 6 + 3 + 2 + 1 + 0 + 4) = 21, which is not divisible by 9.

∴ 5632104 is not divisible by 9.

9. Test of Divisibility By 10:

A number is divisible by 10 only when its unit digit is 0.

Examples : (*a*) Each of the numbers 6340, 5910, 107300 has 0 as its unit digit. So, each one is divisible by 10.

(*b*) The unit digit of each of the numbers 1685, 2734, 7921, 6053, 9718 is other than 0.

So, none of them is divisible by 10.

10. Test of Divisibility By 11:

A number is divisible by 11 if the difference between the sum of digits at odd places and the sum of digits at even places is either 0 or a multiple of 11.

(*a*) Consider the number 75438.

Sum of its digits at odd places = (8 + 4 + 7) = 19.

Sum of its digits at even places = (3 + 5) = 8.

Their difference = (19 − 8) = 11, which is divisible by 11.

∴ 75438 is divisible by 11.

(*b*) Consider the number 497365.

Sum of its digits at odd places = (5 + 3 + 9) = 17.

Sum of its digits at even places = (6 + 7 + 4) = 17.

Their difference = (17 − 17) = 0.

∴ 497365 is divisible by 11.

(*c*) Consider the number 623411.

Sum of its digits at odd places = (1 + 4 + 2) = 7.

Sum of its digits at even places = (1 + 3 + 6) = 10.

Their difference = (10 − 7) = 3, which is not divisible by 11.

∴ 623411 is not divisible by 11.

EXERCISE 17

1. Write first six multiples of:
   - (a) 6
   - (b) 11
   - (c) 19
   - (d) 21
   - (e) 25

2. Write all the factors of each of the following numbers:
   - (a) 18
   - (b) 28
   - (c) 32
   - (d) 45
   - (e) 60

3. Which of the following numbers are divisible by 2?
   - (a) 976
   - (b) 670
   - (c) 843
   - (d) 5694
   - (e) 7358
   - (f) 2890
   - (g) 1985
   - (h) 299

4. Which of the following numbers are divisible by 3?
   - (a) 837
   - (b) 1493
   - (c) 26412
   - (d) 37401
   - (e) 16339
   - (f) 23571
   - (g) 42105
   - (h) 31547

5. Which of the following numbers are divisible by 4?
   - (a) 894
   - (b) 1056
   - (c) 2360
   - (d) 7130
   - (e) 16338
   - (f) 69704
   - (g) 24842
   - (h) 97312

6. Which of the following numbers are divisible by 5?
   - (a) 1980
   - (b) 1785
   - (c) 3206
   - (d) 27905
   - (e) 2730
   - (f) 6309
   - (g) 9915
   - (h) 3617

7. Which of the following numbers are divisible by 6?
   - (a) 3132
   - (b) 5704
   - (c) 8316
   - (d) 9430
   - (e) 7038
   - (f) 17703
   - (g) 7812
   - (h) 8721

8. Which of the following numbers are divisible by 7?
   - (a) 252
   - (b) 1204
   - (c) 5843
   - (d) 8036
   - (e) 9308
   - (f) 3045
   - (g) 7833
   - (h) 5233

9. Which of the following numbers are divisible by 8?
   - (a) 1372
   - (b) 10568
   - (c) 62156
   - (d) 50432
   - (e) 73152
   - (f) 796504
   - (g) 59238
   - (h) 279136

10. Which of the following numbers are divisible by 9?
    - (a) 8316
    - (b) 7509
    - (c) 4186
    - (d) 26901
    - (e) 50553
    - (f) 12501
    - (g) 3499
    - (h) 20367

11. Which of the following numbers are divisible by 10?
    - (a) 1155
    - (b) 2960
    - (c) 8740
    - (d) 2068

12. Which of the following numbers are divisible by 11?
    - (a) 2101
    - (b) 32571
    - (c) 35064
    - (d) 20833
    - (e) 17622
    - (f) 58564
    - (g) 101011
    - (h) 202202

1 9

13. *Separate even and odd numbers from the following:*

    (*a*) 23   (*b*) 36   (*c*) 41   (*d*) 87

    (*e*) 60   (*f*) 74   (*g*) 258   (*h*) 605

14. *Write all even numbers between*

    (*a*) 73 and 87   (*b*) 519 and 531

15. *Write all odd numbers between*

    (*a*) 64 and 80   (*b*) 624 and 640

PRIME AND COMPOSITE NUMBERS

PRIME NUMBERS : *A number having exactly two different factors, namely 1 and itself is called a **prime number.***

Examples : Each of the following numbers is a prime number:

    2, 3, 5, 7, 11, 13, 17, 19, 23, 29, 31, 37

COMPOSITE NUMBERS : *A number having more than two different factors is called a **composite number.***

Examples : Each of the following numbers is a composite number:

    4, 6, 8, 9, 12, 14, 15, 16, 18, 20, 21, 22, 24

Note 1. Clearly, 1 has only one factor, namely 1 itself.

    ∴ 1 is neither prime nor composite.

Note 2. The smallest prime number is 2 and it is the only even prime number.

TO FIND ALL PRIME NUMBERS BETWEEN 1 AND 100:

About 230 B.C. a Greek mathematician Eratosthenes developed the method of finding prime numbers upto 100. This method gives us a grid, known as Sieve of Eratosthenes, given below.

METHOD : Write down the numbers from 1 to 100 in 10 rows and proceed as under.

    Step 1 : Cross out 1.

    Step 2 : Encircle 2 and cross out remaining multiples of 2, i.e. 4, 6, 8, 10, ...

    Step 3 : Encircle 3 and cross out remaining multiples of 3, i.e. 6, 9, 12, 15, ...

    Step 4 : Encircle 5 and cross out remaining multiples of 5, i.e. 10, 15, 20, ...

    Step 5 : Encircle 7 and cross out remaining multiples of 7, i.e. 14, 21, 28, ...

    Step 6 : Now, encircle each one of the remaining numbers.

X	2	3	X	5	X	7	X	X	10
11	12	13	14	15	16	17	18	19	20
21	22	23	24	25	26	27	28	29	30
31	32	33	34	35	36	37	38	39	40
41	42	43	44	45	46	47	48	49	50
51	52	53	54	55	56	57	58	59	60
61	62	63	64	65	66	67	68	69	70
71	72	73	74	75	76	77	78	79	80
81	82	83	84	85	86	87	88	89	90
91	92	93	94	95	96	97	98	99	100

Sieve of Eratosthenes

All the encircled numbers are the prime numbers, and all the crossed out numbers are composite numbers. Thus, there are 25 prime numbers between 1 and 100.

Thus, all prime numbers between 1 and 100 are:

2, 3, 5, 7, 11, 13, 17, 19, 23, 29, 31, 37, 41, 43, 47, 53, 59, 61, 67, 71, 73, 79, 83, 89 and 97.

TWIN PRIMES : *Prime numbers which differ by 2 are called* **twin primes.**

Examples :   (3 and 5), (5 and 7), (11 and 13), (17 and 19), (29 and 31), (41 and 43), (59 and 61), (71 and 73) etc. are all pairs of twin primes.

CO-PRIMES : *Two numbers are said to be **co-primes** if they have only 1 as their common factor.*

Examples: (*a*) 3 and 4 are co-primes.   (*b*) 4 and 9 are co-primes.
(*c*) 8 and 15 are co-primes.   (*d*) 21 and 25 are co-primes.

SOLVED EXAMPLES

Example 1.   *Separate the prime and composite numbers from the following:*
18, 23, 39, 43 and 81

Solution :   We know that a number having exactly two factors is a prime number and the one having more than two factors is a composite number.

Factors of 18 are 1, 2, 3, 6, 9, 18. Thus, 18 has more than two factors.

∴ 18 is a composite number.

Factors of 23 are 1 and 23. Thus, 23 has exactly two factors.

∴ 23 is a prime number.

Factors of 39 are 1, 3, 13, 39. Thus, 39 has more than two factors.

∴ 39 is a composite number.

Factors of 43 are 1 and 43. Thus, 43 has exactly two factors.

∴ 43 is a prime number.

Factors of 81 are 1, 3, 9, 27 and 81. Thus, 81 has more than two factors.

∴ 81 is a composite number.

Hence, out of the given numbers 23 and 43 are prime numbers while 18, 39 and 81 are composite numbers.

PRIME FACTORISATION

Expressing a given number as the product of prime numbers is called the **prime factorisation** of the given numbers.

Example 2. Write the prime factorisation using division method:

(a) 90   (b) 468

Solution : We have:

(a)
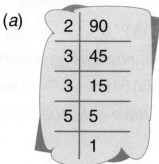

∴ 90 = (2 × 3 × 3 × 5).

(b)
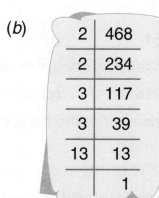

∴ 468 = (2 × 2 × 3 × 3 × 13)

Example 3. Write the prime factorisation by drawing the factor tree.

(a) 180   (b) 630

Solution : We have

(a)
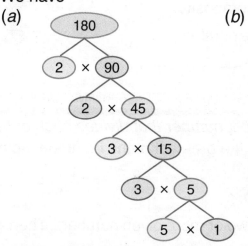

∴ 180 = (2 × 2 × 3 × 3 × 5).

(b)
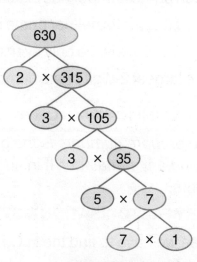

∴ 630 = (2 × 3 × 3 × 5 × 7)

1. *Which of the following numbers are prime numbers?*

   1, 11, 21, 57, 67, 19, 91, 63, 83, 89

2. *Which of the following numbers are composite numbers?*

   1, 79, 97, 51, 61, 87, 81, 78, 93, 47

3. List all prime numbers between 1 and 50.

4. List all prime numbers between 51 and 100.

5. List all twin-primes between 1 and 50.

6. List six consecutive composite numbers less than 100.

7. Give four examples of pairs of co-primes.

8. *Write the prime factorisation of each of the following numbers using division by prime numbers:*

   (*a*) 60   (*b*) 84   (*c*) 180   (*d*) 210   (*e*) 728

9. *Write the prime factorisation of each of the following numbers using factor tree:*

   (*a*) 90   (*b*) 216   (*c*) 300   (*d*) 315   (*e*) 450

10. *Give examples of 4 pairs of prime numbers which have only one composite number between them.*

11. *Fill in the blanks:*

    (*a*) .... is a factor of every number.

    (*b*) The least prime number is ....

    (*c*) The smallest composite number is ....

    (*d*) Each prime number has exactly .... factors.

    (*e*) .... is neither prime nor composite.

    (*f*) .... is the only even prime number.

    (*g*) The largest 2-digit prime number is ....

HIGHEST COMMON FACTOR (H.C.F.) OR GREATEST COMMON DIVISOR (G.C.D.)

H.C.F of two or more numbers is the greatest number that divides each of the numbers without leaving any remainder. It in, in fact, the greatest of the common factors of the given numbers.

1. **H.C.F. BY FACTORISATION METHOD:**

   Suppose we have to find the H.C.F. of two or more given numbers. Then, we proceed as under.

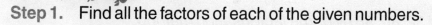

Step 1. Find all the factors of each of the given numbers.

Step 2. Find their common factors.

Step 3. The largest of the common factors is the H.C.F. of the given numbers.

SOLVED EXAMPLES

Example 1. *Find the H.C.F. of 24 and 32.*

Solution : We have

$24 = (1 \times 24); 24 = (2 \times 12); 24 = (3 \times 8)$ and $24 = (4 \times 6)$.

∴ All the factors of 24 are : $\boxed{1, 2, 3, 4, 6, 8, 12, 24}$

Again, $32 = (1 \times 32); 32 = (2 \times 16); 32 = (4 \times 8)$.

∴ All the factors of 32 are : $\boxed{1, 2, 4, 8, 16, 32}$

Common factors of 24 and 32 are : $\boxed{1, 2, 4, 8}$

∴ H.C.F. of 24 and 32 is 8.

Example 2. *Find the H.C.F. of 18, 24 and 30.*

Solution : We have

$18 = 1 \times 18; 18 = 2 \times 9; 18 = 3 \times 6$.

∴ All the factors of 18 are : $\boxed{1, 2, 3, 6, 9, 18}$

Again, $24 = 1 \times 24; 24 = 2 \times 12; 24 = 3 \times 8; 24 = 4 \times 6$.

∴ All the factors of 24 are : $\boxed{1, 2, 3, 4, 6, 8, 12, 24}$

Next, $30 = 1 \times 30; 30 = 2 \times 15; 30 = 3 \times 10; 30 = 5 \times 6$.

∴ All the factors of 30 are : $\boxed{1, 2, 3, 5, 6, 10, 15, 30}$

∴ Common factors of 18, 24 and 30 are : $\boxed{1, 2, 3, 6}$

∴ H.C.F. of 18, 24 and 30 = 6.

2. H.C.F. BY PRIME FACTORISATION METHOD:

Example 3. *Find the H.C.F. of 72 and 90 by prime factorisation method.*

Solution : By prime factorisation, we have

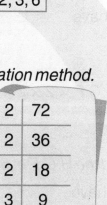

$72 = 2 \times 2 \times 2 \times 3 \times 3, 90 = 2 \times 3 \times 3 \times 5$.

∴ H.C.F. of 72 and 90

= Product of common prime factors of 72 and 90

$= (2 \times 3 \times 3) = 18$.

Hence, the H.C.F. of 72 and 90 is 18.

2	72
2	36
2	18
3	9
3	3
	1

2	90
3	45
3	15
5	5
	1

Example 4. *Find the H.C.F. of 32, 80, 96 by prime factorisation method.*

Solution :

2	32
2	16
2	8
2	4
2	2
	1

2	80
2	40
2	20
2	10
5	5
	1

2	96
2	48
2	24
2	12
2	6
3	3
	1

∴ $32 = 2 \times 2 \times 2 \times 2 \times 2$, $80 = 2 \times 2 \times 2 \times 2 \times 5$ and $96 = 2 \times 2 \times 2 \times 2 \times 2 \times 3$.

∴ H.C.F. = Product of all common factors of 32, 80, 96

$= 2 \times 2 \times 2 \times 2 = 16$.

Hence, the H.C.F. of 32, 80, 96 is 16.

3. H.C.F. BY COMMON DIVISION METHOD :

Step 1 : Arrange the given numbers in a line in any order.

Step 2 : Divide the numbers by the lowest common prime number. Write the quotients below the numbers.

Step 3 : Then divide the quotients by the lowest common prime number.

Step 4 : Repeat the process till there are no common prime numbers to divide by.

Step 5 : The product of the divisors is the required H.C.F.

Example 5. *Find the H.C.F. of 60 and 72.*

Solution : We have

2	60, 72
2	30, 36
3	15, 18
	5, 6

∴ H.C.F. = $2 \times 2 \times 3 = 12$.

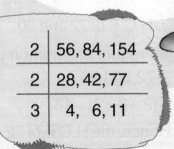

Example 6. *Find the H.C.F. of 56, 84 and 154.*

Solution : We have

2	56, 84, 154
2	28, 42, 77
3	4, 6, 11

∴ H.C.F. = $2 \times 7 = 14$.

3. H.C.F. BY DIVISION METHOD:

Suppose we have to find the H.C.F. of two large numbers.

Then, we proceed as under :

Step 1 : Divide the larger number by the smaller number. Obtain the remainder.

Step 2 : Divide the divisor by the remainder.

Step 3 : Repeat the process of dividing the previous divisor by the remainder last obtained till 0 is obtained as remainder.

Then, the last divisor is the required H.C.F.

Example 7. *Find the H.C.F. of 135 and 180 by division method.*

Solution :

```
135 ) 180 ( 1
      135
      ‾‾‾‾‾
   45 ) 135 ( 3
        135
        ‾‾‾‾
          0
```

∴ H.C.F. of 135 and 180 is 45.

H.C.F. of three numbers = H.C.F. of [(H.C.F. of any two numbers) and 3ʳᵈ number]

Example 8. *Find the H.C.F. of 217, 385 and 735.*

Solution : First we find the H.C.F. of any two numbers.

Let us take 217 and 385.

```
217 ) 385 ( 1
      217
      ‾‾‾‾
  168 ) 217 ( 1
        168
        ‾‾‾‾
      49 ) 168 ( 3
           147
           ‾‾‾
        21 ) 49 ( 2
             42
             ‾‾‾
           7 ) 21 ( 3
               21
               ‾‾‾
                0
```

So, the H.C.F. of 217 and 385 is 7.

Now, we find the H.C.F. of 7 and 735.

```
7 )735( 105
   7
   ——
   35
   35
   ——
    0
```

Thus, 7 divides 735 completely.

∴ H.C.F. of 7 and 735 is 7.

Hence, the H.C.F. of 217, 385 and 735 is 7.

Example 9. *Find the H.C.F. of 594, 792 and 1848 by the division method.*

Solution : We first find the H.C.F. of 594 and 792.

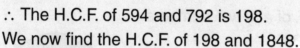

```
198 )792( 1
     594
     ————
 198 )594( 3
      594
      ————
        0
```

∴ The H.C.F. of 594 and 792 is 198.

We now find the H.C.F. of 198 and 1848.

```
198 )1948( 9
     1782
     ————
   66 )198( 3
       198
       ————
         0
```

∴ The H.C.F. of 198 and 1848 is 66.

Hence, the H.C.F. of 594, 792 and 1848 is 66.

EXERCISE 19

1. Find the H.C.F. of:

   (*a*) 16 and 24   (*b*) 18 and 27   (*c*) 32 and 40

   (*d*) 8, 20 and 32   (*e*) 14, 28 and 35   (*f*) 16, 20 and 36

2. Find, by prime factorisation, the H.C.F. of:

   (a) 45 and 60   (b) 36 and 54   (c) 48 and 60

   (d) 75 and 90   (e) 52 and 78   (f) 72 and 108

   (g) 42 and 112   (h) 54 and 114   (i) 168 and 216

3. Find the H.C.F. of the following numbers, using prime factorisation:

   (a) 24, 40 and 56   (b) 36, 48 and 72   (c) 42, 63 and 105

   (d) 112, 140 and 168 (e) 144, 180 and 252 (f) 91, 49 and 112

4. Find the H.C.F. of the following numbers by the common division method :

   (a) 24 and 80   (b) 18 and 48   (c) 165 and 220

   (d) 48, 80 and 96   (e) 42, 70 and 112   (f) 144, 180 and 192

5. Find the H.C.F. of the following numbers, using division method :

   (a) 96 and 120   (b) 81 and 108   (c) 144 and 312

   (d) 252 and 576   (e) 575 and 920   (f) 605 and 935

6. Find the H.C.F. of the following numbers, using division method :

   (a) 60, 96 and 150   (b) 75, 100 and 140

   (c) 270, 945 and 2175   (d) 902, 1394 and 3321

LEAST COMMON MULTIPLE (L.C.M.)

The **L.C.M.** of two or more given numbers is the smallest multiple of each of the given numbers.

For example, let us consider the numbers 4 and 6.

The multiples of 4 are 4, 8, 12, 16, 20, 24, 28, ...

The multiples of 6 are 6, 12, 18, 24, 30, ...

The common multiples of 4 and 6 are 12, 24, ...

∴ The least common multiple of 4 and 6 is 12.

Hence, the L.C.M. of 4 and 6 = 12.

1. **TO FIND L.C.M. BY PRIME FACTORISATION METHOD:**

   Step 1. Resolve each of the given numbers into product of prime factors.

   Step 2. The L.C.M. of the given numbers is the product of all different prime factors, taking the common prime factors occurring maximum number of times.

Example 1. Find the L.C.M. of 48 and 72 by prime factorisation.

Solution : We first resolve 48 and 72 into products of prime factors as shown below:

2	48
2	24
2	12
2	6
3	3
	1

2	72
2	36
2	18
3	9
3	3
	1

$48 = 2 \times 2 \times 2 \times 2 \times 3$ and $72 = 2 \times 2 \times 2 \times 3 \times 3$

Here, 2 appears maximum 4 times in one of the prime factorisations;

3 appears maximum 2 times in one of the prime factorisations.

Now, we take 2 four times and 3 two times and multiply to get the L.C.M.

$\therefore$ L.C.M. of 48 and 72 $= 2 \times 2 \times 2 \times 2 \times 3 \times 3 = 144$.

Example 2. *Find the L.C.M. of 90, 108 and 144 by prime factorisation method.*

Solution : Resolving each of the given numbers into prime factors, we get :

2	90
3	45
3	15
5	5
	1

2	108
2	54
3	27
3	9
3	3
	1

2	144
2	72
2	36
2	18
3	9
3	3
	1

$90 = 2 \times 3 \times 3 \times 5$, $108 = 2 \times 2 \times 3 \times 3 \times 3$, $144 = 2 \times 2 \times 2 \times 2 \times 3 \times 3$.

2 appears maximum 4 times in one of the prime factorisations;

3 appears maximum 3 times in one of the prime factorisations;

5 appears maximum 1 time in one of the prime factorisations.

So, we take 2 four times, 3 three times and 5 one time and multiply to get the L.C.M.

$\therefore$ L.C.M. of 90, 108 and 144 $= 2 \times 2 \times 2 \times 2 \times 3 \times 3 \times 3 \times 5 = 2160$.

2. L.C.M. BY SHORT DIVISION METHOD (SHORT CUT METHOD)

Step 1: Arrange the given numbers in a line in any order.

Step 2: Divide by a number which divides exactly at least two of the given numbers and carry forward the numbers which are not divisible.

Step 3: Repeat the above process till no two of the numbers are divisible by the same number other than 1.

Step 4: The product of the divisors and the undivided numbers is the required L.C.M. of the given numbers.

Example 3. *Find the L.C.M. of 20, 30 and 50 by short division method.*

Solution : We have

2	20, 30, 50
5	10, 15, 25
	2, 3, 5

$\therefore$ L.C.M. $= (2 \times 5 \times 2 \times 3 \times 5) = 300$.

Example 4. *Find the L.C.M. of 12, 18, 24 and 36 by short division method.*

Solution : We have

2	12,	18,	24,	36
2	6,	9,	12,	18
3	3,	9,	6,	9
3	1,	3,	2,	3
	1,	1,	2,	1

$\therefore$ L.C.M. $= (2 \times 2 \times 3 \times 3 \times 2) = 72$.

Example 5. *Find the L.C.M. of 96, 108 and 180 by short division method.*

Solution : We have

2	96,	108,	180
2	48,	54,	90
3	24,	27,	45
3	8,	9,	15
	8,	3,	5

$\therefore$ L.C.M. $= (2 \times 2 \times 3 \times 3 \times 8 \times 3 \times 5) = 4320$.

EXERCISE 20

1. Find the L.C.M. of the given numbers using prime factorisation method:

   (a) 18, 24   (b) 36, 45   (c) 63, 105

   (d) 28, 56, 84   (e) 36, 54, 81   (f) 27, 54, 90

2. Find the L.C.M. of the given numbers using short division method:

   (a) 25, 30   (b) 32, 48   (c) 42, 70

   (d) 28, 42, 56   (e) 75, 100, 150   (f) 96, 144, 192

   (g) 90, 135, 180   (h) 102, 136, 170   (i) 64, 72, 96, 108

SOME FACTS ABOUT H.C.F. AND L.C.M.

1. Two numbers are said to be co-prime if their H.C.F. is 1.

2. The L.C.M. of two co-prime numbers is equal to their product.

3. If one number is a factor of the other number, then their H.C.F. is the smaller number and their L.C.M. is the larger number.

4. Product of two given numbers is equal to the product of their H.C.F. and L.C.M. Thus, we have:

$$\text{L.C.M. of two given numbers} = \frac{\text{First number} \times \text{Second number}}{\text{H.C.F. of the given numbers}}.$$

SOLVED EXAMPLES

Example 1. Find the H.C.F. and L.C.M. of 680 and 816.

Solution : First we find the H.C.F. of 680 and 816.

$$680\overline{)816}(1$$
$$\underline{680}$$
$$136\overline{)680}(5$$
$$\underline{680}$$
$$0$$

∴ H.C.F. = 136.

Now, L.C.M. = $\dfrac{\text{1st number} \times \text{2nd number}}{\text{Their H.C.F.}}$

$$= \frac{\overset{5}{(\cancel{680} \times 816)}}{\underset{1}{\cancel{136}}} = 4080.$$

∴ L.C.M. = 4080.

Example 2. *The H.C.F. of two numbers is 144 and their L.C.M. is 2880. If one of the numbers is 720, find the other number.*

Solution H.C.F. = 144 and L.C.M. = 2880.

One number = 720.

The other number $= \dfrac{\text{H.C.F.} \times \text{L.C.M.}}{\text{given number}} = \dfrac{(144 \times \overset{4}{\cancel{2880}})}{\cancel{720}} = 576.$

Hence, the other number is 576.

Example 3. *Find the greatest number which divides 148 and 100 leaving remainder 4 in each case.*

Solution : Clearly, we have to find the largest number that divides (148 – 4) i.e. 140 and (100 – 4) i.e. 96 exactly.

∴ Required number = H.C.F of 144 and 96 = 48.

Hence, the required number is 48.

```
96)144(1
    96
    48)96(2
       96
        0
```

Example 4. *Three pieces of timber 42 m, 49 m and 63 m long have to be divided into planks of the same length. What is the greatest possible length of each plank?*

Solution : Required length = H.C.F. of 42 m, 49 m, 63 m.

Now, 42 = 2 × 3 × 7, 49 = 7 × 7 and 63 = 3 × 3 × 7

∴ H.C.F. of (42, 49 and 63) = 7.

Hence, the required length of each plank = 7 m.

Example 5. *Five bells begin to toll together and toll respectively at intervals of 6, 7, 8 and 12 seconds. After how much time will they toll together again?*

Solution : Required time = {L.C.M. of 6, 7, 8, 12} seconds

= (2 × 2 × 3 × 7 × 2) seconds

= 168 seconds = 2 min 48 sec.

So, all the bells will toll together after 2 min. 48 sec.

2	6,	7,	8,	12
2	3,	7,	4,	6
3	3,	7,	2,	3
	1,	7,	2,	1

EXERCISE 21

1. Find the H.C.F. and L.C.M of :

   (a) 87 and 145 (b) 161 and 207 (c) 270 and 450

2. The H.C.F. of two numbers is 12 and their L.C.M. is 180. If one of the numbers is 36, find the other.

3. The H.C.F. of two numbers is 30 and their L.C.M. is 2310. If one of the numbers is 210, find the other.

4. The product of two numbers is 2925 and their H.C.F. is 15. Find the L.C.M. of these numbers.

5. The product of two numbers is 3750 and their L.C.M. is 150. Find the H.C.F. of these numbers.

6. Find the largest number which divides 209 and 260 leaving remainder 5 in each case.

7. Two ropes of lengths 16 m and 24 m are to be cut into small pieces of equal lengths. What will be the maximum length of each piece?

8. Three drums contain respectively 36 litres, 45 litres and 72 litres of oil. Find the capacity of the largest container which can measure the content of each drum an exact number of times.

9. Find the least number which is exactly divisible by each one of the numbers 12, 16 and 24.

10. Find the least number of stones so that heaps of 15, 20 or 30 stones can be made.

11. Six bells commence tolling together and toll at intervals of 2, 4, 6, 8, 10 and 12 seconds respectively. After how much time will they toll together again?

THINGS TO REMEMBER

1. A number which has only two distinct factors i.e., 1 and the number itself, is called a prime number.

2. A number which has more than two factors is called a composite number.

3. 1 is neither a prime nor a composite number.

4. If a number is expressed in the form of product of prime numbers, then this form is called the prime factorisation of the given number.

5. The Highest common Factor (H.C.F.) of two or more given numbers is the greatest among all their common factors.

6. If a number is a factor of another number, the smaller number is the H.C.F. of the given numbers.

7. H.C.F. of 3 numbers = H.C.F. of [(H.C.F. of any two) and the third number]

8. The Lowest Common Multiple (L.C.M.) of two or more numbers is the smallest among their common multiples.

9. If one of the two given numbers is a multiple of the other, the greater number is the L.C.M. of the given numbers.

10. To determine the L.C.M. of given numbers, we first find their prime factorisation. Then we take the product of each prime factor with the maximum number of times it has appeared, to calculate the L.C.M.

11. For any two given numbers, we have
(First number × Second number) = (Their H.C.F. × Their L.C.M.)

ACTIVITY TIME

Activity To Find The H.C.F. Of Two Given Numbers By Paper Cutting and Pasting

Let us find the H.C.F. of two numbers, say 64 and 28.

Step 1. Cut out a rectangular paper strip of length 64 cm. Label it A. Next, cut out paper strips of lengths 28 cm of the same width and place them over strip A so as to cover it fully. We find that on placing two strips of length 28 cm each, a length of 8 cm is left uncovered out of strip A.

64 cm

28 cm

Strip A

28 cm   28 cm   8 cm

Step 2. Now cut out strips of 8 cm and place them on a strip of 28 cm so as to cover it fully. We find that on placing three strips of length 8 cm each, a length of 4 cm is left uncovered.

8 cm   8 cm   8 cm   4 cm

Step 3. Next cut out strips of length 4 cm and place them on a strip of length 8 cm so as to cover it fully. We find that on placing two strips of length 4 cm each, nothing is left out.

4 cm   4 cm

Hence, the H.C.F. of 64 and 28 is 4.

C.C.E. DRILL - 5

QUESTION BAG - 1

(OBJECTIVE - TYPE QUESTIONS)

Tick (✓) the correct answer :

1. The sum of the first five multiples of 6 is
   (a) 30   (b) 60   (c) 90   (d) 120

2. Which is the only number having only one factor?
   (a) 0   (b) 1   (c) 2   (d) 3

3. Which of the following numbers is not divisible by 3 ?
   (a) 3162   (b) 5482   (c) 7956   (d) 8085

4. Two consecutive prime numbers whose difference is 2 are called
   (a) Twin primes   (b) Co-primes
   (c) Even numbers   (d) Composite numbers

5. Which of the following is not correctly matched ?
   (a) Only even number which is prime → 2
   (b) Smallest composite number → 1
   (c) Multiple of every number → 0
   (d) Factor of every number → 1

6. The prime factorisation of 88 is
   (a) 2 × 2 × 11   (b) 2 × 44   (c) 2 × 22 × 2   (d) 2 × 2 × 2 × 11

7. How many prime numbers are there from 1 to 100 ?
   (a) 18   (b) 22   (c) 25   (d) 27

8. There are 3 prime numbers between
   (a) 40 and 50   (b) 50 and 60
   (c) 70 and 80   (d) Both (a) and (c)

9. There is only one prime number between
   (a) 30 and 40   (b) 60 and 70
   (c) 80 and 90   (d) 90 and 100

10. H.C.F of 36 and 84 is
    (a) 4   (b) 6   (c) 12   (d) 18

11. L.C.M. of 24, 36 and 40 is

    (a) 120   (b) 240   (c) 360   (d) 480

12. Which of the following is a pair of co-primes?

    (a) (16, 62)   (b) (18, 25)   (c) (21, 35)   (d) (23, 92)

13. The smallest number that is divisible by each one of 9, 12 and 15 is

    (a) 60   (b) 90   (c) 120   (d) 180

14. Three bags of wheat contain 120 kg, 125 kg and 100 kg wheat. It each bag is to be emptied in smaller sacks of equal weights, how much wheat is to be filled in each small sack ?

    (a) 5 kg   (b) 10 kg   (c) 15 kg   (d) 25 kg

QUESTION BAG-2

1. *Circle the prime numbers:*

    39 51 19 71 27 59 73 55 91 67 83 97 15 43

2. *Check divisibility of each of the following numbers by 2, 3, 4, 5, 6, 7, 8, 9, 10 and 11 Put a (✓) for 'divisible' and a (x) for 'not divisible'.*

	Number	2	3	4	5	6	8	9	10	11
(a)	99880									
(b)	46632									
(c)	67968									
(d)	726354									
(e)	50505									

3. *In the following table, factors of two numbers A and B are given. Complete the table by finding the H.C.F and L.C.M. of A and B.*

	A	B	H.C.F	L.C.M.
(a)	2 × 3 × 3	2 × 5 × 7		
(b)	2 × 3 × 5	3 × 3 × 5		
(c)	2 × 3 × 3 × 7	2 × 3 × 11		
(d)	3 × 3 × 5 × 7	2 × 3 × 5 × 11		
(e)	2 × 3 × 3 × 5	2 × 2 × 3 × 5		
(f)	2 × 2 × 7	2 × 3 × 7		

4. *Find the H.C.F by common division method :*

    (a) 72, 54 and 96   (b) 180 and 450   (c) 108, 144 and 60

5. *Find the H.C.F by long division method:*

    (a) 575 and 874   (b) 649 and 913

    (c) 736 and 1632   (d) 408, 510 and 1054

6. *Find the L.C.M. by common division method :*

   (*a*) 15, 36 and 40
   (*b*) 93, 62 and 120
   (*c*) 112, 140 and 168
   (*d*) 121, 132 and 330

7. Three bells ring at intervals of 20 minutes, 30 minutes and 45 minutes respectively. After how much time will the bells ring together?

8. *State whether each of the following statements is true or false :*

   (*a*) The sum of two numbers is equal to the sum of their H.C.F. and L.C.M ....

   (*b*) If a number is divisible by 6, it must be divisible by 12. ....

   (*c*) If a number is divisible by 6, it must be divisible by 3. ....

   (*d*) The H.C.F. of 3 and 9 is 3 and their L.C.M. is 9. ....

   (*e*) If a number is divisible by 25, it must be divisible by 5. ....

   (*f*) If a number A is a factor of a number B, then B is also a factor of A. ....

   (*g*) The H.C.F. of 26 and 27 is 1. ....

   (*h*) A factor of a number cannot be greater than the number. ....

   (*i*) Co-prime numbers are prime also. ....

   (*j*) If A is divisible by B, then A is divisible by any of the factors of B. ....

   (*k*) Every two consecutive numbers are co-prime. ....

   (*l*) L.C.M. of any two distinct numbers is always greater than their H.C.F. ....

   (*m*) In finding H.C.F. by long division method, the last quotient obtained gives the H.C.F. ....

   (*n*) 91 is a composite number. ....

FRACTIONS

Fraction is a part of a whole such as $\frac{2}{3}$, $\frac{4}{7}$, $\frac{5}{9}$ etc.

In $\frac{2}{3}$, we say that numerator = 2 and denominator = 3.

In $\frac{4}{7}$, we say that numerator = 4 and denominator = 7.

In $\frac{5}{9}$, we say that numerator = 5 and denominator = 9.

TYPES OF FRACTIONS

LIKE FRACTIONS

Fractions with same denominators are called **like fractions.**

Examples : $\frac{2}{9}$, $\frac{3}{9}$, $\frac{4}{9}$, $\frac{5}{9}$ etc. are all like fractions.

UNLIKE FRACTIONS

Fractions with different denominators are called **unlike fractions.**

Examples : $\frac{1}{2}$, $\frac{1}{4}$, $\frac{3}{8}$, $\frac{5}{7}$ etc. are all unlike fractions.

UNIT FRACTIONS

Fractions with numerator 1 are called **unit fractions.**

Examples : $\frac{1}{1}$, $\frac{1}{2}$, $\frac{1}{3}$, $\frac{1}{7}$, $\frac{1}{10}$, $\frac{1}{16}$ etc. are all unit fractions.

PROPER FRACTIONS

A fraction whose numerator is less than its denominator is called a **proper fraction.**

Examples : $\frac{3}{4}$, $\frac{5}{7}$, $\frac{6}{11}$, $\frac{14}{19}$, $\frac{20}{27}$ etc. are all proper fractions.

IMPROPER FRACTIONS

A fraction whose numerator is greater than or equal to its denominator is called an **improper fraction.**

Examples : $\frac{5}{4}$, $\frac{7}{5}$, $\frac{7}{7}$, $\frac{8}{3}$, $\frac{11}{6}$ etc. are all improper fractions.

MIXED NUMBERS (OR MIXED FRACTIONS)

When an improper fraction is written as a combination of a whole number and a proper fraction, it is called a **mixed number (or mixed fraction).**

Examples: $1\frac{2}{7}, 1\frac{3}{5}, 2\frac{3}{4}, 4\frac{5}{7}$ are all mixed numbers.

To Convert A Mixed Number Into An Improper Fraction

$$2\frac{3}{8} = 2 + \frac{3}{8} = \frac{2}{1} + \frac{3}{8} = \frac{2 \times 8}{1 \times 8} + \frac{3}{8} = \frac{16}{8} + \frac{3}{8} = \frac{16+3}{8} = \frac{19}{8}.$$

A Quicker Way:

$$2\frac{3}{8} = \frac{2 \times 8 + 3}{8} = \frac{16+3}{8} = \frac{19}{8}.$$

$$3\frac{2}{5} = \frac{3 \times 5 + 2}{5} = \frac{15+2}{5} = \frac{17}{5}.$$

$$6\frac{1}{4} = \frac{6 \times 4 + 1}{4} = \frac{24+1}{4} = \frac{25}{4}.$$

To Convert An Improper Fraction Into A Mixed Number

Rule : Divide the numerator by the denominator. The quotient obtained is the whole number part and the remainder is the numerator of the fractional part of the mixed numeral.

Example: $\frac{23}{9} = 2 + \frac{5}{9} = 2\frac{5}{9}.$

```
            2  ← Quotient
        9 ) 2 3 (
            1 8
            5  ← Remainder
```

EQUIVALENT FRACTIONS

As we have studied earlier :

An equivalent fraction of a given fraction can be obtained by multiplying or dividing its numerator and denominator by the same non-zero number.

Example 1. *Write five fractions equivalent to $\frac{1}{2}$.*

Solution : We have :

$$\frac{1}{2} = \frac{1 \times 2}{2 \times 2} = \frac{1 \times 3}{2 \times 3} = \frac{1 \times 4}{2 \times 4} = \frac{1 \times 5}{2 \times 5} = \frac{1 \times 6}{2 \times 6}$$

$$\frac{1}{2} = \frac{2}{4} = \frac{3}{6} = \frac{4}{8} = \frac{5}{10} = \frac{6}{12} = \dots$$

Hence, the fractions equivalent to $\frac{1}{2}$ are $\frac{2}{4}, \frac{3}{6}, \frac{4}{8}, \frac{5}{10}$ and $\frac{6}{12}$.

Example 2. *Write three fractions equivalent to $\frac{3}{4}$.*

Solution : We have :

$$\frac{3}{4} = \frac{3 \times 2}{4 \times 2} = \frac{3 \times 3}{4 \times 3} = \frac{3 \times 4}{4 \times 4}$$

$$\therefore \quad \frac{3}{4} = \frac{6}{8} = \frac{9}{12} = \frac{12}{16}.$$

Hence, the fractions equivalent to $\frac{3}{4}$ are $\frac{6}{8}, \frac{9}{12}$ and $\frac{12}{16}$.

Example 3. *Replace ☐ by the correct number:*

$$\frac{2}{7} = \frac{8}{☐}$$

Solution : To get 8 in the numerator, we multiply 2 by 4.

So, we multiply the denominator also by 4.

$$\therefore \quad \frac{2}{7} = \frac{2 \times 4}{7 \times 4} = \frac{8}{28}.$$

Hence, missing numeral = 28.

Example 4. *Write an equivalent fraction of $\frac{5}{9}$ with denominator 45.*

Solution : Let $\frac{5}{9} = \frac{?}{45}$

Then, we have to find the missing numeral. To get 45 in the denominator, we multiply 9 by 5. So, we multiply the numerator also by 5.

$$\therefore \quad \frac{5}{9} = \frac{5 \times 5}{9 \times 5} = \frac{25}{45}.$$

Hence, $\frac{5}{9}$ and $\frac{25}{45}$ are equivalent fractions.

Example 5. *Write an equivalent fraction of $\frac{35}{42}$, with denominator 18.*

Solution : We have

$$\frac{35}{42} = \frac{35 \div 7}{42 \div 7} = \frac{5}{6} = \frac{5 \times 3}{6 \times 3} = \frac{15}{18}.$$

Hence, $\frac{35}{42}$ and $\frac{15}{18}$ are equivalent fractions.

To Test Whether Two Given Fractions are Equivalent or Not:

We know that:

> **Two fractions are equivalent if**
>
> **(Numerator of first × Denominator of second)**
>
> **= (Denominator of first × Numerator of second)**

Example 6. *Check whether $\frac{3}{7}$ and $\frac{9}{21}$ are equivalent fractions.*

Solution : Cross multiply as shown : $\frac{3}{7} \diagup\!\!\!\!\diagdown \frac{9}{21}$

We have : $3 \times 21 = 63$ and $7 \times 9 = 63$.

Thus, the two cross products are equal.

Hence, $\frac{3}{7}$ and $\frac{9}{21}$ are equivalent fractions.

1. Write the fractions for the shaded parts and the unshaded parts:

   (a)   (b)   (c)

   Shaded = ...   Shaded = ...   Shaded = ...

   Unshaded = ...   Unshaded = ...   Unshaded = ...

2. Circle each one of the unit fractions given below:

   $\dfrac{6}{1}, \dfrac{1}{4}, \dfrac{3}{6}, \dfrac{1}{7}, \dfrac{9}{1}, \dfrac{1}{10}, \dfrac{5}{5}, \dfrac{1}{11}$

3. Circle each pair of like fractions given below:

   (a) $\dfrac{3}{5}, \dfrac{4}{5}$ (b) $\dfrac{2}{5}, \dfrac{2}{7}$ (c) $\dfrac{5}{9}, \dfrac{7}{9}$ (d) $\dfrac{6}{7}, \dfrac{6}{11}$

4. Circle each pair of unlike fractions given below:

   (a) $\dfrac{1}{4}, \dfrac{1}{7}$ (b) $\dfrac{3}{4}, \dfrac{3}{5}$ (c) $\dfrac{4}{9}, \dfrac{7}{9}$ (d) $\dfrac{5}{11}, \dfrac{7}{11}$

5. Circle each one of the proper fractions given below:

   (a) $\dfrac{5}{3}$ (b) $\dfrac{6}{7}$ (c) $\dfrac{3}{3}$ (d) $\dfrac{8}{11}$ (e) $\dfrac{6}{1}$

6. Circle each one of the improper fractions given below:

   (a) $\dfrac{7}{8}$ (b) $\dfrac{4}{4}$ (c) $\dfrac{11}{6}$ (d) $\dfrac{8}{1}$ (e) $\dfrac{1}{1}$

7. Convert each of the following into an improper fraction:

   (a) $3\dfrac{3}{5}$ (b) $2\dfrac{5}{7}$ (c) $6\dfrac{2}{3}$ (d) $4\dfrac{5}{6}$ (e) $7\dfrac{1}{7}$

8. Convert each of the following into a mixed number:

   (a) $\dfrac{11}{4}$ (b) $\dfrac{17}{8}$ (c) $\dfrac{23}{6}$ (d) $\dfrac{19}{5}$ (e) $\dfrac{15}{7}$

9. Write four fractions equivalent to each of the following:

   (a) $\dfrac{2}{3}$ (b) $\dfrac{5}{6}$ (c) $\dfrac{4}{7}$ (d) $\dfrac{3}{5}$ (e) $\dfrac{8}{11}$

10. Replace ☐ in each of the following by the correct numeral:

   (a) $\dfrac{3}{5} = \dfrac{12}{☐}$ (b) $\dfrac{6}{13} = \dfrac{☐}{52}$ (c) $\dfrac{7}{17} = \dfrac{☐}{85}$ (d) $\dfrac{11}{27} = \dfrac{33}{☐}$

11. Find an equivalent fraction of $\dfrac{7}{11}$ having denominator 33.

12. Find an equivalent fraction of $\dfrac{5}{6}$ having numerator 35.

13. Find an equivalent fraction of $\dfrac{45}{54}$ having numerator 5.

14. Find an equivalent fraction of $\dfrac{35}{40}$ having denominator 8.

15. *Check whether the given fractions are equivalent or not:*

(a) $\dfrac{3}{4}$ and $\dfrac{15}{20}$ (b) $\dfrac{4}{5}$ and $\dfrac{12}{20}$ (c) $\dfrac{2}{3}$ and $\dfrac{10}{15}$

(d) $\dfrac{5}{8}$ and $\dfrac{15}{24}$ (e) $\dfrac{7}{11}$ and $\dfrac{28}{44}$ (f) $\dfrac{3}{10}$ and $\dfrac{12}{50}$

FRACTIONS IN LOWEST TERMS OR IN SIMPLEST FORM

A fraction is said to be in lowest terms or in simplest form if the H.C.F. of the numerator and the denominator is 1.

Example 1.   *Show that the fraction $\dfrac{25}{36}$ is in the lowest terms.*

Solution :   The given fraction is $\dfrac{25}{36}$.

The factors of 25 are 1, 5, 25.

The factors of 36 are 1, 2, 3, 4, 6, 9, 12, 18, 36.

Common factor of 25 and 36 is 1 only.

∴   H.C.F. of 25 and 36 is 1.

Hence, $\dfrac{25}{36}$ is in its lowest terms.

Example 2.   *Show that the fraction $\dfrac{21}{35}$ is not in its lowest terms.*

Solution :   Here numerator = 21 and denominator = 35.

Factors of 21 are : 1, 3, 7, 21.

Factors of 35 are : 1, 5, 7, 35

Common factors of 21 and 35 are : 1, 7.

∴ H.C.F. of 21 and 35 = 7.

Hence, $\dfrac{21}{35}$ is not in its lowest terms.

How to Reduce a Fraction to its Lowest Terms or in Simplest Form?

Rule 1. To reduce a given fraction to is its lowest lerms, we divide the numerator and the denominator of the given fraction by their H.C.F.

Rule 2. Divide the numerator and the denominator of the given fraction by their common factors till we are left with only the common factor 1.

Example 3. *Reduce $\dfrac{18}{24}$ to its lowest terms.*

Solution : Here, numerator = 18 and denominator = 24.

Let us find the H.C.F. of 18 and 24.

Factors of 18 are : 1, 2, 3, 6, 9, 18

Factors of 24 are : 1, 2, 3, 4, 6, 8, 12, 24

Common factors of 18 and 24 are : 1, 2, 3, 6.

∴   H.C.F. of 18 and 24 = 6.

∴ $\dfrac{18}{24} = \dfrac{18 \div 6}{24 \div 6} = \dfrac{3}{4}$.

Hence, $\dfrac{18}{24}$ in its lowest terms is $\dfrac{3}{4}$.

Alternative Method :

$$\frac{18}{24} = \frac{18\overset{6}{\cancel{}}\overset{3}{\cancel{}}}{24\underset{8}{\cancel{}}\underset{4}{\cancel{}}} = \frac{3}{4} .$$

Example 4. *Reduce $\dfrac{28}{42}$ to its lowest terms.*

Solution : Here, numerator = 28 and denominator = 42.

Let us find the H.C.F. of 28 and 42.

∴   H.C.F. of 28 and 42 = $(2 \times 7) = 14$.

∴ $\dfrac{28}{42} = \dfrac{28 \div 14}{42 \div 14} = \dfrac{2}{3}$.

Hence, $\dfrac{28}{42}$ in its lowest terms = $\dfrac{2}{3}$.

2	28, 42
7	14, 21
	2, 3

Example 5. *Reduce $\dfrac{72}{90}$ to the simplest form.*

Solution : Here, numerator = 72 and denominator = 90.

Let us find the H.C.F. of 72 and 90.

∴ H.C.F. of 72 and 90 = $(2 \times 3 \times 3) = 18$.

$$\frac{72}{90} = \frac{72 \div 18}{90 \div 18} = \frac{4}{5} .$$

∴ Hence, $\dfrac{72}{90}$ in the simplest form is $\dfrac{4}{5}$.

2	72, 90
3	36, 45
3	12, 15
	4, 5

Which of the following fractions are in simplest form?

1. $\dfrac{21}{40}$ 2. $\dfrac{24}{35}$ 3. $\dfrac{15}{20}$ 4. $\dfrac{36}{81}$ 5. $\dfrac{24}{57}$ 6. $\dfrac{28}{39}$

Reduce each of the following fractions to simplest form :

7. $\dfrac{9}{27}$ 8. $\dfrac{16}{24}$ 9. $\dfrac{42}{48}$ 10. $\dfrac{45}{54}$ 11. $\dfrac{40}{72}$ 12. $\dfrac{38}{95}$

13. $\dfrac{35}{63}$ 14. $\dfrac{56}{70}$ 15. $\dfrac{64}{80}$ 16. $\dfrac{44}{66}$ 17. $\dfrac{72}{80}$ 18. $\dfrac{51}{68}$

COMPARISON OF FRACTIONS

Comparison of Fractions with Like Denominators and Unlike Numerators

Rule: *Out of the two given like fractions, the one having greater numerator is greater.*

Examples: (a) $\dfrac{4}{7} > \dfrac{2}{7}$ (b) $\dfrac{9}{13} > \dfrac{6}{13}$ (c) $\dfrac{7}{8} > \dfrac{5}{8}$

Arranging Some Given Like Fractions in Ascending or Descending order:

Rule : *Three or more like fractions can be arranged in ascending or descending order by arranging their numerators in ascending or descending order respectively.*

Example 1. *Arrange the fractions* $\dfrac{1}{9}, \dfrac{7}{9}, \dfrac{2}{9}, \dfrac{5}{9}, \dfrac{4}{9}$ *in the ascending order.*

Solution : We know that:

$$1 < 2 < 4 < 5 < 7$$

$$\therefore \dfrac{1}{9} < \dfrac{2}{9} < \dfrac{4}{9} < \dfrac{5}{9} < \dfrac{7}{9}.$$

These fractions are in ascending order.

Example 2 . *Arrange the fractions* $\dfrac{3}{17}, \dfrac{15}{17}, \dfrac{7}{17}, \dfrac{11}{17}, \dfrac{6}{17}$ *in the descending order.*

Solution : We know that

$$15 > 11 > 7 > 6 > 3$$

$$\therefore \dfrac{15}{17} > \dfrac{11}{17} > \dfrac{7}{17} > \dfrac{6}{17} > \dfrac{3}{17}.$$

These fractions are clearly in descending order.

Comparison of Fractions with Like Numerators and Unlike Denominators:

RULE: *Out of the given fractions with same numerator, the fraction with smaller denominator is greater.*

Examples : (a) $\dfrac{3}{5} > \dfrac{3}{7}$ (b) $\dfrac{5}{11} > \dfrac{5}{16}$ (c) $\dfrac{7}{10} > \dfrac{7}{12}$

Example 3. Arrange the fractions $\dfrac{3}{7}, \dfrac{3}{13}, \dfrac{3}{4}, \dfrac{3}{11}, \dfrac{3}{5}$ in the ascending order.

Solution : The given fractions have the same numerator.
So, the one with larger denominator is smaller.
Now, 13 > 11 > 7 > 5 > 4

$\therefore \dfrac{3}{13} < \dfrac{3}{11} < \dfrac{3}{7} < \dfrac{3}{5} < \dfrac{3}{4}$.

These fractions are clearly in ascending order.

Example 4. Arrange the fractions $\dfrac{2}{19}, \dfrac{2}{9}, \dfrac{2}{15}, \dfrac{2}{3}, \dfrac{2}{5}$ in the descending order.

Solution : The given fractions have the same numerator. So, the one with smaller denominator is larger.
Now, 3 < 5 < 9 < 15 < 19

$\therefore \dfrac{2}{3} > \dfrac{2}{5} > \dfrac{2}{9} > \dfrac{2}{15} > \dfrac{2}{19}$.

These fractions are clearly in descending order.

EXERCISE 24

1. Which is the greater fraction in each of the following pairs ?

   (a) $\dfrac{3}{4}, \dfrac{1}{4}$ (b) $\dfrac{4}{7}, \dfrac{6}{7}$ (c) $\dfrac{7}{9}, \dfrac{5}{9}$ (d) $\dfrac{8}{13}, \dfrac{11}{13}$ (e) $\dfrac{13}{27}, \dfrac{23}{27}$ (f) $\dfrac{17}{21}, \dfrac{20}{21}$

2. Which is the smaller fraction in each of the following pairs ?

   (a) $\dfrac{1}{3}, \dfrac{1}{5}$ (b) $\dfrac{5}{6}, \dfrac{5}{7}$ (c) $\dfrac{4}{9}, \dfrac{4}{7}$ (d) $\dfrac{7}{10}, \dfrac{7}{13}$ (e) $\dfrac{8}{9}, \dfrac{8}{11}$ (f) $\dfrac{6}{7}, \dfrac{6}{5}$

3. Arrange the following fractions in ascending order :

   (a) $\dfrac{9}{11}, \dfrac{3}{11}, \dfrac{7}{11}, \dfrac{6}{11}, \dfrac{10}{11}$ (b) $\dfrac{8}{15}, \dfrac{2}{15}, \dfrac{11}{15}, \dfrac{7}{15}, \dfrac{13}{15}$

   (c) $\dfrac{5}{19}, \dfrac{13}{19}, \dfrac{7}{19}, \dfrac{3}{19}, \dfrac{11}{19}$ (d) $\dfrac{12}{25}, \dfrac{23}{25}, \dfrac{9}{25}, \dfrac{13}{25}, \dfrac{11}{25}$

4. Arrange the following fractions in descending order:

   (a) $\dfrac{3}{7}, \dfrac{3}{5}, \dfrac{3}{11}, \dfrac{3}{8}, \dfrac{3}{14}$ (b) $\dfrac{8}{9}, \dfrac{8}{15}, \dfrac{8}{11}, \dfrac{8}{17}, \dfrac{8}{13}$

   (c) $\dfrac{5}{8}, \dfrac{5}{6}, \dfrac{5}{11}, \dfrac{5}{14}, \dfrac{5}{12}$ (d) $\dfrac{10}{21}, \dfrac{10}{17}, \dfrac{10}{19}, \dfrac{10}{23}, \dfrac{10}{11}$

Comparison of Fractions with Unlike Numerators and Unlike Denominators

To compare two or more such fractions, we follow the steps given below:

Step 1 : Find the L.C.M. of denominators of given unlike fractions.

Step 2 : Convert the given unlike fractions into equivalent like fractions with the L.C.M. as common denominator.

Step 3 : Compare the like fractions so obtained.

If one or more of the given fractions is/are mixed fractions, convert them into improper fractions before following the above steps.

SOLVED EXAMPLES

Example 1. *Compare $\frac{5}{6}$ and $\frac{4}{9}$.*

Solution: The given fractions are unlike fractions.

L.C.M. of 6 and 9 = $(3 \times 2 \times 3) = 18$.

Now, $\frac{5}{6} = \frac{5 \times 3}{6 \times 3} = \frac{15}{18}$.

And, $\frac{4}{9} = \frac{4 \times 2}{9 \times 2} = \frac{8}{18}$.

Clearly, $\frac{15}{18} > \frac{8}{18}$.

Hence, $\frac{5}{6} > \frac{4}{9}$.

$$\begin{array}{c|cc} 3 & 6, & 9 \\ \hline & 2, & 3 \end{array}$$

Example 2. *Compare $2\frac{5}{6}$ and $2\frac{3}{4}$.*

Solution: We have

$2\frac{5}{6} = \frac{2 \times 6 + 5}{6} = \frac{12 + 5}{6} = \frac{17}{6}$.

And, $2\frac{3}{4} = \frac{2 \times 4 + 3}{4} = \frac{8 + 3}{4} = \frac{11}{4}$.

$\therefore$ Given fractions are $\frac{17}{6}$ and $\frac{11}{4}$.

L.C.M. of 6 and 4 = $(2 \times 3 \times 2) = 12$.

Now, $\frac{17}{6} = \frac{17 \times 2}{6 \times 2} = \frac{34}{12}$.

And, $\frac{11}{4} = \frac{11 \times 3}{4 \times 3} = \frac{33}{12}$.

Clearly, $\frac{34}{12} > \frac{33}{12}$.

So, $\frac{17}{6} > \frac{11}{4}$.

Hence, $2\frac{5}{6} > 2\frac{3}{4}$.

$$\begin{array}{c|cc} 2 & 6, & 4 \\ \hline & 3, & 2 \end{array}$$

Example 3. *Arrange the following fractions in ascending order :*

$$\frac{5}{8}, \frac{3}{4}, \frac{7}{12}, \frac{2}{3}$$

Solution : Given fractions are $\frac{5}{8}, \frac{3}{4}, \frac{7}{12}, \frac{2}{3}$.

We shall change them into equivalent fractions with a common denominator.

This common denominator is the L.C.M. of 8, 4, 12, 3.

2	8, 4, 12, 3
2	4, 2, 6, 3
3	2, 1, 3, 3
	2, 1, 1, 1

∴ L.C.M. of 8, 4, 12, 3 = $(2 \times 2 \times 3 \times 2) = 24$.

Changing each of the given fractions into an equivalent fraction with denominator 24, we get :

$$\frac{5}{8} = \frac{5 \times 3}{8 \times 3} = \frac{15}{24}, \qquad \frac{3}{4} = \frac{3 \times 6}{4 \times 6} = \frac{18}{24},$$

$$\frac{7}{12} = \frac{7 \times 2}{12 \times 2} = \frac{14}{24}, \qquad \frac{2}{3} = \frac{2 \times 8}{3 \times 8} = \frac{16}{24}.$$

Clearly, $\frac{14}{24} < \frac{15}{24} < \frac{16}{24} < \frac{18}{24}$.

∴ $\frac{7}{12} < \frac{5}{8} < \frac{2}{3} < \frac{3}{4}$.

Hence, the given fractions in ascending order are $\frac{7}{12}, \frac{5}{8}, \frac{2}{3}, \frac{3}{4}$.

Example 4. *Arrange the following fractions in descending order :*

$$\frac{3}{5}, \frac{1}{2}, \frac{7}{10}, \frac{5}{6}$$

Solution : Given fractions are $\frac{3}{5}, \frac{1}{2}, \frac{7}{10}, \frac{5}{6}$.

We shall change them into equivalent fractions with a common denominator, which is the L.C.M. of 5, 2, 10, 6.

2	5, 2, 10, 6
5	5, 1, 5, 3
	1, 1, 1, 3

Therefore, L.C.M. of 5, 2, 10, 6 = $(2 \times 5 \times 3) = 30$.

Changing each of the given fractions into equivalent fraction with denominator 30, we get:

$$\frac{3}{5} = \frac{3 \times 6}{5 \times 6} = \frac{18}{30}, \qquad \frac{1}{2} = \frac{1 \times 15}{2 \times 15} = \frac{15}{30},$$

$$\frac{7}{10} = \frac{7 \times 3}{10 \times 3} = \frac{21}{30}, \qquad \frac{5}{6} = \frac{5 \times 5}{6 \times 5} = \frac{25}{30}.$$

Clearly, $\dfrac{25}{30} > \dfrac{21}{30} > \dfrac{18}{30} > \dfrac{15}{30}$

$\therefore \quad \dfrac{5}{6} > \dfrac{7}{10} > \dfrac{3}{5} > \dfrac{1}{2}$.

Hence, the given fractions in descending order are $\dfrac{5}{6}, \dfrac{7}{10}, \dfrac{3}{5}, \dfrac{1}{2}$.

EXERCISE 25

1. *Fill in each placeholder with >, < or = to make the statement true:*

   (a) $\dfrac{2}{5} \bigcirc \dfrac{7}{8}$ 　　(b) $\dfrac{3}{4} \bigcirc \dfrac{2}{5}$ 　　(c) $\dfrac{17}{4} \bigcirc \dfrac{13}{3}$

   (d) $\dfrac{5}{8} \bigcirc \dfrac{4}{7}$ 　　(e) $\dfrac{4}{6} \bigcirc \dfrac{6}{9}$ 　　(f) $\dfrac{13}{6} \bigcirc \dfrac{11}{5}$

   (g) $\dfrac{7}{10} \bigcirc \dfrac{5}{9}$ 　　(h) $\dfrac{3}{10} \bigcirc \dfrac{7}{25}$ 　　(i) $\dfrac{3}{8} \bigcirc \dfrac{2}{9}$

2. *Compare the following:*

   (a) $2\dfrac{3}{5}, 2\dfrac{3}{4}$ 　　(b) $3\dfrac{1}{3}, 3\dfrac{3}{10}$ 　　(c) $2\dfrac{1}{7}, 1\dfrac{7}{9}$

   (d) $4\dfrac{2}{7}, 4\dfrac{1}{3}$ 　　(e) $5\dfrac{1}{6}, 5\dfrac{1}{4}$ 　　(f) $\dfrac{2}{1}, 2\dfrac{1}{10}$

3. *Arrange the following fractions in an ascending order :*

   (a) $\dfrac{5}{6}, \dfrac{7}{9}, \dfrac{2}{3}, \dfrac{11}{12}$ 　　(b) $\dfrac{4}{5}, \dfrac{7}{10}, \dfrac{8}{15}, \dfrac{1}{2}$

   (c) $\dfrac{1}{3}, \dfrac{3}{10}, \dfrac{5}{6}, \dfrac{2}{5}$ 　　(d) $\dfrac{7}{8}, \dfrac{5}{12}, \dfrac{15}{16}, \dfrac{17}{24}$

4. *Arrange the following fractions in a descending order :*

   (a) $\dfrac{1}{2}, \dfrac{3}{4}, \dfrac{5}{8}, \dfrac{9}{16}$ 　　(b) $\dfrac{2}{7}, \dfrac{11}{35}, \dfrac{9}{14}, \dfrac{13}{28}$ 　　(c) $\dfrac{3}{4}, \dfrac{7}{8}, \dfrac{7}{12}, \dfrac{17}{24}$

   (d) $\dfrac{2}{5}, \dfrac{3}{10}, \dfrac{7}{15}, \dfrac{1}{2}$ 　　(e) $\dfrac{5}{9}, \dfrac{3}{12}, \dfrac{1}{3}, \dfrac{4}{15}$ 　　(f) $\dfrac{3}{8}, \dfrac{1}{2}, \dfrac{5}{6}, \dfrac{2}{3}$

THINGS TO REMEMBER

1. A fraction indicates one or more parts of a whole.

2. The numbers like one-half, one-third, two-thirds, three-fourths, two-fifths etc. are called *fractional numbers* and the symbols $\frac{1}{2}, \frac{1}{3}, \frac{2}{3}, \frac{3}{4}, \frac{2}{5}$ etc. representing them are called *fractions*.

3. A fraction obtained by multiplying or dividing the numerator and denominator by the same non-zero number is called an *equivalent fraction* of the given fraction.

4. A fraction with numerator less than its denominator is called a *proper fraction*.

5. A fraction with numerator greater than or equal to its denominator is called an *improper fraction*.

6. Fractions with same denominators are called like *fractions*.

7. Fractions with different denominators are called *unlike fractions*.

8. Fractions with 1 as numerator are called *unit fractions*.

9. A fraction is said to be *in its lowest terms or in simplest form* if the H.C.F. of its numerator and denominator is 1.

10. If we compare two fractions with same denominators, then the one with greater numerator is greater.

11. If we compare two fractions with same numerators, then the one with smaller denominator is greater.

12. A combination of a whole number and a proper fraction is a mixed numeral.

13. To compare two fractions with unlike numerators and unlike denominators, we find the L.C.M. of their denominators and then convert them into equivalent like fractions with the L.C.M. as common denominators. We then compare the like fractions so obtained.

C.C.E. DRILL - 6

(OBJECTIVE - TYPE QUESTIONS)

Tick (✓) the correct answer :

1. Which of the following figures has $\frac{3}{8}$ shaded ?

   (a)   (b)   (c)   (d)

2. Which of the following is an improper fraction?

   (a) $\frac{2}{3}$ (b) $\frac{16}{17}$ (c) $\frac{5}{4}$ (d) $\frac{19}{50}$

3. Which fraction is greater than $\frac{1}{2}$?

   (a) $\frac{1}{4}$ (b) $\frac{2}{7}$ (c) $\frac{3}{8}$ (d) $\frac{3}{4}$

4. The fraction equivalent to $\frac{5}{7}$ is

   (a) $\frac{25}{28}$ (b) $\frac{35}{49}$ (c) $\frac{15}{14}$ (d) $\frac{40}{63}$

5. The mixed numeral for the fraction $\frac{37}{8}$ is

   (a) $4\frac{5}{8}$ (b) $3\frac{13}{8}$ (c) $4\frac{1}{8}$ (d) $5\frac{4}{8}$

6. Which of the following fractions is the greatest ?

   (a) $\frac{13}{15}$ (b) $\frac{13}{17}$ (c) $\frac{13}{19}$ (d) $\frac{13}{20}$

7. A box has 25 balls of which 9 are red and the rest yellow. Aniket picks one-third of the red balls and half of the yellow balls. What fraction of the balls are left in the box ?

   (a) $\frac{11}{16}$ (b) $\frac{11}{25}$ (c) $\frac{14}{25}$ (d) $\frac{16}{25}$

8. Which of the following is a pair of like fractions ?

   (a) $\frac{5}{7}, \frac{7}{5}$ (b) $\frac{2}{3}, \frac{6}{9}$ (c) $\frac{7}{9}, \frac{7}{11}$ (d) $\frac{13}{17}, \frac{13}{21}$

9. Which of the following fractions is in its lowest terms ?

   (a) $\frac{28}{79}$ (b) $\frac{31}{93}$ (c) $\frac{27}{156}$ (d) $\frac{57}{152}$

10. Which of the following statements is incorrect ?

    (a) $\frac{2}{3} > \frac{2}{5}$ (b) $\frac{7}{9} > \frac{5}{9}$ (c) $\frac{10}{11} = \frac{100}{121}$ (d) $\frac{3}{8} > \frac{7}{12}$

1. Find the equivalent fraction of $\frac{75}{90}$ having
    (a) numerator 15   (b) denominator 42
    (c) denominator 270   (d) numerator 300

2. Complete the following table :

Improper Fraction	....	$\frac{86}{9}$	....	$\frac{227}{15}$	....	$\frac{120}{21}$
Mixed Numeral	$5\frac{6}{7}$	....	$8\frac{11}{13}$	....	$7\frac{17}{54}$	....

3. Compare :
    (a) $\frac{1}{8}$ ◯ $\frac{1}{7}$ (b) $\frac{2}{7}$ ◯ $\frac{5}{7}$ (c) $\frac{3}{5}$ ◯ $\frac{2}{7}$ (d) $\frac{5}{8}$ ◯ $\frac{7}{9}$

4. Rearrange in descending order :
    (a) $\frac{2}{5}, \frac{3}{4}, \frac{1}{3}, \frac{6}{7}, \frac{5}{8}, \frac{8}{9}$ (b) $\frac{2}{9}, \frac{1}{21}, \frac{4}{7}, \frac{11}{63}$

5. State whether each of the following statements is true or false :
    (a) $\frac{6}{12}$ and $\frac{1}{2}$ are equivalent fractions.   ....
    (b) $\frac{4}{5}$ and $\frac{4}{9}$ are like fractions.   ....
    (c) To reduce a fraction to its lowest terms, we divide the numerator and denominator by their L.C.M.   ....
    (d) A proper fraction is always less than 1.   ....
    (e) $\frac{7}{7}$ is a proper fraction.   ....
    (f) Unlike fractions can be converted into like fractions by taking the H.C.F of their denominators as the common denominator.   ....
    (g) In unlike fractions with the same numerator, the fraction with the greater denominator is greater.   ....
    (h) If a given fraction is in its lowest terms, then its numerator and denominator are both prime numbers.   ....

6. Fill in the blanks:
    (a) $\frac{23}{6}$ written as a mixed numeral is ....
    (b) $7\frac{3}{7}$ expressed as an improper fraction is ....
    (c) $\frac{35}{65}$ expressed in lowest terms is ....
    (d) If the denominator of a fraction is increased, the value of the fraction ....
    (e) When I fill $\frac{5}{9}$ of a bucket with water, ... is still empty.

8 ADDITION AND SUBTRACTION OF FRACTIONS

In class IV, we have learnt the addition and subtraction of like fractions. In this chapter, we shall study the addition and subtraction of all types of fractions.

ADDITION OF LIKE FRACTIONS

We know that :

$$\text{Sum of like fractions} = \frac{\text{Sum of numerators}}{\text{Common denominator}}$$

Example 1. *Find the sum :*

(a) $\dfrac{3}{5} + \dfrac{2}{5}$ (b) $\dfrac{5}{8} + \dfrac{7}{8}$ (c) $\dfrac{4}{9} + \dfrac{5}{9} + \dfrac{7}{9}$

Solution :

(a) $\dfrac{3}{5} + \dfrac{2}{5} = \dfrac{3+2}{5} = \dfrac{5^1}{5_1} = \dfrac{1}{1} = 1.$

(b) $\dfrac{5}{8} + \dfrac{7}{8} = \dfrac{5+7}{8} = \dfrac{12^3}{8_2} = \dfrac{3}{2} = 1\dfrac{1}{2}.$

(c) $\dfrac{4}{9} + \dfrac{5}{9} + \dfrac{7}{9} = \dfrac{4+5+7}{9} = \dfrac{16}{9} = 1\dfrac{7}{9}.$

EXERCISE 26

Find the sum of the following :

1. $\dfrac{5}{7} + \dfrac{2}{7}$

2. $\dfrac{2}{9} + \dfrac{5}{9}$

3. $\dfrac{3}{11} + \dfrac{9}{11}$

4. $\dfrac{6}{7} + \dfrac{3}{7}$

5. $\dfrac{5}{8} + \dfrac{5}{8}$

6. $\dfrac{5}{12} + \dfrac{11}{12}$

7. $\dfrac{1}{4} + \dfrac{1}{4} + \dfrac{3}{4}$

8. $\dfrac{4}{15} + \dfrac{7}{15} + \dfrac{8}{15}$

9. $\dfrac{1}{10} + \dfrac{7}{10} + \dfrac{3}{10}$

10. $\dfrac{9}{16} + \dfrac{7}{16} + \dfrac{3}{16}$

11. $\dfrac{16}{21} + \dfrac{4}{21} + \dfrac{1}{21}$

12. $\dfrac{12}{19} + \dfrac{8}{19} + \dfrac{6}{19}$

ADDITION OF UNLIKE FRACTIONS

When we add two or more unlike fractions, we follow the steps given below :

Step 1 : Find the L.C.M. of denominators of unlike fractions.

Step 2 : Convert unlike fractions into equivalent like fractions with their L.C.M. as common denominator.

Step 3 : Add the like fractions so obtained.

SOLVED EXAMPLES

Example 1. *Find the sum of $\frac{3}{4}$ and $\frac{5}{6}$.*

Solution : Given fractions are $\frac{3}{4}$ and $\frac{5}{6}$.

$$\begin{array}{c|c} 2 & 4 - 6 \\ \hline & 2 - 3 \end{array}$$

L.C.M of 4 and 6 = $2 \times 2 \times 3 = 12$.

Now, $\frac{3}{4} = \frac{3 \times 3}{4 \times 3} = \frac{9}{12}$. And, $\frac{5}{6} = \frac{5 \times 2}{6 \times 2} = \frac{10}{12}$.

$\therefore \quad \frac{3}{4} + \frac{5}{6} = \frac{9}{12} + \frac{10}{12} = \frac{9+10}{12} = \frac{19}{12} = 1\frac{7}{12}$.

Example 2. *Find the sum :* $\frac{3}{4} + \frac{2}{5} + \frac{1}{2}$.

Solution : Given fractions are : $\frac{3}{4}, \frac{2}{5}, \frac{1}{2}$.

$$\begin{array}{c|c} 2 & 4 - 5 - 2 \\ \hline & 2 - 5 - 1 \end{array}$$

L.C.M. of 4, 5 and 2 = $2 \times 2 \times 5 = 20$.

$\therefore \quad \frac{3}{4} = \frac{3 \times 5}{4 \times 5} = \frac{15}{20}, \quad \frac{2}{5} = \frac{2 \times 4}{5 \times 4} = \frac{8}{20}, \quad \frac{1}{2} = \frac{1 \times 10}{2 \times 10} = \frac{10}{20}$.

$\therefore \quad \frac{3}{4} + \frac{2}{5} + \frac{1}{2} = \frac{15}{20} + \frac{8}{20} + \frac{10}{20} = \frac{15+8+10}{20} = \frac{33}{20} = 1\frac{13}{20}$.

EXERCISE 27

Add :

1. $\frac{2}{5}$ and $\frac{3}{10}$

2. $\frac{4}{7}$ and $\frac{2}{3}$

3. $\frac{4}{9}$ and $\frac{5}{6}$

4. $\frac{3}{4}$ and $\frac{11}{12}$

Find the sum :

5. $\frac{5}{12} + \frac{7}{16}$

6. $\frac{5}{8} + \frac{7}{12}$

7. $\frac{1}{6} + \frac{7}{10}$

8. $\frac{8}{15} + \frac{9}{20}$

9. $\frac{11}{12} + \frac{13}{18}$

10. $\frac{1}{2} + \frac{2}{3} + \frac{3}{4}$

11. $\frac{1}{6} + \frac{3}{8} + 3$

12. $\frac{5}{7} + \frac{9}{14} + \frac{1}{2}$

13. $\frac{5}{9} + \frac{7}{12} + \frac{1}{3}$

14. $\frac{3}{4} + \frac{5}{8} + \frac{7}{12}$

15. $\frac{3}{8} + \frac{5}{16} + \frac{13}{24}$

16. $\frac{5}{6} + \frac{7}{12} + \frac{11}{18}$

17. $\frac{1}{2} + \frac{1}{3} + \frac{1}{4} + \frac{1}{6}$

18. $\frac{1}{1} + \frac{2}{3} + \frac{3}{4} + \frac{5}{8}$

Example 1. *Find the sum of* $3\dfrac{2}{7}$ *and* $2\dfrac{3}{7}$.

Solution : We have

$$3\dfrac{2}{7} + 2\dfrac{3}{7} = \dfrac{3 \times 7 + 2}{7} + \dfrac{2 \times 7 + 3}{7}$$

$$= \dfrac{23}{7} + \dfrac{17}{7} = \dfrac{23 + 17}{7} = \dfrac{40}{7} = 5\dfrac{5}{7}.$$

Example 2. *Find the sum :* $1\dfrac{3}{5} + 2\dfrac{7}{10}$.

Solution : We have

$$1\dfrac{3}{5} + 2\dfrac{7}{10} = \dfrac{1 \times 5 + 3}{5} + \dfrac{2 \times 10 + 7}{10} = \dfrac{8}{5} + \dfrac{27}{10}$$

$$= \dfrac{8 \times 2}{5 \times 2} + \dfrac{27}{10} \qquad [\textit{Since L.C.M. of } 5, \ 10 = 10]$$

$$= \dfrac{16}{10} + \dfrac{27}{10} = \dfrac{16 + 27}{10} = \dfrac{43}{10} = 4\dfrac{3}{10}.$$

Example 3. *Add* $1\dfrac{5}{12}$, $2\dfrac{4}{9}$ *and* $3\dfrac{1}{6}$.

Solution : We have

$$1\dfrac{5}{12} + 2\dfrac{4}{9} + 3\dfrac{1}{6} = \dfrac{1 \times 12 + 5}{12} + \dfrac{2 \times 9 + 4}{9} + \dfrac{3 \times 6 + 1}{6}$$

$$= \dfrac{17}{12} + \dfrac{22}{9} + \dfrac{19}{6}$$

$$= \dfrac{17 \times 3}{12 \times 3} + \dfrac{22 \times 4}{9 \times 4} + \dfrac{19 \times 6}{6 \times 6} \qquad [\textit{Since L.C.M. of } 12, 9, 6 \textit{ is } 36]$$

$$= \dfrac{51}{36} + \dfrac{88}{36} + \dfrac{114}{36} = \dfrac{51 + 88 + 114}{36}$$

$$= \dfrac{253}{36} = 7\dfrac{1}{36}.$$

2	12 − 9 − 6
3	6 − 9 − 3
	2 − 3 − 1

$\therefore$ L.C.M of 12, 9, 6
$= 2 \times 3 \times 2 \times 3 = 36$

EXERCISE 28

Find the following sums :

1. $4\dfrac{2}{5} + 3\dfrac{1}{5}$

2. $3\dfrac{4}{7} + 5\dfrac{2}{7}$

3. $6\dfrac{1}{4} + 3\dfrac{3}{8}$

4. $4\dfrac{1}{6} + 5\dfrac{7}{12}$

5. $2\dfrac{3}{7} + \dfrac{9}{14}$

6. $2\dfrac{4}{9} + \dfrac{2}{3}$

7. $1\dfrac{3}{4} + 2\dfrac{2}{3} + 3\dfrac{1}{6}$

8. $2\dfrac{4}{5} + 1\dfrac{3}{10} + 2\dfrac{1}{2}$

9. $2\dfrac{5}{9} + 3\dfrac{1}{3} + 1\dfrac{5}{6}$ 10. $3\dfrac{2}{5} + 1\dfrac{1}{10} + \dfrac{4}{15}$ 11. $2\dfrac{3}{5} + 8 + \dfrac{7}{10}$ 12. $7\dfrac{1}{2} + \dfrac{5}{9} + \dfrac{2}{3}$

SUBTRACTION OF FRACTIONS

SUBTRACTION OF LIKE FRACTIONS

We have learnt that :

$$\text{Difference of Like Fractions} = \frac{\text{Difference between the numerators}}{\text{Common Denominator}}.$$

Example : *Subtract* $\dfrac{4}{9}$ *from* $\dfrac{7}{9}$.

Solution : We have

$$\frac{7}{9} - \frac{4}{9} = \frac{7-4}{9} = \frac{\cancel{3}^{1}}{\cancel{9}_{3}} = \frac{1}{3}.$$

EXERCISE 29

Find the difference :

1. $\dfrac{9}{4} - \dfrac{1}{4}$ 2. $\dfrac{3}{8} - \dfrac{1}{8}$ 3. $\dfrac{7}{10} - \dfrac{3}{10}$ 4. $\dfrac{11}{15} - \dfrac{8}{15}$ 5. $\dfrac{7}{20} - \dfrac{3}{20}$

6. $\dfrac{5}{6} - \dfrac{1}{6}$ 7. $\dfrac{3}{2} - \dfrac{1}{2}$ 8. $\dfrac{5}{18} - \dfrac{1}{18}$ 9. $\dfrac{9}{28} - \dfrac{5}{28}$

SUBTRACTION OF UNLIKE FRACTIONS

To find the difference between two unlike fractions, we follow the following steps :

Step 1 : Find the L.C.M. of denominators of unlike fractions.

Step 2 : Convert unlike fractions into equivalent like fractions with their L.C.M. as common denominator.

Step 3 : Find the difference between the like fractions so obtained.

SOLVED EXAMPLES

Example 1. Find the difference :

    (a) $\dfrac{7}{8} - \dfrac{5}{12}$ (b) $2 - \dfrac{5}{9}$

Solution : (a) We have to find : $\dfrac{7}{8} - \dfrac{5}{12}$.

          L.C.M. of 8 and 12 $= 4 \times 2 \times 3 = 24$

$$\begin{array}{r|l} 4 & 8 - 12 \\ \hline & 2 - 3 \end{array}$$

Now, $\dfrac{7}{8} = \dfrac{7 \times 3}{8 \times 3} = \dfrac{21}{24}$.   And, $\dfrac{5}{12} = \dfrac{5 \times 2}{12 \times 2} = \dfrac{10}{24}$.

$\therefore$ $\dfrac{7}{8} - \dfrac{5}{12} = \dfrac{21}{24} - \dfrac{10}{24} = \dfrac{21-10}{24} = \dfrac{11}{24}$.

(b) We have to find : $\dfrac{2}{1} - \dfrac{5}{9}$.

L.C.M. of 1 and 9 is 9.

$\therefore$ $\dfrac{2}{1} - \dfrac{5}{9} = \dfrac{18}{9} - \dfrac{5}{9} = \dfrac{18-5}{9} = \dfrac{13}{9} = 1\dfrac{4}{9}$.

Example 2. *Find the difference between $\dfrac{4}{9}$ and $\dfrac{5}{12}$.*

Solution : Given fractions are $\dfrac{4}{9}$ and $\dfrac{5}{12}$.

L.C.M. of 9 and 12 = 3 × 3 × 4 = 36.

$$
\begin{array}{c|c}
3 & 9 - 12 \\
\hline
3 & 3 - 4
\end{array}
$$

Now, $\dfrac{4}{9} = \dfrac{4 \times 4}{9 \times 4} = \dfrac{16}{36}$.   And, $\dfrac{5}{12} = \dfrac{5 \times 3}{12 \times 3} = \dfrac{15}{36}$.

Clearly, $\dfrac{16}{36} > \dfrac{15}{36}$

$\therefore$ $\dfrac{4}{9} > \dfrac{5}{12}$.

Now, $\dfrac{4}{9} - \dfrac{5}{12} = \dfrac{16}{36} - \dfrac{15}{36} = \dfrac{16-15}{36} = \dfrac{1}{36}$.

Example 3. *Subtract $5\dfrac{1}{6}$ from $10\dfrac{2}{3}$.*

Solution : $10\dfrac{2}{3} - 5\dfrac{1}{6} = \dfrac{10 \times 3 + 2}{3} - \dfrac{5 \times 6 + 1}{6} = \dfrac{32}{3} - \dfrac{31}{6}$

$= \dfrac{32 \times 2}{3 \times 2} - \dfrac{31}{6}$ *[Since L.C.M. of 3 and 6 is 6]*

$= \dfrac{64}{6} - \dfrac{31}{6} = \dfrac{64-31}{6}$

$= \dfrac{\cancel{33}^{11}}{\cancel{6}_2} = \dfrac{11}{2} = 5\dfrac{1}{2}$.

Example 4. *Subtract $\dfrac{7}{10}$ from $3\dfrac{1}{5}$.*

Solution : $3\dfrac{1}{5} - \dfrac{7}{10} = \dfrac{3 \times 5 + 1}{5} - \dfrac{7}{10} = \dfrac{16}{5} - \dfrac{7}{10}$

$= \dfrac{32}{10} - \dfrac{7}{10}$ *[Since L.C.M. of 5 and 10 is 10]*

$= \dfrac{32-7}{10} = \dfrac{\cancel{25}^5}{\cancel{10}_2} = \dfrac{5}{2} = 2\dfrac{1}{2}$.

EXERCISE 30

Find the difference of :

1. $\dfrac{1}{2}$ and $\dfrac{1}{3}$

2. $\dfrac{1}{6}$ and $\dfrac{2}{3}$

3. $\dfrac{3}{4}$ and $\dfrac{5}{6}$

4. $\dfrac{3}{8}$ and $\dfrac{5}{12}$

5. $\dfrac{7}{10}$ and $\dfrac{8}{15}$

6. $\dfrac{7}{20}$ and $\dfrac{19}{15}$

Find the difference :

7. $\dfrac{4}{5} - \dfrac{3}{10}$

8. $6 - \dfrac{3}{5}$

9. $\dfrac{17}{16} - \dfrac{11}{24}$

10. $1 - \dfrac{8}{15}$

11. $5 - \dfrac{5}{8}$

12. $\dfrac{53}{6} - 7$

13. $3\dfrac{3}{4} - 2\dfrac{1}{2}$

14. $6\dfrac{2}{3} - 4\dfrac{1}{9}$

15. $5\dfrac{2}{3} - 2\dfrac{3}{4}$

16. $5\dfrac{5}{12} - 4\dfrac{1}{6}$

17. $5\dfrac{1}{8} - 3\dfrac{1}{12}$

18. $5\dfrac{3}{10} - 3\dfrac{7}{15}$

19. $7\dfrac{4}{9} - 3\dfrac{5}{12}$

20. $5\dfrac{1}{6} - 1\dfrac{7}{10}$

21. $3 - 2\dfrac{1}{8}$

22. $5 - 1\dfrac{6}{7}$

23. $3\dfrac{3}{4} - \dfrac{7}{10}$

24. $1\dfrac{11}{24} - \dfrac{7}{8}$

MIXED PROBLEMS ON ADDITION AND SUBTRACTION

Example 1. *Simplify* : $\dfrac{7}{9} - \dfrac{2}{3} + \dfrac{5}{6}$.

Solution : L.C.M. of 9, 3, 6 = 3 × 3 × 2 = 18.

3	9	−3	−6
	3	−1	−2

Now, $\dfrac{7}{9} = \dfrac{7 \times 2}{9 \times 2} = \dfrac{14}{18}$,

$\dfrac{2}{3} = \dfrac{2 \times 6}{3 \times 6} = \dfrac{12}{18}$,

$\dfrac{5}{6} = \dfrac{5 \times 3}{6 \times 3} = \dfrac{15}{18}$.

$\therefore \quad \dfrac{7}{9} - \dfrac{2}{3} + \dfrac{5}{6} = \dfrac{14}{18} - \dfrac{12}{18} + \dfrac{15}{18}$

$\qquad = \dfrac{14 - 12 + 15}{18}$

$\qquad = \dfrac{17}{18}$.

Example 2. *Simplify :* $4\dfrac{1}{3} - 2\dfrac{3}{4} + 5\dfrac{1}{6}$.

Solution : $4\dfrac{1}{3} - 2\dfrac{3}{4} + 5\dfrac{1}{6} = \dfrac{4\times 3 + 1}{3} - \dfrac{2\times 4 + 3}{4} + \dfrac{5\times 6 + 1}{6}$

$= \dfrac{13}{3} - \dfrac{11}{4} + \dfrac{31}{6}$

$= \dfrac{13\times 4}{3\times 4} - \dfrac{11\times 3}{4\times 3} + \dfrac{31\times 2}{6\times 2}$

$= \dfrac{52}{12} - \dfrac{33}{12} + \dfrac{62}{12} = \dfrac{52 - 33 + 62}{12} = \dfrac{114 - 33}{12}$

$= \dfrac{81^{27}}{12_4} = \dfrac{27}{4} = 6\dfrac{3}{4}$.

2	3 – 4 – 6
3	3 – 2 – 3
	1 – 2 – 1

∴ L.C.M of 3, 4, 6
$= 2 \times 3 \times 2 = 12$

EXERCISE 31

Simplify :

1. $\dfrac{1}{2} + \dfrac{3}{4} - \dfrac{5}{8}$

2. $\dfrac{7}{8} - \dfrac{1}{6} + \dfrac{5}{12}$

3. $\dfrac{1}{4} - \dfrac{5}{9} + \dfrac{7}{12}$

4. $\dfrac{3}{5} + \dfrac{7}{10} - \dfrac{1}{2}$

5. $\dfrac{3}{10} - \dfrac{8}{15} + \dfrac{2}{5}$

6. $\dfrac{4}{9} - \dfrac{5}{12} + \dfrac{1}{4}$

7. $2\dfrac{1}{3} + 3\dfrac{1}{6} - 1\dfrac{5}{12}$

8. $4\dfrac{1}{4} - 2\dfrac{3}{8} + 3\dfrac{1}{3}$

9. $6\dfrac{5}{9} - 4\dfrac{1}{3} - 2\dfrac{1}{6}$

10. $10 - 3\dfrac{1}{5} - 5\dfrac{3}{10}$

11. Subtract the sum of $5\dfrac{1}{2}$ and $6\dfrac{3}{8}$ from the sum of $7\dfrac{3}{4}$ and $6\dfrac{1}{2}$.

12. Subtract the difference of $6\dfrac{2}{3}$ and $5\dfrac{1}{6}$ from the difference of 4 and $2\dfrac{1}{3}$.

WORD PROBLEMS

(On Addition and Subtraction of Fractions)

Example 1. *An empty basket weighs* $1\dfrac{3}{4}$ *kg. Mona put* $2\dfrac{1}{2}$ *kg of mangoes in the basket. What is the total weight of basket and mangoes together ?*

Solution : Weight of the empty basket $= 1\dfrac{3}{4}$ kg $= \dfrac{1\times 4 + 3}{4}$ kg $= \dfrac{7}{4}$ kg.

Weight of mangoes in the basket $= 2\dfrac{1}{2}$ kg $= \dfrac{2\times 2 + 1}{2}$ kg $= \dfrac{5}{2}$ kg.

$\therefore$ Total weight of basket and mangoes

$$= \left(\frac{7}{4} + \frac{5}{2}\right) kg = \left(\frac{7}{4} + \frac{10}{4}\right) kg = \frac{(7+10)}{4} kg = \frac{17}{4} kg = 4\frac{1}{4} kg.$$

Hence, the total weight of basket and mangoes together is $4\frac{1}{4}$ kg.

Example 2. *A board $3\frac{7}{16}$ cm thick is glued to a board $4\frac{3}{8}$ cm thick. What is the combined thickness of the boards?*

Solution : Thickness of one board $= 3\frac{7}{16}$ cm $= \frac{3 \times 16 + 7}{16}$ cm $= \frac{55}{16}$ cm.

Thickness of another board $= 4\frac{3}{8}$ cm $= \frac{4 \times 8 + 3}{8}$ cm $= \frac{35}{8}$ cm.

Thickness of combined board $= \left(\frac{55}{16} + \frac{35}{8}\right)$ cm $= \left(\frac{55}{16} + \frac{70}{16}\right)$ cm

$$= \left(\frac{55 + 70}{16}\right) cm = \frac{125}{16} cm = 7\frac{13}{16} cm.$$

Example 3. *A vessel had $4\frac{1}{4}$ litres of milk. Out of it, a cat drank $\frac{3}{8}$ litres. How much milk was left in the vessel ?*

Solution : Quantity of milk in the vessel $= 4\frac{1}{4} l = \frac{17}{4} l.$

Quantity of milk drank by the cat $= \frac{3}{8} l.$

Quantity of the milk left in the vessel $= \left(\frac{17}{4} - \frac{3}{8}\right) l = \left(\frac{34}{8} - \frac{3}{8}\right) l$

$$= \left(\frac{34 - 3}{8}\right) l = \frac{31}{8} l = 3\frac{7}{8} l.$$

Hence, $3\frac{7}{8}$ litres of milk was left in the vessel.

Example 4. *Arun jumped 5 metres in a long jump and his classmate Varun jumped $1\frac{5}{8}$ metres less than Arun. How long was Varun's jump ?*

Solution : Clearly, Varun's jump is $\left(5 - 1\frac{5}{8}\right)$ m.

Now, $5 - 1\frac{5}{8} = \frac{5}{1} - \frac{1 \times 8 + 5}{8} = \frac{5}{1} - \frac{13}{8}$

$$= \frac{40}{8} - \frac{13}{8} = \frac{40 - 13}{8} = \frac{27}{8} = 3\frac{3}{8}.$$

Hence, the length of Varun's jump $= 3\frac{3}{8}$ metres.

Example 5. *What must be added to* $4\frac{5}{6}$ *to make* $5\frac{2}{9}$?

Solution : Sum of two fractions $= 5\frac{2}{9} = \frac{5 \times 9 + 2}{9} = \frac{47}{9}$.

One of the fractions $= 4\frac{5}{6} = \frac{4 \times 6 + 5}{6} = \frac{29}{6}$.

$$\begin{array}{c|cc} 2 & 9 & -6 \\ \hline & 3 & -2 \end{array}$$

$\therefore$ L.C.M of 9, 6
$= 3 \times 3 \times 2 = 18$

$\therefore$ The fraction to be added $= \frac{47}{9} - \frac{29}{6} = \frac{47 \times 2}{9 \times 2} - \frac{29 \times 3}{6 \times 3}$

[*Since L.C.M. of 9, 6 is 18*]

$$= \frac{94}{18} - \frac{87}{18} = \frac{94 - 87}{18} = \frac{7}{18}.$$

Hence, the fraction to be added is $\frac{7}{18}$.

Example 6. *What must be subtracted from* $6\frac{3}{4}$ *to get* $4\frac{1}{6}$?

Solution : Larger fraction $= 6\frac{3}{4} = \frac{6 \times 4 + 3}{4} = \frac{27}{4}$.

Remainder $= 4\frac{1}{6} = \frac{4 \times 6 + 1}{6} = \frac{25}{6}$.

$$\begin{array}{c|cc} 2 & 4 & -6 \\ \hline & 2 & -3 \end{array}$$

$\therefore$ L.C.M of 4, 6
$= 2 \times 2 \times 3 = 12$

$\therefore$ The fraction to be subracted $= \frac{27}{4} - \frac{25}{6} = \frac{27 \times 3}{4 \times 3} - \frac{25 \times 2}{6 \times 2}$

[*Since L.C.M. of 4, 6 is 12*]

$$= \frac{81}{12} - \frac{50}{12} = \frac{81 - 50}{12} = \frac{31}{12} = 2\frac{7}{12}.$$

Hence, the required fraction to be subtracted is $2\frac{7}{12}$.

Example 7. *From a rope 7 metres long, two pieces of length* $2\frac{3}{5}$ *metres and* $3\frac{3}{10}$ *metres were cut off. What is the length of the remaining rope ?*

Solution : Total length of the rope $= 7$ metres.

Total length cut off $= 2\frac{3}{5}\text{m} + 3\frac{3}{10}\text{m} = \left(\frac{2 \times 5 + 3}{5} + \frac{3 \times 10 + 3}{10}\right)\text{m} = \left(\frac{13}{5} + \frac{33}{10}\right)\text{m}$

$$= \left(\frac{26}{10} + \frac{33}{10}\right)\text{m} = \left(\frac{26 + 33}{10}\right)\text{m} = \frac{59}{10}\text{m}.$$

Length of the remaining rope $= \left(7 - \frac{59}{10}\right)\text{m}$

$$= \left(\frac{70}{10} - \frac{59}{10}\right)\text{m} = \frac{(70 - 59)}{10}\text{m} = \frac{11}{10}\text{m} = 1\frac{1}{10}\text{m}.$$

Hence, the length of the remaining rope is $1\frac{1}{10}$ m .

1. A frog took three jumps. The first jump was $\frac{3}{5}$ m long, the second was $\frac{3}{4}$ m long and the third was $\frac{7}{10}$ m long. How far did the frog jump in all ?

2. Renu took $2\frac{3}{4}$ hours to paint a table and $1\frac{1}{3}$ hours to paint a chair. How much time did she take in all ?

3. Rohit purchased $4\frac{1}{2}$ kg of potatoes, $3\frac{1}{4}$ kg of onions, $\frac{3}{4}$ kg of tomatoes and $1\frac{1}{8}$ kg of peas. What is the total quantity of vegetables purchased by Rohit ?

4. A piece of length $3\frac{4}{5}$ metres is cut off from a rope $7\frac{1}{4}$ metres long. What is the length of the remaining piece ?

5. A gas cylinder contained 35 litres of gas. $23\frac{3}{5}$ litres of gas is used. How much of gas is left in the cylinder ?

6. A drum full of rice weighs $40\frac{1}{6}$ kg. If the empty drum weighs $13\frac{3}{4}$ kg, find the weight of rice in the drum.

7. The heights of Deepak and Vikas are $148\frac{5}{6}$ cm and $153\frac{3}{4}$ cm respectively. Who is taller and by how much ?

8. What must be subtracted from $6\frac{4}{5}$ to get $2\frac{7}{10}$?

9. What must be added to $7\frac{1}{6}$ to get $9\frac{1}{9}$?

10. A man travelled $47\frac{1}{2}$ km in one day. He covered $29\frac{1}{3}$ km by scooter, $8\frac{5}{6}$ km on bicycle and the remaining distance on foot. How much did he travel on foot ?

11. A basket contains three types of $19\frac{1}{3}$ kg of fruits. There are $8\frac{1}{9}$ kg of apples, $3\frac{1}{6}$ kg of oranges and rest pears. What is the weight of pears in the basket ?

12. Meena purchased 12 metres of cloth. She used $7\frac{3}{4}$ metres of it for curtains and $1\frac{5}{6}$ metres for a bed-sheet. How much cloth is left ?

13. Which is greater ?

The difference between $2\frac{3}{4}$ and $5\frac{1}{6}$.   Or

The sum of $1\frac{3}{12}$ and $1\frac{1}{3}$.

THINGS TO REMEMBER

1. Sum of like fractions = $\dfrac{Sum\ of\ numerators}{Common\ denominator}$.

2. When we add two or more unlike fractions we convert them into equivalent fractions with a denominator equal to the L.C.M. of the denominators of the given fractions. Now, these like fractions can be added as given above.

3. Difference of like fractions = $\dfrac{Difference\ of\ numerators}{Common\ denominator}$.

4. When we find the difference of two unlike fractions we convert them into equivalent fractions with a denominator equal to the L.C.M. of the denominators of the given fractions. Now, these like fractions can be subtracted as given above.

C.C.E. DRILL - 7

QUESTION BAG - 1

(OBJECTIVE - TYPE QUESTIONS)

Tick(✓) the correct answer :

1. $\frac{1}{3} + \frac{1}{6} = ?$

    (a) $\frac{2}{9}$ 　　　　(b) $\frac{1}{18}$ 　　　　(c) $\frac{1}{2}$ 　　　　(d) 1

2. $2\frac{1}{3} + 4\frac{1}{2} = ?$

    (a) $6\frac{1}{6}$ 　　　　(b) $6\frac{1}{5}$ 　　　　(c) $6\frac{2}{5}$ 　　　　(d) $6\frac{5}{6}$

3. The difference between $\frac{9}{10}$ and $\frac{7}{15}$ is

    (a) $\frac{2}{15}$ 　　　　(b) $\frac{7}{20}$ 　　　　(c) $\frac{11}{15}$ 　　　　(d) $\frac{13}{30}$

4. $5\frac{6}{7} - 3\frac{4}{5} = ?$

    (a) $2\frac{1}{2}$ 　　　　(b) $2\frac{2}{35}$ 　　　　(c) $2\frac{3}{5}$ 　　　　(d) $2\frac{11}{35}$

5. $3\frac{3}{4} + 1\frac{1}{2} = ?$

    (a) $4\frac{1}{4}$ 　　　　(b) $4\frac{3}{4}$ 　　　　(c) $5\frac{1}{4}$ 　　　　(d) $5\frac{3}{4}$

6. The sum of $2\frac{3}{8}$, $2\frac{5}{16}$ and $2\frac{7}{24}$ is

    (a) $7\frac{1}{24}$ 　　　(b) $6\frac{47}{48}$ 　　　(c) $6\frac{23}{24}$ 　　　(d) $6\frac{17}{48}$

7. Anita put $\frac{1}{4}$ cup of flour in a bowl. Meena mixed $\frac{1}{6}$ cup of flour in it. How much more flour should Arti mix in it to make it equal to 1 cup of flour ?

    (a) $\frac{5}{6}$ 　　　　(b) $\frac{3}{8}$ 　　　　(c) $\frac{5}{12}$ 　　　　(d) $\frac{7}{12}$

8. Shikha ate $\frac{2}{5}$ of a cake and Anandi ate $\frac{1}{4}$ of the same cake. What part of the cake was left ?

    (a) $\frac{7}{10}$ 　　　　(b) $\frac{13}{20}$ 　　　　(c) $\frac{7}{20}$ 　　　　(d) $\frac{11}{20}$

9. Anuj ate $\frac{3}{4}$ of a pizza and Shaloo ate $\frac{2}{3}$ of the same pizza. How much more did Anuj eat than shaloo ?

   (a) $\frac{1}{6}$ (b) $\frac{1}{12}$ (c) $\frac{5}{6}$ (d) $\frac{5}{12}$

QUESTION BAG - 2

1. *State whether the following statement is true or false :*

   $\frac{3}{4} + \frac{4}{3} = 1$

2. A recipe needs $\frac{2}{5}$ cup of milk and $\frac{1}{3}$ cup of cream. How much more milk than cream is required ?

3. *Add :*

   (a) $\frac{4}{5} + \frac{2}{3} + \frac{1}{10}$ (b) $3\frac{2}{9} + 1\frac{5}{6}$ (c) $5\frac{3}{4} + 2\frac{2}{3}$

4. *Subtract :*

   (a) $12\frac{2}{5} - 6\frac{7}{8}$ (b) $5\frac{3}{4} - 2\frac{5}{6}$ (c) $\frac{3}{14} - \frac{4}{21}$

   (d) $11\frac{1}{6} - 9\frac{7}{8}$ (e) $3\frac{16}{21} - 2\frac{9}{24}$

5. *Simplify :*

   (a) $\frac{3}{4} - \frac{1}{8} + \frac{1}{6}$ (b) $2\frac{2}{3} - 1\frac{1}{4} + 3\frac{1}{6}$ (c) $1\frac{5}{8} - 2\frac{2}{3} + 3\frac{7}{12}$

6. If a length of $3\frac{2}{3}$ metres is cut from a wire which is $5\frac{1}{2}$ metres long, how much of the wire is left ?

7. How much is $10\frac{1}{12}$ more than the sum of $1\frac{1}{6}$ and $2\frac{7}{15}$?

8. *Simplify :* $12\frac{5}{11} - 6\frac{17}{22} + 1\frac{10}{33}$

9. From a 20m roll of cloth, three pieces of lengths $2\frac{5}{8}$ m, $3\frac{1}{3}$ m and $3\frac{2}{5}$ m are cut out. What length of the cloth is left :

9 MULTIPLICATION & DIVISION OF FRACTIONS

MULTIPLICATION OF A FRACTION BY A WHOLE NUMBER

We know that *multiplication means repeated addition.*

For example,

$$3 \times 4 = 3 \text{ repeated 4 times} = 3 + 3 + 3 + 3 = 12.$$

We make use of the same definition in multiplying a fraction and a whole number.

Example 1 .   *Multiply $\frac{1}{2}$ by 3.*

Solution :   We have :

$$\frac{1}{2} \times 3 = \frac{1}{2} \text{ repeated 3 times}$$

$$= \frac{1}{2} + \frac{1}{2} + \frac{1}{2} = \frac{1+1+1}{2} = \frac{3}{2} = 1\frac{1}{2}.$$

Let us apply the rule given below :

Rule: A fraction × A whole number = $\dfrac{\text{Numerator of the fraction} \times \text{Whole number}}{\text{Denominator of the fraction}}$

Using this rule, we have :

$$\frac{1}{2} \times 3 = \frac{1 \times 3}{2} = \frac{3}{2} = 1\frac{1}{2}.$$

Let us try another example.

Example 2 .   *Multiply $\frac{3}{4}$ by 5.*

Solution :   We have :

$$\frac{3}{4} \times 5 = \frac{3}{4} \text{ repeated 5 times}$$

$$= \frac{3}{4} + \frac{3}{4} + \frac{3}{4} + \frac{3}{4} + \frac{3}{4} = \frac{3+3+3+3+3}{4} = \frac{15}{4} = 3\frac{3}{4}.$$

Using the above rule, we have

$$\frac{3}{4} \times 5 = \frac{3 \times 5}{4} = \frac{15}{4} = 3\frac{3}{4}.$$

Example 3. Multiply $\frac{5}{9}$ by 15.

Solution : We have :

$$\frac{5}{9} \times 15 = \frac{5 \times \cancel{15}^5}{\cancel{9}_3} = \frac{25}{3} = 8\frac{1}{3}.$$

Example 4. Multiply $3\frac{5}{6}$ by 8.

Solution : We have :

$$3\frac{5}{6} \times 8 = \frac{23}{6} \times 8 = \frac{23 \times \cancel{8}^4}{\cancel{6}_3} = \frac{92}{3} = 30\frac{2}{3}.$$

EXERCISE 33

Multiply :

1. $\frac{1}{2} \times 5$

2. $\frac{1}{3} \times 8$

3. $\frac{2}{3} \times 7$

4. $\frac{3}{5} \times 6$

5. $\frac{5}{6} \times 8$

6. $\frac{7}{8} \times 12$

7. $\frac{13}{21} \times 9$

8. $\frac{17}{18} \times 14$

9. $\frac{21}{25} \times 10$

10. $2\frac{1}{2} \times 6$

11. $3\frac{2}{3} \times 8$

12. $4\frac{1}{6} \times 21$

13. $5\frac{3}{8} \times 20$

14. $3\frac{7}{15} \times 25$

15. $10\frac{7}{13} \times 26$

16. $2\frac{10}{21} \times 28$

MULTIPLICATION OF A FRACTION BY A FRACTION

Rule: Product of two fractions $= \dfrac{\textbf{Product of their numerators}}{\textbf{Product of their denominators}}$.

If any of the fractions is a mixed numeral or a whole number, change it into an improper fraction and multiply.

SOLVED EXAMPLES

Example 1. Multiply $\frac{7}{10}$ by $\frac{5}{21}$.

Solution : We have :

$$\frac{7}{10} \times \frac{5}{21} = \frac{\cancel{7}^1 \times \cancel{5}^1}{\cancel{10}_2 \times \cancel{21}_3} = \frac{1}{6}.$$

Example 2. Multiply $7\frac{1}{12}$ by $\frac{8}{15}$.

Solution : We have :

$$7\frac{1}{12} \times \frac{8}{15} = \frac{85}{12} \times \frac{8}{15} = \frac{\cancel{85}^{17} \times \cancel{8}^2}{\cancel{12}_3 \times \cancel{15}_3} = \frac{34}{9} = 3\frac{7}{9}.$$

Example 3 . Multiply 35 by $6\frac{1}{14}$.

Solution : We have :

$$35 \times 6\frac{1}{14} = \frac{35}{1} \times \frac{85}{14} = \frac{\cancel{35}^{5} \times 85}{1 \times \cancel{14}_{2}} = \frac{425}{2} = 212\frac{1}{2}.$$

Example 4 . Find the product of $6\frac{2}{3}$ and $1\frac{7}{8}$.

Solution : We have :

$$6\frac{2}{3} \times 1\frac{7}{8} = \frac{20}{3} \times \frac{15}{8} = \frac{\cancel{20}^{5} \times \cancel{15}^{5}}{\cancel{3}_{1} \times \cancel{8}_{2}} = \frac{25}{2} = 12\frac{1}{2}.$$

EXERCISE 34

Multiply :

1. $\dfrac{3}{4} \times \dfrac{5}{7}$

2. $\dfrac{5}{6} \times \dfrac{9}{10}$

3. $\dfrac{14}{27} \times \dfrac{12}{35}$

4. $2\dfrac{3}{5} \times \dfrac{7}{13}$

5. $6\dfrac{5}{12} \times \dfrac{6}{11}$

6. $\dfrac{8}{21} \times 6\dfrac{3}{4}$

7. $\dfrac{9}{46} \times 7\dfrac{2}{3}$

8. $28 \times 2\dfrac{10}{21}$

9. $4\dfrac{4}{15} \times 3\dfrac{1}{8}$

10. $6\dfrac{3}{16} \times 7\dfrac{7}{11}$

11. $3\dfrac{6}{25} \times 6\dfrac{1}{9}$

12. $12\dfrac{5}{6} \times 1\dfrac{5}{22}$

13. $4\dfrac{9}{14} \times 1\dfrac{8}{13}$

14. $15\dfrac{3}{10} \times 4\dfrac{1}{6}$

15. $5\dfrac{10}{21} \times 1\dfrac{17}{46}$

16. $17\dfrac{2}{5} \times 2\dfrac{2}{29}$

17. $23\dfrac{7}{16} \times 2\dfrac{14}{25}$

18. $40\dfrac{6}{7} \times 2\dfrac{19}{22}$

19. $\dfrac{3}{5} \times \dfrac{1}{6} \times \dfrac{2}{3}$

20. $2\dfrac{1}{4} \times 1\dfrac{1}{5} \times 3\dfrac{1}{3}$

WORD PROBLEMS ON MULTIPLICATION OF FRACTIONS

Example 1 . The cost of 1 litre of milk is Rs $26\frac{3}{5}$. What is the cost of $12\frac{1}{2}$ litres of milk?

Solution : Cost of 1 litre of milk = Rs $26\frac{3}{5}$.

$$\text{Cost of } 12\frac{1}{2} \text{ litres of milk} = \text{Rs} \left(26\frac{3}{5} \times 12\frac{1}{2} \right)$$

$$= \text{Rs} \left(\frac{133}{\cancel{5}_{1}} \times \frac{\cancel{25}^{5}}{2} \right)$$

$$= \text{Rs} \frac{665}{2} = \text{Rs } 332.50.$$

Hence, the cost of $12\frac{1}{2}$ litres of milk is Rs 332.50.

Example 2. *Rahul can walk $5\frac{2}{5}$ km in an hour. How much distance will he cover in $3\frac{1}{3}$ hours ?*

Solution : Distance covered by Rahul in 1 hour $= 5\frac{2}{5}$ km.

Distance covered by Rahul in $3\frac{1}{3}$ hours $= \left(5\frac{2}{5} \times 3\frac{1}{3}\right)$ km $= \left(\frac{27}{5} \times \frac{10}{3}\right)$ km

$$= \frac{27^9 \times 10^2}{5_1 \times 3_1} = 18 \text{ km.}$$

$\therefore$ Rahul will cover 18 km in $3\frac{1}{3}$ hours.

Example 3. *Find the perimeter of a rectangular field whose length and breadth are $16\frac{1}{2}$ m and $12\frac{3}{4}$ m respectively.*

Solution : Length of the field $= 16\frac{1}{2}$ m $= \frac{33}{2}$ m.

Breadth of the field $= 12\frac{3}{4}$ m $= \frac{51}{4}$ m.

$\therefore$ Perimeter of the field $= 2 \text{ (length + breadth)} = 2 \times \left(\frac{33}{2} + \frac{51}{4}\right)$ m

$$= 2 \times \left(\frac{66}{4} + \frac{51}{4}\right) \text{ m} = 2 \times \left(\frac{66 + 51}{4}\right) \text{ m}$$

$$= \left(\frac{2^1}{1} \times \frac{117}{4_2}\right) \text{ m} = \frac{117}{2} \text{ m} = 58\frac{1}{2} \text{ m.}$$

Hence, the perimeter of the field is $58\frac{1}{2}$ m.

EXERCISE 35

1. The cost of one pencil is Rs $3\frac{13}{20}$. What is the cost of 12 such pencils ?

2. A bag contains $97\frac{4}{5}$ kg of sugar. How much sugar do 10 such bags contain ?

3. A kilogram of apples cost Rs $16\frac{1}{4}$. What is the cost of $3\frac{1}{5}$ kg of apples ?

4. A metre of cloth costs Rs $107\frac{1}{2}$. Find the cost of $2\frac{1}{5}$ m of cloth.

5. An iron rod has been divided into 8 pieces of equal lengths. If the length of each piece is $6\frac{3}{4}$ m, what was the original length of the iron rod ?

6. One litre of petrol costs Rs $24\frac{4}{5}$. What is the cost of 35 litres of petrol ?

7. A man walks $3\dfrac{3}{4}$ km in 1 hour. How far does he go in $3\dfrac{1}{2}$ hours ?

8. One tin holds $16\dfrac{3}{5}$ litres of oil. How many litres can 25 such tins hold ?

9. A water tank can hold $56\dfrac{1}{4}$ litres of water. How much water is contained in the tank when it is $\dfrac{2}{5}$ full ?

10. An aeroplane covers 1020 km in an hour. How much distance will it cover in $4\dfrac{1}{6}$ hours ?

11. Find the perimeter of a square plot of land whose each side is $6\dfrac{1}{2}$ metres.

12. Find the perimeter of a rectangular park whose length and breadth are $45\dfrac{1}{2}$ m and $34\dfrac{3}{4}$ m respectively.

FRACTION OF A FRACTION

Let us consider $\dfrac{1}{2}$ of $\dfrac{1}{4}$.

We define : $\dfrac{1}{2}$ **of** $\dfrac{1}{4} = \dfrac{1}{4} \times \dfrac{1}{2}$.

With this definition, we have :

$$\dfrac{1}{2} \text{ of } \dfrac{1}{4} = \dfrac{1}{4} \times \dfrac{1}{2} = \dfrac{1 \times 1}{4 \times 2} = \dfrac{1}{8}.$$

SOLVED EXAMPLES

Example 1. *Find $\dfrac{3}{4}$ of $\dfrac{2}{3}$.*

Solution : $\dfrac{3}{4}$ of $\dfrac{2}{3} = \dfrac{2}{3} \times \dfrac{3}{4} = \dfrac{2^1 \times 3^1}{3_1 \times 4_2} = \dfrac{1}{2}$.

$\therefore \quad \dfrac{3}{4}$ of $\dfrac{2}{3} = \dfrac{1}{2}$.

Example 2. *Find $\dfrac{3}{4}$ of $4\dfrac{2}{3}$.*

Solution : $\dfrac{3}{4}$ of $4\dfrac{2}{3} = 4\dfrac{2}{3} \times \dfrac{3}{4} = \dfrac{14}{3} \times \dfrac{3}{4} = \dfrac{14^7 \times 3^1}{3_1 \times 4_2} = \dfrac{7}{2} = 3\dfrac{1}{2}$.

$\therefore \quad \dfrac{3}{4}$ of $4\dfrac{2}{3} = 3\dfrac{1}{2}$.

Example 3. Find $\dfrac{5}{7}$ of 42.

Solution : $\dfrac{5}{7}$ of $42 = 42 \times \dfrac{5}{7} = \dfrac{42}{1} \times \dfrac{5}{7} = \dfrac{\cancel{42}^{6} \times 5}{1 \times \cancel{7}_{1}} = 30.$

Hence, $\dfrac{5}{7}$ of 42 is 30.

Example 4. Tanvy bought $7\dfrac{1}{2}$ kg of apples. Later she found that $\dfrac{1}{5}$ of them were rotten. Find the weight of rotten apples and that of good ones.

Solution : Total weight of apples bought $= 7\dfrac{1}{2}$ kg $= \dfrac{15}{2}$ kg.

Weight of rotten apples $= \dfrac{1}{5}$ of $\dfrac{15}{2}$ kg

$= \left(\dfrac{15}{2} \times \dfrac{1}{5} \right)$ kg

$= \left(\dfrac{\cancel{15}^{3} \times 1}{2 \times \cancel{5}_{1}} \right)$ kg $= \dfrac{3}{2}$ kg $= 1\dfrac{1}{2}$ kg.

Weight of good apples $= \left(7\dfrac{1}{2} \text{ kg} \right) - \left(1\dfrac{1}{2} \text{ kg} \right)$

$= \left(\dfrac{15}{2} - \dfrac{3}{2} \right)$ kg

$= \dfrac{(15-3)}{2}$ kg $= \dfrac{12}{2}$ kg $= 6$ kg.

Example 5. A parking lot can hold 96 cars at a time. At a certain instant it was found that $\dfrac{7}{8}$ of the parking lot was occupied. How many more cars it could accommodate at that time ?

Solution : Number of cars which could be parked in all = 96.

Number of cars parked at that time $= \dfrac{7}{8}$ of 96

$= 96 \times \dfrac{7}{8} = \dfrac{96}{1} \times \dfrac{7}{8} = \dfrac{\cancel{96}^{12} \times 7}{1 \times \cancel{8}_{1}} = 84.$

Number of cars in the parking lot = 84.

Number of more cars to be accommodated = (96 – 84) = 12.

Hence, 12 more cars could be accommodated at that time.

Example 6. $\dfrac{2}{3}$ of the students in a school are boys and $\dfrac{3}{4}$ of these boys are players. What fraction of the students are male players ?

Solution :   Male players = $\frac{3}{4}$ of $\frac{2}{3}$ of all students

$$= \left(\frac{2}{3} \times \frac{3}{4} \right) \text{ of all students}$$

$$= \left(\frac{\overset{1}{\cancel{2}}}{\underset{1}{\cancel{3}}} \times \frac{\overset{1}{\cancel{3}}}{\underset{2}{\cancel{4}}} \right) \text{ of all students} = \frac{1}{2} \text{ of all students}$$

Hence, $\frac{1}{2}$ of all students are male players.

EXERCISE 36

Find :

1. $\frac{1}{2}$ of $\frac{1}{3}$

2. $\frac{1}{7}$ of $\frac{1}{9}$

3. $\frac{2}{3}$ of $\frac{6}{7}$

4. $\frac{3}{7}$ of $\frac{14}{15}$

5. $\frac{5}{8}$ of $\frac{16}{25}$

6. $\frac{2}{5}$ of $1\frac{9}{16}$

7. $\frac{4}{11}$ of $4\frac{2}{5}$

8. $\frac{3}{4}$ of 56

9. $\frac{4}{9}$ of 36

10. $\frac{8}{11}$ of 44

11. $\frac{9}{13}$ of 78

12. $\frac{6}{7}$ of 42

13. A bag can hold 96 kg sugar. How much sugar is there in the bag when it is $\frac{5}{8}$ full ?

14. A test was given to a class of 42 students. If $\frac{6}{7}$ of these students passed, then how many failed ?

15. There are 140 members of a committee. In a meeting, three-fourth of the members were present. How many members were absent ?

16. Mona's school is 6 km away from her house. She covers $\frac{2}{3}$ of the distance in a rickshaw. Due to some fault in the rickshaw she had to cover the remaining distance on foot. How far did she walk ?

17. The capacity of a parking place is that of 84 cars. At a particular time, $\frac{3}{4}$ of the parking place is occupied. How many more cars can be parked at that time ?

18. $\frac{3}{8}$ of the population of a village consists of women. If $\frac{2}{3}$ of the women of that village are illiterate, what fraction of the population in that village consists of illiterate women ?

$\left[\textbf{Hint.} \text{ Illiterate women} = \frac{2}{3} \text{ of } \frac{3}{8} \text{ of the population of the village.} \right]$

DIVISION OF FRACTIONS

MULTIPLICATIVE INVERSE OR RECIPROCAL OF NUMBERS

If two numbers are such that their product is 1, then each is called the **multiplicative inverse** or **reciprocal** of the other.

Example 1.   We have : $\dfrac{3}{4} \times \dfrac{4}{3} = \dfrac{3 \times 4}{4 \times 3} = 1.$

∴   Reciprocal of $\dfrac{3}{4}$ is $\dfrac{4}{3}$. And, reciprocal of $\dfrac{4}{3}$ is $\dfrac{3}{4}$.

Example 2.   We have : $\dfrac{13}{7} \times \dfrac{7}{13} = \dfrac{13 \times 7}{7 \times 13} = 1.$

∴   Reciprocal of $\dfrac{13}{7}$ is $\dfrac{7}{13}$. And, reciprocal of $\dfrac{7}{13}$ is $\dfrac{13}{7}$.

Example 3.   We have : $3 \times \dfrac{1}{3} = \dfrac{3}{1} \times \dfrac{1}{3} = \dfrac{3 \times 1}{1 \times 3} = 1.$

∴   Reciprocal of 3 is $\dfrac{1}{3}$. And, reciprocal of $\dfrac{1}{3}$ is 3.

Example 4.   We have : $1 \times 1 = 1.$

∴   Reciprocal of 1 is 1.

Example 5.   Since there is no number which when multiplied with 0 gives 1, so the reciprocal of 0 does not exist.

How to Write the Reciprocal of a Number ?

To write the multiplicative inverse or the reciprocal of a fraction, we interchange the denominator and the numerator of that fraction.

Example 1.   Write the reciprocal of each of the following :

(a) $\dfrac{5}{11}$ (b) $\dfrac{19}{20}$ (c) $1\dfrac{2}{15}$ (d) 6

Solution :   (a) Reciprocal of $\dfrac{5}{11}$ is $\dfrac{11}{5}$.

(b) Reciprocal of $\dfrac{19}{20}$ is $\dfrac{20}{19}$.

(c) Reciprocal of $1\dfrac{2}{15}$ = Reciprocal of $\dfrac{17}{15} = \dfrac{15}{17}$.

(d) Reciprocal of 6 = Reciprocal of $\dfrac{6}{1} = \dfrac{1}{6}$.

DIVISION OF A FRACTION BY A FRACTION

Rule : *In order to divide a fraction by another fraction, we multiply the dividend by the reciprocal of the divisor.*

Example 2. *Find*: $\dfrac{3}{14} \div \dfrac{2}{7}$.

Solution : Reciprocal of $\dfrac{2}{7} = \dfrac{7}{2}$.

$$\therefore \quad \frac{3}{14} \div \frac{2}{7} = \frac{3}{14} \times \frac{7}{2} = \frac{3 \times \cancel{7}^{1}}{\cancel{14}_{2} \times 2} = \frac{3}{4}.$$

Example 3. *Find*: $14\dfrac{1}{4} \div \dfrac{3}{4}$.

Solution : Reciprocal of $\dfrac{3}{4} = \dfrac{4}{3}$.

$$\therefore \quad 14\frac{1}{4} \div \frac{3}{4} = \frac{57}{4} \div \frac{3}{4} = \frac{57}{4} \times \frac{4}{3} = \frac{\cancel{57}^{19} \times \cancel{4}^{1}}{\cancel{4}_{1} \times \cancel{3}_{1}} = 19.$$

Example 4. *Find*: $19\dfrac{3}{5} \div 1\dfrac{13}{15}$.

Solution : Reciprocal of $1\dfrac{13}{15} = $ Reciprocal of $\dfrac{28}{15} = \dfrac{15}{28}$.

$$\therefore \quad 19\frac{3}{5} \div 1\frac{13}{15} = \frac{98}{5} \div \frac{28}{15} = \frac{98}{5} \times \frac{15}{28} = \frac{\cancel{98}^{7} \times \cancel{15}^{3}}{\cancel{5}_{1} \times \cancel{28}_{2}} = \frac{21}{2} = 10\frac{1}{2}.$$

DIVISION OF A FRACTION BY A WHOLE NUMBER

Rule : **(A fraction) ÷ (A whole number)**

= (The fraction) × (Reciprocal of the whole number).

Example 5. *Find*: $\dfrac{7}{11} \div 14$.

Solution : Reciprocal of $14 = $ Reciprocal of $\dfrac{14}{1} = \dfrac{1}{14}$.

$$\therefore \quad \frac{7}{11} \div 14 = \frac{7}{11} \div \frac{14}{1} = \frac{7}{11} \times \frac{1}{14} = \frac{\cancel{7}^{1} \times 1}{11 \times \cancel{14}_{2}} = \frac{1}{22}.$$

Example 6. *Find*: $8\dfrac{1}{3} \div 5$.

Solution : Reciprocal of $5 = \dfrac{1}{5}$.

$$\therefore \quad 8\frac{1}{3} \div 5 = \frac{25}{3} \div 5 = \frac{25}{3} \times \frac{1}{5} = \frac{\cancel{25}^{5} \times 1}{3 \times \cancel{5}_{1}} = \frac{5}{3} = 1\frac{2}{3}.$$

Rule : (A whole number) ÷ (A fraction)

= (The whole number) × (Reciprocal of the fraction)

Example 7. *Find*: $42 \div \dfrac{6}{7}$.

Solution : Reciprocal of $\dfrac{6}{7}$ is $\dfrac{7}{6}$.

$$\therefore \quad 42 \div \frac{6}{7} = 42 \times \frac{7}{6} = \frac{\overset{7}{\cancel{42}} \times 7}{1 \times \cancel{6}_1} = 49.$$

Example 8. *Find*: $56 \div 8\dfrac{2}{5}$.

Solution : Reciprocal of $8\dfrac{2}{5}$ = Reciprocal of $\dfrac{42}{5} = \dfrac{5}{42}$.

$$\therefore \quad 56 \div 8\frac{2}{5} = 56 \div \frac{42}{5} = 56 \times \frac{5}{42} = \frac{56}{1} \times \frac{5}{42} = \frac{\overset{4}{\cancel{56}} \times 5}{1 \times \cancel{42}_3} = \frac{20}{3} = 6\frac{2}{3}.$$

Example 9. *Write 5 paise as the fraction of a rupee.*

Solution : 1 rupee = 100 paise.

$$\therefore \quad \text{Required fraction} = 5 \div 100 = \frac{5}{1} \times \frac{1}{100} = \frac{\overset{1}{\cancel{5}} \times 1}{1 \times \cancel{100}_{20}} = \frac{1}{20}.$$

EXERCISE 37

1. Find the multiplicative inverse of each of the following :

(a) $\dfrac{3}{5}$ (b) $\dfrac{9}{16}$ (c) $\dfrac{1}{8}$ (d) $\dfrac{10}{19}$ (e) 15   (f) $\dfrac{12}{7}$

(g) $\dfrac{24}{13}$ (h) $2\dfrac{6}{7}$ (i) $3\dfrac{9}{14}$ (j) $6\dfrac{5}{8}$ (k) 1   (l) 0

Divide and find the quotient :

2. $\dfrac{6}{7} \div 3$ 3. $\dfrac{7}{12} \div 21$ 4. $4\dfrac{2}{3} \div 7$ 5. $17\dfrac{3}{5} \div 33$

6. $\dfrac{7}{9} \div \dfrac{2}{3}$ 7. $\dfrac{7}{24} \div \dfrac{5}{12}$ 8. $\dfrac{9}{26} \div 4\dfrac{2}{13}$ 9. $8\dfrac{1}{6} \div 4\dfrac{2}{3}$

10. $10\dfrac{5}{7} \div 1\dfrac{11}{14}$ 11. $100 \div 33\dfrac{1}{3}$ 12. $88 \div 3\dfrac{1}{7}$ 13. $84 \div 7\dfrac{7}{8}$

14. $15\dfrac{8}{9} \div 3\dfrac{2}{3}$ 15. $16\dfrac{2}{3} \div 2\dfrac{2}{9}$ 16. $5\dfrac{7}{10} \div 3\dfrac{1}{6}$

17. Express 25 minutes as a fraction of an hour.

18. Express 35 paise as a fraction of a rupee.

19. Express 325 *ml* as a fraction of a litre.

20. Express 65 cm as a fraction of a metre.

21. Express 125 m as a fraction of a km.

WORD PROBLEMS ON DIVISION OF FRACTIONS

Example 1. *The cost of $3\frac{1}{2}$ metres of cloth is Rs $57\frac{3}{4}$. Find the cost of one metre of cloth.*

Solution: Cost of $3\frac{1}{2}$ m of cloth $=$ Rs $57\frac{3}{4}$.

Cost of 1 m of cloth $=$ Rs $\left(57\frac{3}{4} \div 3\frac{1}{2}\right) =$ Rs $\left(\frac{231}{4} \div \frac{7}{2}\right)$

$=$ Rs $\left(\frac{231}{4} \times \frac{2}{7}\right) =$ Rs $\frac{33}{2} =$ Rs $16\frac{1}{2}$.

Hence, the cost of 1 m of cloth is Rs $16\frac{1}{2}$.

Example 2. *A cord of length $71\frac{1}{2}$ m has been cut into 26 pieces of equal length. What is the length of each piece?*

Solution: Whole length of the cord $= 71\frac{1}{2}$ m $= \frac{143}{2}$ m.

Number of pieces formed $= 26$.

$\therefore$ Length of each piece $= \left(\frac{143}{2} \div 26\right)$ m $= \left(\frac{143}{2} \times \frac{1}{26}\right)$ m

$= \left(\frac{143^{11} \times 1}{2 \times 26_2}\right)$ m $= \frac{11}{4}$ m $= 2\frac{3}{4}$ m.

Hence, the length of each piece is $2\frac{3}{4}$ metres.

Example 3. *How many pieces of length $1\frac{3}{4}$ metres can be cut from a ribbon of length 63 metres?*

Solution: Whole length of the ribbon $= 63$ m.

Length of each piece $= 1\frac{3}{4}$ m $= \frac{7}{4}$ m.

Number of pieces formed $= 63 \div \frac{7}{4} = \left(63 \times \frac{4}{7}\right) = \left(\frac{63^9 \times 4}{7_1}\right) = 36$.

∴   The given length of ribbon can be cut into 36 pieces of equal length.

Example 4. *The area of a room is $65\frac{1}{4}$ square metres. If its breadth is $5\frac{7}{16}$ metres, find its length.*

Solution :   We know that : area = length × breadth.

Area of the room $= 65\frac{1}{4}$ sq. m.

Breadth of the room $= 5\frac{7}{16}$ m.

∴   Length of the room = Area ÷ Breadth

$$= \left(65\frac{1}{4} \div 5\frac{7}{16}\right) m = \left(\frac{261}{4} \div \frac{87}{16}\right) m$$

$$= \left(\frac{261}{4} \times \frac{16}{87}\right) m = \left(\frac{261^{3} \times 16^{4}}{4_{1} \times 87_{1}}\right) m = 12 \ m.$$

Hence, the length of the room is 12 m.

Example 5. *The product of two fractions is $9\frac{3}{5}$. If one of the fractions is $9\frac{3}{7}$, find the other.*

Solution :   Product of two fractions $= 9\frac{3}{5}$.

One of the fractions $= 9\frac{3}{7}$.

The other fraction $= \left(9\frac{3}{5} \div 9\frac{3}{7}\right) = \left(\frac{48}{5} \div \frac{66}{7}\right) = \left(\frac{48}{5} \times \frac{7}{66}\right)$

$$= \frac{48^{8} \times 7}{5 \times 66_{11}} = \frac{56}{55} = 1\frac{1}{55}.$$

Hence, the other fraction is $1\frac{1}{55}$.

❋ EXERCISE 38

1. If the cost of $3\frac{1}{4}$ kg of sugar is Rs $106\frac{3}{5}$ find the cost of 1 kg of sugar.

2. If the cost of $2\frac{3}{4}$ litres of petrol is Rs $145\frac{1}{5}$ find the cost of 1 litre of petrol.

3. A bag of salt weighs $2\frac{1}{4}$ kg. If $40\frac{1}{2}$ kg of salt is to be put in such bags, how many bags will be required ?

4. 14 tins hold $178\frac{1}{2}$ litres of oil. How much oil is there in 1 tin ?

5. If a car travels $283\frac{1}{2}$ km in $4\frac{2}{3}$ hours, how far does it go in 1 hour ?

6. If $367\frac{1}{2}$ kg of rice is contained in 35 bags of equal weights, how much does each bag weigh ?

7. Suchi cuts 54 m of cloth into pieces, each of length $3\frac{3}{8}$ metres. How many pieces does she get ?

8. Mona cuts $36\frac{1}{8}$ m of cloth into 17 pieces of equal lengths. What is the length of each piece ?

9. The area of a rectangle is $37\frac{4}{5}$ square cm. If its length is $6\frac{3}{4}$ cm, find its breadth.

10. The product of two fractions is 5. If one of them is $13\frac{4}{7}$, find the other.

THINGS TO REMEMBER

1. Product of two fractions $= \dfrac{\text{Product of their numerators}}{\text{Product of their denominators}}$.

2. Reciprocal of a fraction $= \dfrac{\text{Its denominator}}{\text{Its numerator}}$.

3. The product of a fraction and its reciprocal is 1.

4. 0 has no reciprocal.

5. To divide a given fraction by another fraction, multiply the first fraction with the reciprocal of the second.

ACTIVITY TIME

Activity To Find The Product Of Fractions Using A Squared Paper.

Let us find the product : $\dfrac{1}{4} \times \dfrac{3}{5}$.

Take a squared paper.

Since the denominators of the given fractions are 4 and 5, cut out a 4 x 5 rectangle from the squared paper as shown below:

Now shade $\dfrac{1}{4}$ of the rectangle horizontally as shown.

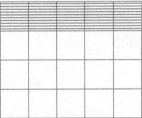

Again shade $\dfrac{3}{5}$ of the rectangle vertically as shown.

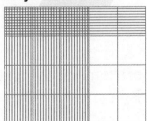

Now observe the rectangle and find out what fraction of the rectangle has both horizontal (red) and vertical (green) lines. Clearly, it is 3 parts out of 20 i.e. $\dfrac{3}{20}$.

$\therefore \dfrac{1}{4} \times \dfrac{3}{5} = \dfrac{3}{20}$.

Try to find some more products in the same manner.

C.C.E. DRILL - 8

QUESTION BAG - 1

(OBJECTIVE - TYPE QUESTIONS)

Tick (✓) the correct answer :

1. Rita had $\frac{5}{6}$ of a cake. She ate $\frac{2}{3}$ of it . What part of the cake did she eat?

   (a) $\frac{5}{9}$ 　　　　(b) $\frac{3}{10}$ 　　　　(c) $\frac{4}{5}$ 　　　　(d) $\frac{10}{12}$

2. Reciprocal of $3\frac{1}{2}$ is

   (a) $\frac{7}{2}$ 　　　　(b) $\frac{2}{7}$ 　　　　(c) $1\frac{2}{3}$ 　　　　(d) $2\frac{1}{3}$

3. What is the sum of the reciprocals of 8 and $\frac{1}{6}$?

   (a) $6\frac{1}{8}$ 　　　　(b) $\frac{8}{49}$ 　　　　(c) $8\frac{1}{6}$ 　　　　(d) $\frac{6}{49}$

4. Sachin reads $\frac{3}{5}$ of a book. He finds that there are still 80 pages left to be read. Total number of pages in the book are

   (a) 100 　　　　(b) 200 　　　　(c) 300 　　　　(d) 400

5. Jim has a rope of length $5\frac{1}{2}$ m. He cuts off one-third of it. What is the length of the part cut off?

   (a) $1\frac{1}{2}$ 　　　　(b) $1\frac{5}{6}$ m 　　　　(c) $1\frac{3}{4}$ m 　　　　(d) $1\frac{3}{8}$ m

6. The daily consumption of milk of a family is $2\frac{3}{4}$ litres. The quantity of milk consumed by the family in the month of June is

   (a) 77 litres 　　(b) $82\frac{1}{2}$ litres 　　(c) $85\frac{1}{4}$ litres 　　(d) $87\frac{1}{2}$ litres

7. On dividing $7\frac{1}{5}$ by $1\frac{1}{35}$, we get

   (a) 7 　　　　(b) 35 　　　　(c) $\frac{1}{36}$ 　　　　(d) 36

QUESTION BAG-2

1. *Fill in the blanks:*

   (a) $\frac{1}{4}$ of a rupee = ...P

   (b) $\frac{2}{3}$ of a year = ...months

   (c) $\frac{5}{6}$ of a day = ...hours

   (d) $\frac{3}{8}$ of a kg = ...gm

   (e) $\frac{11}{25}$ of a litre = ...ml

   (f) $\frac{7}{15}$ of an hour = ...min

2. *Fill in the place holders:*

   (a) $\boxed{} \div 2\frac{3}{4} = 0$

   (b) $\frac{6}{7} \div \boxed{} = 1$

   (c) $3\frac{2}{5} \div 3\frac{2}{5} = \boxed{}$

   (d) $\frac{3}{11} \div 1 = \boxed{}$

   (e) $0 \div 7\frac{5}{6} = \boxed{}$

   (f) $\frac{3}{8} \div \frac{2}{3} = \frac{3}{8} \times \boxed{}$

   (g) $9\frac{2}{7} \times 3\frac{5}{9} \times 0 \times 1\frac{2}{3} = \boxed{}$

   (h) $100 \div 3\frac{1}{3} = \boxed{}$

   (i) $5 \div \frac{1}{5} = \boxed{}$

   (j) $11 \div \frac{1}{11} = \boxed{}$

   (k) $\frac{1}{2} \div \frac{1}{10} = \boxed{}$

   (l) $\frac{1}{5} \div \frac{1}{20} = \boxed{}$

   (m) $1 \div \frac{3}{5} = \boxed{}$

   (n) $\frac{5}{6} \div \frac{6}{5} = \boxed{}$

   (o) $8\frac{8}{9} \div 0 = \boxed{}$

   (p) $49 \div \frac{7}{9} = \boxed{}$

3. (a) How many one-thirds are there in 2?

   (b) How many one-sixths are there in one-third?

   (c) How many two-thirds are there in 6?

   (d) How many four - fifths are there in 4?

4. *Simplify:*

   (a) $3\frac{7}{9} \times 1\frac{3}{4}$

   (b) $4\frac{3}{8} \times 1\frac{2}{5}$

   (c) $2\frac{3}{4} \times 4\frac{4}{5} \times 6\frac{3}{8}$

   (d) $2\frac{3}{9} \times 3\frac{2}{7}$

   (e) $2\frac{1}{3} \times 3\frac{2}{5} \times 1\frac{1}{2}$

5. *Write the multiplicative inverse of:*

   (a) $9\frac{4}{11}$

   (b) $2\frac{5}{8}$

   (c) $15\frac{3}{10}$

6. *Divide:*

   (a) $8\dfrac{2}{5} \div 1\dfrac{1}{15}$ (b) $47\dfrac{2}{9} \div 9\dfrac{4}{9}$ (c) $3\dfrac{11}{38} \div 1\dfrac{18}{57}$

7. Amisha can swim $1\dfrac{3}{5}$ m in 1 second. What distance can she swim in 1 minute?

8. Acar goes $45\dfrac{1}{3}$ km in 1 hour. How much distance will it cover in $1\dfrac{4}{5}$ hours?

9. *Simplify:* $5\dfrac{11}{17} \times 1\dfrac{9}{8} \div \dfrac{24}{63}$

10. Divide the product of $1\dfrac{4}{13}$ and $7\dfrac{4}{5}$ by $3\dfrac{12}{13}$.

11. The product of two numbers is 4. One of the numbers is $5\dfrac{1}{3}$. Find the other.

12. When I have travelled $4\dfrac{1}{2}$ km, I have completed $\dfrac{3}{7}$ of my journey. What is the total length of my journey?

13. $8\dfrac{3}{4}$ m of ribbon was cut into 14 pieces of equal length. Find the length of each piece.

14. Find the fraction by which $16\dfrac{7}{11}$ is multiplied to get 244.

15. *Fill in the blanks:*

   (a) The multiplicative inverse of $1\dfrac{2}{3}$ is ....

   (b) $9 \div \dfrac{1}{2}$ means there are .... halves in 9.

   (c) There are .... halves in $12\dfrac{1}{2}$.

   (d) The number which is its own reciprocal is ....

   (e) The reciprocal of a whole number is always a .... fraction.

   (f) The product of a number and its reciprocal is ....

   (g) Dividing by $\dfrac{1}{5}$ is the same as multiplying by ....

   (h) If 1 is divided by a fraction, the quotient is the .... of the fraction.

16. *State whether each of the following statements is true or false:*

   (a) The reciprocal of a mixed number is a proper fraction. ....

   (b) Any fraction $\div\ 0 = 0$. ....

   (c) The reciprocal of 0 is 0 . ...

   (d) $2 \div 3 = \dfrac{3}{2}$

   (e) We can change the order of fractions in multiplication. ....

   (f) $\dfrac{3}{4} \times \dfrac{5}{6} = \dfrac{3 \times 5}{4 \times 6}$ ....

   (g) $3\dfrac{1}{4} \times 3\dfrac{1}{4} = 9\dfrac{1}{16}$ ....

   (h) The reciprocal of a fraction is always greater than 1. ....

10 DECIMALS

Let us recall what we have learnt about decimals in class IV.

DECIMAL FRACTIONS

*The fractions in which the denominators are 10, 100, 1000 etc. are known as **decimal fractions.***

Examples. $\dfrac{7}{10}$, $\dfrac{64}{100}$, $\dfrac{219}{100}$, $\dfrac{3567}{1000}$ etc. are all decimal fractions.

We have

$$\frac{1}{10} = .1, \quad \frac{2}{10} = .2, \quad \frac{3}{10} = .3, \quad \ldots\ldots\ldots\ldots, \quad \frac{9}{10} = .9$$

$$\frac{1}{100} = .01, \quad \frac{2}{100} = .02, \quad \frac{3}{100} = .03, \quad \ldots\ldots\ldots\ldots, \quad \frac{9}{100} = .09.$$

$$\frac{10}{100} = .10, \quad \frac{11}{100} = .11, \quad \frac{12}{100} = .12, \quad \ldots\ldots\ldots\ldots, \quad \frac{99}{100} = .99.$$

$$\frac{1}{1000} = .001, \quad \frac{2}{1000} = .002, \quad \frac{3}{1000} = .003, \quad \ldots\ldots\ldots\ldots, \quad \frac{9}{1000} = .009.$$

$$\frac{10}{1000} = .010, \quad \frac{11}{1000} = .011, \quad \frac{12}{1000} = .012, \quad \ldots\ldots\ldots\ldots, \quad \frac{99}{1000} = .099.$$

$$\frac{100}{1000} = .100, \quad \frac{101}{1000} = .101, \quad \frac{102}{1000} = .102, \quad \ldots\ldots\ldots\ldots, \quad \frac{999}{1000} = .999.$$

The dot (.) in a decimal representation is called ***decimal point.***

DECIMALS : The numbers written in decimal form are called ***decimal numbers*** or simply ***decimals.***

Thus, each of the numbers .7, .64, 2.19 and 3.567 is a decimal.

A decimal number has two parts - whole number part and decimal part, separated by a decimal point. The whole number part is to the left of the decimal point and the decimal part is to its right.

In 352.89, whole number part = 352 and decimal part = .89.

The absence of any of the parts is shown by 0.

Thus, .63 may be written as 0.63. And, 89 may be written as 89.0.

Also, we read :

(a)   0.54 as **decimal five four.**

(b)   16.08 as **sixteen point zero eight.**

(c)   235.975 as **two hundred thirty-five point nine seven five.**

PLACE - VALUE CHART

For decimal numbers, we have the place value chart as shown below :

Ten-thousands	Thousands	Hundreds	Tens	Ones	Decimal Point	Tenths	Hundredths	Thousandths
10000	1000	100	10	1	.	$\frac{1}{10}$ (0.1)	$\frac{1}{100}$ (0.01)	$\frac{1}{1000}$ (0.001)

We may arrange a decimal number 1238.654 in the place value chart as follows :-

Thousands 1000	Hundreds 100	Tens 10	Ones 1	Decimal Point	Tenths $\frac{1}{10}$	Hundredths $\frac{1}{100}$	Thousandths $\frac{1}{1000}$
1	2	3	8	.	6	5	4

Thus, in 1238.654, we have :

Place value of 1 = 1000 ;

Place value of 2 = 200 ;

Place value of 3 = 30 ;

Place value of 8 = 8 ;

Place value of 6 = $\frac{6}{10}$;

Place value of 5 = $\frac{5}{100}$;

Place value of 4 = $\frac{4}{1000}$.

Hence, we may write 1238.654 in **expanded form** as :

$$1000 + 200 + 30 + 8 + \frac{6}{10} + \frac{5}{100} + \frac{4}{1000}$$

1238.654 is called the **ordinary** or **short form.**

EXERCISE 39

1. Write the following decimals in words :

   (a) 16.23   (b) 0.871   (c) 86.047   (d) 103.005

   (e) 1.01   (f) 2305.61   (g) 30.108   (h) 140.062

2. Write the following decimals in figures :

   (a) thirty-five point six five   (b) one hundred eight point zero seven

   (c) six point nine three two   (d) decimal five zero three

   (e) three hundred forty point nine   (f) four hundred sixteen point one zero six

   (g) three thousand six point zero zero nine

   (h) two hundred point one two

3. Write the place value of each digit in each of the following decimals :

   (a) 237.641   (b) 29.053   (c) 8.204   (d) 2035.647

4. Write the following decimals in expanded form :

   (a) 19.35   (b) 23.04   (c) 137.506   (d) 0.613

   (e) 8.137   (f) 2605.034   (g) 0.008   (h) 407.65

5. Write each of the following in short form :

   (a) $20 + 7 + \dfrac{3}{10} + \dfrac{6}{100}$ (b) $400 + 30 + 6 + \dfrac{1}{10} + \dfrac{3}{100} + \dfrac{5}{1000}$

   (c) $40 + \dfrac{8}{10} + \dfrac{3}{100} + \dfrac{4}{1000}$ (d) $500 + 7 + \dfrac{2}{100} + \dfrac{3}{1000}$

   (e) $3000 + 200 + 1 + \dfrac{6}{10} + \dfrac{7}{1000}$ (f) $600 + 9 + \dfrac{7}{10} + \dfrac{6}{1000}$

LIKE AND UNLIKE DECIMALS

DECIMAL PLACES

The number of digits contained in the decimal part of a decimal number is the number of decimal places in it.

Examples : The number 6.38 has two decimal places and 14.749 has three decimal places.

LIKE DECIMALS

Decimals having the same number of decimal places are called **like decimals.**

Examples : The decimals 5.67, 0.89, 13.74, 8.60 are like decimals, each having 2 places of decimal.

UNLIKE DECIMALS

Decimals having different number of decimal places are called **unlike decimals.**

Examples : The numbers 12.53, 8.968 and 0.7 are unlike decimals. Note that these numbers have two places of decimals, three places of decimals and one place of decimal respectively.

AN IMPORTANT RESULT:

We have :

$$0.7 = \frac{7}{10} = \frac{7 \times 10}{10 \times 10} = \frac{70}{100} = 0.70$$

$$0.70 = \frac{70}{100} = \frac{70 \times 10}{100 \times 10} = \frac{700}{1000} = 0.700$$

$$\therefore 0.7 = 0.70 = 0.700$$

Putting any number of zeros to the extreme right side of the decimal part does not change the decimal number.

We may write, 6.83 = 6.830 = 6.8300 etc.

Thus, we may convert unlike decimals into like decimals.

Example 1. *Convert 16.23, 8.7, 0.534, 118.84 into a set of like decimals.*

Solution : The maximum number of decimal places contained in a decimal of the given set of numbers is three.

So, we convert each one of the given decimals into an equivalent decimal having three decimal places, by annexing zero or zeros to the right of the decimal part.

We may write :

16.23 = 16.230, 8.7 = 8.700, 0.534 = 0.534, 118.84 = 118.840

Thus, 16.230, 8.700, 0.534, 118.840 is a set of like decimals.

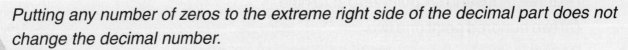

ORDER RELATION IN DECIMALS

Rule : Suppose we have to compare two decimals. Then, we take the following steps:

Step 1 : Convert the given decimals into like decimals.

Step 2 : First compare the whole number parts. The decimal with the greater whole number part is greater.

Step 3 : If the whole number parts are equal, compare the tenths digits. The decimal with the bigger digit in the tenths place is greater.

Step 4 : If the tenths digits are equal, compare the hundredths digits, and so on.

The following examples will make the idea more clear.

Example 2. *Compare* 36.54 *and* 29.63.

Solution : The given numbers are 36.54 and 29.63. Let us compare their whole number parts. Clearly, 36 > 29.

∴   36.54 > 29.63.

Example 3. *Compare* 13.5 *and* 13.05.

Solution : Converting the given numbers into like decimals, they become 13.50 and 13.05.

Clearly, their whole number parts are the same.

Now, compare their tenths digits.

Clearly, 5 tenths > 0 tenths.

∴ 13.50 > 13.05.

Hence, 13.5 > 13.05.

Example 4. *Compare* 0.64 *and* 0.645.

Solution   : Converting the given numbers into like decimals, they become 0.640 and 0.645.

Clearly their whole number parts are same.

Their tenths digits as well as hundredths digits are same.

Now, compare their thousandths digits.

Clearly, 0 thousandth < 5 thousandths.

So,   0.640 < 0.645.

Hence, 0.64 < 0.645.

Example 5. *Write the following decimals in ascending order :*

6.01, 3.85, 0.876, 0.9, 8.23, 3.852

Solution : The given decimals are :

6.010, 3.850, 0.876, 0.900, 8.230, 3.852

3.850 and 3.852 have the same whole number parts, same tenths digits and same hundredths digits. So, we compare their thousandths digits.

Since 0 < 2, so 3.850 < 3.852.

Again, 0.876 and 0.900 have the same whole number parts. So, we compare their tenths digits.

Since 8 < 9, so 0.876 < 0.900.

Finally, we have 0 < 3 < 6 < 8.

So, 0.876 < 0.900 < 3.850 < 3.852 < 6.010 < 8.230

Hence,   0.876 < 0.9 < 3.85 < 3.852 < 6.01 < 8.23.

1. Convert each of the following sets of unlike decimals into like decimals :

   (a) 9.5, 102.86   (b) 4.8, 6.06   (c) 0.3, 1.457

   (d) 48.001, 7.14, 3.9   (e) 101.01, 19.708, 10.6   (f) 0.5, 5.7, 17.716

2. Fill in the placeholders with >, < or = to make the following statements correct :

   (a) 0.707 ☐ 1   (b) 6.803 ☐ 6.85   (c) 7.56 ☐ 7.567

   (b) 2.01 ☐ 2.001   (e) 1.93 ☐ 1.905   (f) 0.04 ☐ 0.4

   (g) 2.64 ☐ 2.640   (h) 2.068 ☐ 2.68   (i) 0.69 ☐ 0.96

   (j) 0.010 ☐ 0.009   (k) 1.013 ☐ 0.975   (l) 0.07 ☐ 0.1

3. Arrange the following decimals in ascending order :

   (a) 0.34, 0.06, 0.1, 0.61, 0.01   (b) 3.05, 2.901, 4.03, 2.91, 3.005, 2.109

   (b) 1.28, 0.82, 2.08, 0.78, 1.8, 2.8   (d) 1.1, 1.01, 10.1, 10.01, 1.001, 10.001

   (e) 78.8, 87.98, 77.9, 78.89, 87.9, 87.88   (f) 0.3, 0.003, 0.03, 3.03, 30.3, 30.03

   (g) 4.37, 3.47, 4.73, 3.74, 4.7, 3.4

4. Arrange the following decimals in descending order :

   (a) 0.1, 0.01, 0.001, 1.1, 1.01   (b) 3.1, 0.75, 3.01, 0.57, 2.3, 2.03

   (c) 1.93, 2.01, 2.1, 1.9, 2.13, 1.87   (d) 55.5, 5.55, 55.05, 5.5, 5.05, 55.55

   (e) 6.06, 6.6, 6.006, 0.66, 0.06, 0.6   (f) 2.002, 2.22, 2.02, 2.2, 2.012, 2.021

   (g) 1.9, 2.6, 1.09, 2.06, 1.009, 2.006

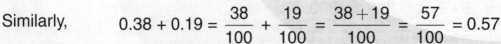

ADDITION OF DECIMALS

Let us find : 0.2 + 0.7

Then, we have : $0.2 + 0.7 = \dfrac{2}{10} + \dfrac{7}{10} = \dfrac{2+7}{10} = \dfrac{9}{10} = 0.9$

Similarly, $0.38 + 0.19 = \dfrac{38}{100} + \dfrac{19}{100} = \dfrac{38+19}{100} = \dfrac{57}{100} = 0.57$

Observing the above patterns, we get the following rule for addition of decimals.

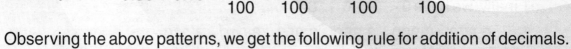

Rule : *In order to add two or more decimals , we proceed according to the following steps :*

Step 1 : Either the given decimals are like decimals, otherwise change them to like decimals.

Step 2 : Write the addends one below the other so that the decimal points of all the addends are in the same column.

The digits having the same place values should be in the same column.

Step 3 : Add as in the case of ordinary numbers.

Step 4 : In the sum, put the decimal point directly below the decimal points of the addends.

SOLVED EXAMPLES

Example 1 . *Add :* 8.76 *and* 9.58.

Solution : We have :

$$\begin{array}{r} 8.76 \\ +9.58 \\ \hline 18.34 \end{array}$$

Example 2 . *Add :* 6.04, 13.5, 2.687 *and* 108.96.

Solution : Converting the given numbers into like decimals, we get :

6.040, 13.500, 2.687 and 108.960.

Writing them in column form and adding, we get :

$$\begin{array}{r} 6.040 \\ 13.500 \\ 2.687 \\ +108.960 \\ \hline 131.187 \end{array}$$

SUBTRACTION OF DECIMALS

Let us find : 0.85 − 0.54.

We have : $0.85 - 0.54 = \dfrac{85}{100} - \dfrac{54}{100} = \dfrac{85-54}{100} = \dfrac{31}{100} = 0.31$

Similarly, $42.96 - 28.38 = (42 + .96) - (28 + .38)$

$= \left(42 + \dfrac{96}{100}\right) - \left(28 + \dfrac{38}{100}\right) = (42 - 28) + \left(\dfrac{96-38}{100}\right)$

$= 14 + \dfrac{58}{100} = 14 + .58 = 14.58.$

The above subtraction may also be shown as :

$$
\begin{array}{r}
4\,2\,.\,9\,6 \\
-\ 2\,8\,.\,3\,8 \\
\hline
\boxed{1\,4\,.\,5\,8} \\
\end{array}
$$

Observing the above examples, we get the following rule for subtraction of decimals :

Rule :   *In order to find the difference of two decimal numbers, we proceed according to the following steps.*

Step 1 :   Convert the given decimals into like decimals.

Step 2 :   Write the smaller number under the larger one so that the decimal points of both the numbers are in the same column.

Step 3 :   Subtract as in the case of ordinary numbers.

Step 4 :   In the difference, put the decimal point directly under the decimal points of the given numbers.

Example 3.   *Subtract* 12.85 *from* 72.4.

Solution :   Converting the given numbers into like decimals we get 12.85 and 72.40. Writing them in column form and subtracting, we get :

$$
\begin{array}{r}
7\,2\,.\,4\,0 \\
-\ 1\,2\,.\,8\,5 \\
\hline
\boxed{5\,9\,.\,5\,5} \\
\end{array}
$$

∴ 72.4 − 12.85 = 59.55.

Example 4.   *Simplify :* 37.9 − 18.3 + 113.42 − 46.58.

Solution :   Writing each of the given numbers with two decimal places, we have :

37.9 − 18.3 + 113.42 − 46.58 = 37.90 − 18.30 + 113.42 − 46.58

Adding positive numbers and negative numbers separately, we get :

$$
\begin{array}{r}
3\,7\,.\,9\,0 \\
+\,1\,1\,3\,.\,4\,2 \\
\hline
\boxed{1\,5\,1\,.\,3\,2} \\
\end{array}
\qquad
\begin{array}{r}
1\,8\,.\,3\,0 \\
+\ 4\,6\,.\,5\,8 \\
\hline
\boxed{6\,4\,.\,8\,8} \\
\end{array}
$$

Now, subtracting the sum of negative numbers from the sum of positive numbers, we get :

$$
\begin{array}{r}
1\,5\,1\,.\,3\,2 \\
-\;6\,4\,.\,8\,8 \\
\hline
8\,6\,.\,4\,4 \\
\hline
\end{array}
$$

Hence, $37.9 - 18.3 + 113.42 - 46.58 = 86.44$.

EXERCISE 41

1. Add :

(a)
$$
\begin{array}{r}
8\,.\,9\,4 \\
+\;3\,.\,2\,7 \\
\hline
\end{array}
$$

(b)
$$
\begin{array}{r}
4\,3\,.\,6\,7 \\
+\;\;8\,.\,4\,5 \\
\hline
\end{array}
$$

(c)
$$
\begin{array}{r}
1\,6\,.\,2\,8 \\
2\,4\,.\,8\,7 \\
+\;\;8\,.\,9 \\
\hline
\end{array}
$$

(d)
$$
\begin{array}{r}
1\,5\,3\,.\,4\,6 \\
4\,7\,.\,8\,9 \\
6\,.\,3 \\
+\;1\,0\,2\,.\,5\,4 \\
\hline
\end{array}
$$

(e)
$$
\begin{array}{r}
5\,6\,.\,8\,7 \\
4\,3\,2\,.\,9\,3 \\
1\,8\,.\,7\,6 \\
+\;\;\;\;0\,.\,3\,8 \\
\hline
\end{array}
$$

(f)
$$
\begin{array}{r}
5\,.\,8\,0\,7 \\
3\,0\,.\,9 \\
0\,.\,6\,3 \\
+\;1\,3\,8\,.\,0\,7 \\
\hline
\end{array}
$$

2. Add the following decimals :

(a) 18.4, 7.89, 0.365, 104.6

(b) 216.87, 39.09, 8.8, 17.6

(c) 1.9, 19.39, 109.899, 919.99

(d) 425.78, 3087.9, 98.08, 0.8

(e) 9.008, 18.678, 403.96, 38.8

(f) 0.23, 17.77, 7.777, 77.7

3. Find the sum :

(a) $175.6 + 86.54 + 245.356 + 7.8$

(b) $29.87 + 146.9 + 37.635 + 0.78 + 1.907$

(c) $123.45 + 56.78 + 91.06 + 1.789$

(d) $84.6 + 9.78 + 0.935 + 243.7 + 0.006$

(e) $5.936 + 20 + 796.04 + 813$

4. Find the difference :

(a)
$$
\begin{array}{r}
1\,3\,.\,0\,4 \\
-\;\;9\,.\,8\,7 \\
\hline
\end{array}
$$

(b)
$$
\begin{array}{r}
6\,0\,.\,5\,0 \\
-\;5\,4\,.\,6\,5 \\
\hline
\end{array}
$$

(c)
$$
\begin{array}{r}
8\,4\,.\,0\,0 \\
-\;3\,6\,.\,2\,3 \\
\hline
\end{array}
$$

(d)
$$
\begin{array}{r}
1\,0\,.\,0\,1\,2 \\
-\;\;7\,.\,2\,3\,6 \\
\hline
\end{array}
$$

(e)
$$
\begin{array}{r}
8\,2\,7\,.\,0\,0\,3 \\
-\;7\,3\,9\,.\,7\,6\,4 \\
\hline
\end{array}
$$

(f)
$$
\begin{array}{r}
2\,5\,6\,.\,3\,1\,4 \\
-\;\;7\,8\,.\,7\,6\,5 \\
\hline
\end{array}
$$

5. Subtract :

(a) 7.83 from 21.7

(b) 41.6 from 80

(c) 23.46 from 70.1

(d) 39.65 from 49.21

(e) 16.764 from 74.67

(f) 21.34 from 101.2

(g) 48.5 from 113.416

(h) 62.125 from 80.12

6. *Find the difference :*
   (a) 207.3 − 198.86   (b) 500 − 71.48   (c) 301 − 37.6
   (d) 1000 − 136.325   (e) 753.126 − 197.039   (f) 248.24 − 89.673

7. *Simplify :*
   (a) 63.8 + 14.37 − 28.609 − 9.07   (b) 103.5 − 27.38 + 75.6 − 38.9
   (c) 66.66 − 6.666 − 3.033   (d) 500 − 37.8 + 1.4 − 137.63

8. What should be added to 78.9 to get 93.06?

9. What should be subtracted from 103.1 to get 84.56?

10. By how much should 100 be decreased to get 18.8?

11. By how much should 43.786 be increased to get 50?

12. The sum of two numbers is 43.12. If one of the numbers is 18.576, find the other number..

13. Mona went to the market with Rs 50.60 in her purse. She purchased a geometry box for Rs 29.75. How much money is now left in Mona's purse?

14. A drum contained 60 litres of milk. Out of this, 15.75 litres of milk was taken out in one bucket and 8.5 litres in another bucket. How much milk is left in the drum?

CONVERTING DECIMALS INTO FRACTIONS

To convert a decimal into a fraction, we

(a) write the decimal without the decimal point as the numerator of the fraction.

(b) write 1 followed by as many zeros as there are decimal places in the given decimal as the denominator of the fraction.

(c) simplify the fraction if possible.

SOLVED EXAMPLES

Example 1. *Convert the following decimals into fractions :*
    (a) 0.7   (b) 0.83   (c) 0.259   (d) 23.7

Solution : We have :

(a) $0.7 = \dfrac{7}{10}$ (b) $0.83 = \dfrac{83}{100}$

(c) $0.259 = \dfrac{259}{1000}$ (d) $23.7 = \dfrac{237}{10} = 23\dfrac{7}{10}$

Example 2. *Convert the following decimals into fractions :*
    (a) 0.003   (b) 16.04   (c) 3.005   (d) 8.254

Solution : We have :

(a) $0.003 = \dfrac{3}{1000}$.

(b) $16.04 = \dfrac{1604}{100} = \dfrac{401}{25} = 16\dfrac{1}{25}$.

(c) $3.005 = \dfrac{3005}{1000} = \dfrac{601}{200} = 3\dfrac{1}{200}$.

(d) $8.254 = \dfrac{8254}{1000} = \dfrac{4127}{500} = 8\dfrac{127}{500}$.

CONVERTING FRACTIONS INTO DECIMALS

When the denominator of a fraction is 10 or a power of 10, we can easily change it into decimal as we have learnt earlier.

Example 3. *Convert the following fractions into decimals :*

(a) $\dfrac{17}{10}$　　　(b) $\dfrac{237}{100}$　　　(c) $\dfrac{1049}{1000}$　　　(d) $\dfrac{1007}{100}$

Solution : We have :

(a) $\dfrac{17}{10} = 1\dfrac{7}{10} = 1 + \dfrac{7}{10} = 1 + .7 = 1.7$

(b) $\dfrac{237}{100} = 2\dfrac{37}{100} = 2 + \dfrac{37}{100} = 2 + .37 = 2.37$

(c) $\dfrac{1049}{1000} = 1\dfrac{49}{1000} = 1 + \dfrac{49}{1000} = 1 + .049 = 1.049$

(d) $\dfrac{1007}{100} = 10\dfrac{7}{100} = 10 + \dfrac{7}{100} = 10 + .07 = 10.07$

Sometimes a fraction can be converted into an equivalent fraction with denominator 10 or a power of 10, as shown below.

Example 4. *Convert the following decimals into fractions :*

(a) $\dfrac{3}{4}$　　(b) $\dfrac{3}{2}$　　(c) $\dfrac{5}{8}$　　(d) $\dfrac{129}{4}$

Solution : We have :

(a) $\dfrac{3}{4} = \dfrac{3 \times 25}{4 \times 25} = \dfrac{75}{100} = .75$.

(b) $\dfrac{3}{2} = 1\dfrac{1}{2} = 1 + \dfrac{1}{2} = 1 + .5 = 1.5$.

(c) $\dfrac{5}{8} = \dfrac{5 \times 125}{8 \times 125} = \dfrac{625}{1000} = .625$.

(d) $\dfrac{129}{4} = 32\dfrac{1}{4} = 32 + \dfrac{1}{4} = 32 + \dfrac{1 \times 25}{4 \times 25} = 32 + \dfrac{25}{100} = 32 + .25 = 32.25$.

TO CONVERT A FRACTION INTO DECIMAL BY DIVISION METHOD

Step 1 : *Divide the numerator by the denominator.*

Step 2 : *Complete the division. Let a non-zero remainder be left.*

Step 3 : *Insert a decimal point in the dividend and the quotient.*

Step 4 : *Put a zero on the right of the decimal point in the dividend as well as on the right of the remainder. Divide again just as whole numbers.*

Step 5 : *Repeat step 4 till the remainder is zero.*

The following examples will make the ideas more clear.

Example 5. *Convert* $\dfrac{15}{4}$ *into decimal fraction.*

Solution : We have :

```
       3.75
   4 ) 15.00
       12
       ──
        30
        28
        ──
         20
         20
         ──
          0
```

$$\therefore \frac{15}{4} = 3.75$$

Example 6. *Convert* $6\dfrac{3}{8}$ *into decimal fraction.*

Solution : We have : $6\dfrac{3}{8} = \dfrac{6 \times 8 + 3}{8} = \dfrac{51}{8}$.

```
        6.375
   8 ) 51.000
       48
       ──
        30
        24
        ──
         60
         56
         ──
          40
          40
          ──
           0
```

$$\therefore 6\frac{3}{8} = \frac{51}{8} = 6.375$$

EXERCISE 42

Convert the following decimals into fractions :

1. 0.3	2. 0.6	3. 0.35	4. 0.345
5. 4.8	6. 7.03	7. 2.75	8. 8.01
9. 6.05	10. 8.12	11. 16.25	12. 9.005
13. 4.44	14. 4.444	15. 70.625	16. 92.85
17. 65.75	18. 12.375	19. 24.015	20. 45.54

Convert the following fractions into decimals :

21. $\dfrac{19}{10}$	22. $\dfrac{347}{100}$	23. $\dfrac{1057}{1000}$	24. $\dfrac{3018}{100}$
25. $\dfrac{19035}{1000}$	26. $\dfrac{1}{4}$	27. $\dfrac{2}{5}$	28. $\dfrac{7}{8}$
29. $\dfrac{15}{16}$	30. $3\dfrac{3}{4}$	31. $4\dfrac{5}{8}$	32. $6\dfrac{3}{20}$
33. $8\dfrac{1}{25}$	34. $9\dfrac{6}{25}$	35. $\dfrac{8}{125}$	36. $7\dfrac{19}{125}$
37. $\dfrac{123}{250}$	38. $6\dfrac{17}{50}$	39. $\dfrac{37}{40}$	40. $2\dfrac{19}{40}$
41. $\dfrac{347}{500}$	42. $18\dfrac{3}{5}$	43. $16\dfrac{3}{8}$	44. $26\dfrac{19}{20}$

MULTIPLICATION OF DECIMALS

MULTIPLICATION OF A DECIMAL BY A WHOLE NUMBER

Example 1. *Find the following products :*

(a) 2.6×14 (b) 3.42×16 (c) 1.157×9

What do you observe ?

Solution : (a) $2.6 \times 14 = \dfrac{26}{10} \times \dfrac{14}{1} = \dfrac{26 \times \overset{7}{14}}{\underset{5}{10} \times 1} = \dfrac{182}{5} = 36.4$

We observe here that :

$26 \times 14 = 364$ has the same digits as in 36.4.

Number of decimal places in the product is the

same as in given decimal.

(b) $3.42 \times 16 = \dfrac{342}{100} \times \dfrac{16}{1} = \dfrac{342 \times \overset{4}{\cancel{16}}}{\underset{25}{\cancel{100}} \times 1} = \dfrac{1368}{25} = 54.72$

We observe here that :

$342 \times 16 = 5472$ has the same digits as in 54.72.

Number of decimal places in the product is the same as in given decimal.

(c) $1.157 \times 9 = \dfrac{1157}{1000} \times \dfrac{9}{1} = \dfrac{1157 \times 9}{1000} = \dfrac{10413}{1000} = 10.413$

We observe here that :

$1159 \times 7 = 10413$ has the same digits as in 10.413.

Number of decimal places in the product is the same as in given decimal.

Thus, in order to multiply a decimal by a whole number, we adopt the following rule.

Working Rule : In order to multiply a decimal by a whole number we take the following steps :

Step 1 : *Multiply the decimal without the decimal point by the whole number.*

Step 2 : *Place the decimal point so as to obtain as many decimal places in the product as there are in the decimal number.*

The following examples will make the ideas more clear.

Example 2. *Multiply 3.417 by 8.*

Solution : First we multiply 3417 by 8.

$$
\begin{array}{r}
3\ 4\ 1\ 7 \\
\times\ 8 \\
\hline
2\ 7\ 3\ 3\ 6 \\
\end{array}
$$

The given decimal number has 3 decimal places.

So, the product will have 3 decimal places.

$\therefore \qquad 3.417 \times 8 = 27.336.$

Example 3. *Multiply 16.73 by 48.*

Solution : First we multiply 1673 by 48.

$$
\begin{array}{r}
1\ 6\ 7\ 3 \\
\times\ 4\ 8 \\
\hline
1\ 3\ 3\ 8\ 4 \\
6\ 6\ 9\ 2\ 0 \\
\hline
8\ 0\ 3\ 0\ 4 \\
\end{array}
$$

The given decimal has 2 decimal places.

So, the product will have 2 decimal places.

$\therefore \qquad 16.73 \times 48 = 803.04.$

Example 4. *Multiply* 2.376 *by* 134.

Solution : First we multiply 2376 by 134.

```
      2 3 7 6
    ×   1 3 4
    ─────────
      9 5 0 4
    7 1 2 8 0
  2 3 7 6 0 0
  ─────────────
  3 1 8 3 8 4
```

The given decimal has 3 decimal places.

So, the product will have 3 decimal places.

∴ 2.376 × 134 = 318.384.

➤ **MULTIPLICATION OF A DECIMAL BY 10, 100, 1000 ETC.**

Example 5. *Find the following products :*

(*a*) 16.342 × 10   (*b*) 8.167 × 100   (*c*) 13.419 × 1000

What do you observe?

Solution : (*a*) $16.342 \times 10 = \dfrac{16342}{1000} \times \dfrac{10}{1} = \dfrac{16342 \times \cancel{10}^{1}}{\cancel{1000}_{100} \times 1} = \dfrac{16342}{100} = 163.42.$

Observation : When 16.342 is multiplied by 10, the decimal point moves to the right by one place.

(*b*) $8.167 \times 100 = \dfrac{8167}{\cancel{1000}_{10}} \times \dfrac{\cancel{100}^{1}}{1} = \dfrac{8167}{10} = 816.7$

Observation : When 8.167 is multiplied by 100, the decimal point moves to the right by two places.

(*c*) $13.419 \times 1000 = \dfrac{13419}{\cancel{1000}_{1}} \times \dfrac{\cancel{1000}^{1}}{1} = 13419.$

Observation : When 13.419 is multiplied by 1000, the decimal point moves to the right by three places.

In general, we have the following rules.

Rule 1 :   *When a decimal number is multiplied by 10, the decimal point moves to the right by one place.*

Rule 2 :   *When a decimal number is multiplied by 100, the decimal point moves to the right by two places.*

Rule 3 :   *When a decimal number is multiplied by 1000, the decimal point moves to the right by three places. And, so on.*

Example 6. *Find the following products :*

(*a*) 9.67 × 10   (*b*) 18.354 × 100   (*c*) 9.3 × 1000

Solution :   We have :

(*a*) 9.67 × 10 = 96.7 (*Shift decimal point 1 place to the right*)

(*b*) 18.354 × 100 = 1835.4 (*Shift decimal point 2 places to the right*)

(*c*) 9.3 × 1000 = 9.300 × 1000 (*Write 9.3 = 9.300 to have 3 decimal places*)

= 9300 (*Shift decimal point 3 places to the right*)

EXERCISE 43

Find the following products :

1. 36.7 × 8
2. 125.47 × 9
3. 47.35 × 45
4. 31.82 × 124
5. 3.174 × 243
6. 1.806 × 325
7. 10.263 × 116
8. 0.941 × 306
9. 23.06 × 87
10. 0.069 × 549
11. 91.85 × 182
12. 103.75 × 274

Fill in the blanks :

13. 17.54 × 10 = ...
14. 47.653 × 10 = ...
15. 89.5 × 10 = ...
16. 0.07 × 10 = ...
17. 0.008 × 10 = ...
18. 103.24 × 10 = ...
19. 49.752 × 100 = ...
20. 72.12 × 100 = ...
21. 8.5 × 100 = ...
22. 0.01 × 100 = ...
23. 74.5 × 100 = ...
24. 39.1 × 100 = ...
25. 7.935 × 1000 = ...
26. 79.36 × 1000 = ...
27. 145.8 × 1000 = ...
28. 16.03 × 1000 = ...
29. 0.003 × 1000 = ...
30. 0.6 × 1000 = ...

MULTIPLICATION OF TWO DECIMALS

Example 1.   *Find the following products:*

(*a*) 3.27 × 1.6   (*b*) 1.35 × 2.43

What do you observe ?

Solution :   We have :

(*a*) $3.27 \times 1.6 = \frac{327}{100} \times \frac{16}{10} = \frac{5232}{1000} = 5\frac{232}{1000}$

$= 5 + \frac{232}{1000} = 5 + .232 = 5.232.$

Observations :   327 × 16 = 5232 has the same digits as in 5.232.

(Number of decimal places in 3.27) + (Number of decimal places in 1.6)

= 2 + 1 = 3.

∴ Number of decimal places in the product = Sum of decimal places in given decimals.

(b) $1.35 \times 2.43 = \dfrac{135}{100} \times \dfrac{243}{100} = \dfrac{135 \times 243}{10000} = \dfrac{32805}{10000} = 3\dfrac{2805}{10000}$

$= 3 + \dfrac{2805}{10000} = 3 + .2805 = 3.2805.$

Observations : $135 \times 243 = 32805$ has the same digits as in 3.2805.

Number of decimal places in the product = Sum of decimal places in given decimals.

Thus, in order to multiply two decimals we adopt the following rule.

Rule :   *For multiplying two decimals, we take the following rule.*

Step 1 :   *Multiply the two decimals without the decimal points, just like whole numbers.*

Step 2 :   *In the product, place the decimal point so that the number of decimal places in the product is equal to the sum of the decimal places in the given decimals .*

Following examples will make the ideas more clear.

Example 2.   *Multiply 27.8 by 0.57.*

Solution :   First we multiply 278 by 57.

```
      2 7 8
    ×   5 7
    1 9 4 6
  1 3 9 0 0
  1 5 8 4 6
```

Sum of decimal places in given decimals = 1 + 2 = 3.

We put the decimal point in the product so as to have 3 decimal places.

∴ $27.8 \times 0.57 = 15.846.$

Example 3.   *Multiply 136.87 by 7.935.*

Solution :   First we multiply 13687 by 7935.

```
          1 3 6 8 7
        ×   7 9 3 5
          6 8 4 3 5
        4 1 0 6 1 0
      1 2 3 1 8 3 0 0
      9 5 8 0 9 0 0 0
    1 0 8 6 0 6 3 4 5
```

Sum of decimal places in given decimals = 2 + 3 = 5.

So, we put the decimal point in the product so as to have 5 decimal places.

∴ $136.87 \times 7.935 = 1086.06345.$

Example 4. *Multiply* 0.057 *by* 0.08.

Solution : First we multiply 57 by 8.

$$\begin{array}{r} 5\,7 \\ \times\ 8 \\ \hline 4\,5\,6 \end{array}$$

Sum of decimal places in the given decimals $= 3 + 2 = 5$.

Now, we want to take 5 decimal places in the product.

But, the product has 3 digits only.

We make it up by putting two zeros on the left of the product.

$\therefore\ 0.057 \times 0.08 = 0.00456.$

Example 5. *Find the continued product :* $2.74 \times 1.3 \times 0.56$.

Solution : Let us find the product $274 \times 13 \times 56$.

$$\begin{array}{r} 2\,7\,4 \\ \times\ 1\,3 \\ \hline 3\,5\,6\,2 \\ \times\ 5\,6 \\ \hline 2\,1\,3\,7\,2 \\ 1\,7\,8\,1\,0\,0 \\ \hline 1\,9\,9\,4\,7\,2 \end{array}$$

Now, sum of decimal places in given decimals $= 2 + 1 + 2 = 5$.

So, we put the decimal point so as to have 5 decimal places.

$\therefore\quad 2.74 \times 1.3 \times 0.56 = 1.99472.$

EXERCISE 44

Multiply :

1. 1.5 by 0.9
2. 0.6 by 0.4
3. 0.13 by 0.6
4. 2.57 by 1.8
5. 16.34 by 7.9
6. 49.07 by 8.5
7. 34.61 by 9.73
8. 19.84 by 27.98
9. 8.354 by 7.62
10. 9.306 by 23.7
11. 7.564 by 8.76
12. 16.386 by 6.97
13. 39.83 by 0.375
14. 48.48 by 6.56
15. 3.145 by 0.327
16. 0.546 by 0.33
17. 0.3251 by 0.7
18. 0.0325 by 0.09
19. 6.003 by 0.005
20. 0.225 by 0.13
21. 0.001 by 0.01

Find the continued product:

22. $0.2 \times 0.3 \times 2.8$
23. $1.7 \times 0.23 \times 0.9$
24. $0.2 \times 0.2 \times 0.2$
25. $2.3 \times 6.8 \times 5.4$
26. $1.73 \times 8.2 \times 0.6$
27. $0.235 \times 4.6 \times 0.3$

28. If $386 \times 247 = 95342$, fill in the blanks :

(a) $38.6 \times 24.7 = \ldots\ldots\ldots$ (b) $3.86 \times 2.47 = \ldots\ldots\ldots$

(c) $.386 \times 2.47 = \ldots\ldots\ldots$ (d) $0.386 \times 0.247 = \ldots\ldots\ldots$

29. Verify that : $9.8 \times 6.4 = 0.98 \times 64$

30. Verify that : $35.079 \times 8.5 = 350.79 \times 0.85$

31. Verify that : $6.9 \times 5.8 = 5.8 \times 6.9$

WORD PROBLEMS ON MULTIPLICATION OF DECIMALS

Example 1. *The cost of one pen is Rs 14.65. Find the cost of 48 such pens.*

Solution : Cost of 1 pen = Rs 14.65

$\therefore$ Cost of 48 pens = Rs (14.65×48).

$$\begin{array}{r} 1\,4\,6\,5 \\ \times\ 4\,8 \\ \hline 1\,1\,7\,2\,0 \\ 5\,8\,6\,0\,0 \\ \hline 7\,0\,3\,2\,0 \end{array}$$

$\therefore$ $14.65 \times 48 = 703.20$.

Hence, the cost of 48 pens = Rs 703.20.

Example 2. *The cost of 1 metre of ribbon is Rs 3.50. What will be the cost of 9.5 metres of ribbon?*

Solution : Cost of 1 m of ribbon = Rs 3.50

Cost of 9.5 m of ribbon = Rs (3.50×9.5)

$$\begin{array}{r} 3\,5\,0 \\ \times\ 9\,5 \\ \hline 1\,7\,5\,0 \\ 3\,1\,5\,0\,0 \\ \hline 3\,3\,2\,5\,0 \end{array}$$

$\therefore$ $3.50 \times 9.5 = 33.250$, which is the same as 33.25.

Hence, the cost of 9.5 m of ribbon is Rs 33.25.

Example 3. *A generator consumes 2.725 litres of diesel per hour. How much diesel is required to run the generator for 24 hours?*

Solution : Consumption of diesel in 1 hour = 2.725 litres.

Consumption of diesel in 24 hours = (2.725×24) litres .

$$\begin{array}{r} 2\,7\,2\,5 \\ \times\ 2\,4 \\ \hline 1\,0\,9\,0\,0 \\ 5\,4\,5\,0\,0 \\ \hline 6\,5\,4\,0\,0 \end{array}$$

$\therefore$ $2.725 \times 24 = 65.400$.

Hence, the consumption of diesel in 24 hours is 65.400 litres.

EXERCISE 45

1. The cost of one chocolate is Rs 13.85. What is the cost of 16 chocolates ?

2. One metre of cloth costs Rs 106.50. What is the cost of 8.5 metres of cloth ?

3. One kg of rice costs Rs 37.80. What will be the cost of 10.25 kg of rice ?

4. A tin of oil weighs 15.6 kg. What is the weight of 35 tins of oil ?

5. Find the weight of 16 bags of sugar, each weighing 48.450 kg ?

6. A bag of wheat weighs 97.8 kg. How much wheat is contained in 1000 such bags ?

7. If one drum can hold 16.950 litres of oil, how many litres can 36 such drums hold ?

8. A small bottle holds 0.845 kg of sauce. How much sauce will be there in 14 such bottles ?

9. The price of a watch is Rs 982.75. How much money will be needed to buy 46 such watches ?

10. A taxi-driver charges Rs 6.40 per km. How much will he charge for a journey of 16.5 km ?

11. If 1 kg of milk has 0.268 kg of fat, how much fat is there in 10.5 kg of milk?

12. A bus can cover 62.5 km in one hour. How much distance it can cover in 17 hours?

13. A car can cover a distance of 18.4 km on one litre of petrol. How far can it go on 25.5 litres of petrol?

14. The monthly salary of Mr. Nadir is Rs 6723.50 and his monthly expenditure is Rs 3854.75. How much does he save in one year?

15. Amit weighs 50.84 kg. His father is 1.5 times heavier than he is. Calculate his father's weight.

DIVISION OF DECIMALS

DIVISION OF A DECIMAL BY A WHOLE NUMBER

Working Rule : For dividing a decimal by a whole number we take the following steps :

Step 1 : *Perform the division by considering the dividend a whole number.*

Step 2 : *When the division of whole number part of the dividend is complete, put the decimal point in the quotient and proceed with the division as in case of whole numbers.*

SOLVED EXAMPLES

Example 1.   *Divide* 43.128 *by* 12.

Solution :

```
        3 . 5 9 4
   1 2 ) 4 3 . 1 2 8
         3 6
         7 1
         6 0
         1 1 2
         1 0 8
             4 8
             4 8
               0
```

∴ 43.128 ÷ 12 = 3.594.

Example 2.   *Divide :* (*a*) 7.155 *by* 9.   (*b*) 0.5176 *by* 8

Solution :   (*a*)

```
        0 . 7 9 5
      9 ) 7 . 1 5 5
          0
          7 1
          6 3
            8 5
            8 1
              4 5
              4 5
                0
```

(*b*)

```
        0 . 0 6 4 7
      8 ) 0 . 5 1 7 6
          0
          5 1
          4 8
            3 7
            3 2
              5 6
              5 6
                0
```

∴   7.155 ÷ 9 = 0.795.   ∴   0.5176 ÷ 8 = 0.0647

Note : *Sometimes on dividing a decimal by a whole number the last remainder obtained is non-zero. In such cases insert as many zeros on the right of the decimal part of the dividend as is necessary to make the last remainder zero.*
The following examples will make the ideas more clear.

Example 3.   *Divide* 3.45 *by* 25.

Solution :   We have

```
           0 . 1 3 8
    2 5 ) 3 . 4 5 0        ← one zero annexed
          0
          3 4
          2 5
            9 5
            7 5
            2 0 0
            2 0 0
                0
```

∴ 3.45 ÷ 25 = 0.138.

Example 4. *Divide* 112.38 *by* 8.

Solution :   We have

```
        14.0475
    8) 112.3800    ← two zeros annexed
        8
        3 2
        3 2
          3 8
          3 2
            6 0
            5 6
              4 0
              4 0
                0
```

∴   112.38 ÷ 8 = 14.0475.

Example 5. *Divide* 1.877 *by* 25.

Solution :   We have

```
         0.07508
    25) 1.87700    ← two zeros annexed
         0
         1 87
         1 75
           1 27
           1 25
             2 0 0
             2 0 0
                 0
```

∴   1.877 ÷ 25 = 0.07508.

EXERCISE 46

Divide :

1.   41.5 by 5
2.   42.7 by 7
3.   30.6 by 9
4.   60.72 by 12
5.   58.944 by 8
6.   85.956 by 12
7.   857.458 by 14
8.   254.25 by 15
9.   217.44 by 18

10.	132.48 by 23	11.	2.88 by 6	12.	3.44 by 8
13.	0.152 by 19	14.	0.0012 by 6	15.	0.49 by 7
16.	0.448 by 14	17.	2.13 by 15	18.	6.54 by 12
19.	5.52 by 16	20.	0.264 by 15	21.	1.001 by 14
22.	0.477 by 18	23.	1.8 by 24	24.	0.04 by 5

DIVISION OF A DECIMAL BY 10, 100, 1000 etc.

Example 1. *Find the quotient:*

  (*a*) $16.5 \div 10$ (*b*) $230.65 \div 100$ (*c*) $3.4564 \div 1000$

   What do you conclude?

Solution :   We have :

```
        1.65
   10 ) 16.50
        10
        ──
         6 5
         6 0
         ──
           5 0
           5 0
           ──
             0
```

```
          2.3065
   100 ) 230.65
         200
         ───
          306
          300
          ───
           650
           600
           ───
            500
            500
            ───
              0
```

```
          0.0034564
   1000 ) 3.4564000
          0
          ─
          3456
          3000
          ────
           4564
           4000
           ────
            5640
            5000
            ────
             6400
             6000
             ────
              4000
              4000
              ────
                 0
```

$\therefore$ $16.5 \div 10 = 1.65$, $230.65 \div 100 = 2.3065$,
$3.4564 \div 1000 = 0.0034564$.

OBSERVATIONS :

(*a*) *When a decimal is divided by 10, the decimal point moves to the left by one place.*

(*b*) *When a decimal is divided by 100, the decimal point moves to the left by two places.*

(*c*) *When a decimal is divided by 1000, the decimal point moves to the left by three places.*

   And so on.

   Thus, we have :

  (*a*) $0.6 \div 10 = 0.06$ (*b*) $0.6 \div 100 = 0.006$ (*c*) $0.6 \div 1000 = 0.0006$

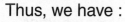

DIVISION BY A MULTIPLE OF 10, 100, 1000 etc.

Example 2. Divide 16.46 by 20.

Solution : Note that we first divide by 10 and then by 2.

$$\therefore \quad 16.46 \div 20 = \frac{16.46}{20} = \frac{16.46}{10 \times 2} = \frac{16.46}{10} \times \frac{1}{2} = \frac{1.646}{2} = 0.823.$$

Example 3. *Divide* 12.15 *by* 300.

Solution : Note that we first divide by 100 and then by 3.

$$\therefore \quad 12.15 \div 300 = \frac{12.15}{300} = \frac{12.15}{100 \times 3}$$

$$= \frac{12.15}{100} \times \frac{1}{3} = \frac{.1215}{3} = 0.0405.$$

Example 4. *Divide* 23.2 *by* 4000.

Solution : Note that we first divide by 1000 and then by 4.

$$\therefore \quad 23.2 \div 4000 = \frac{23.2}{4000} = \frac{23.2}{1000} \times \frac{1}{4} = \frac{23.2}{1000} \times \frac{1}{4} = \frac{.0232}{4} = .0058.$$

EXERCISE 47

Find the quotient :

1. $23.64 \div 10$	2. $5.76 \div 10$	3. $0.347 \div 10$
4. $0.05 \div 10$	5. $317.3 \div 100$	6. $95.87 \div 100$
7. $8.923 \div 100$	8. $0.769 \div 100$	9. $0.08 \div 100$
10. $1342.8 \div 1000$	11. $476.35 \div 1000$	12. $38.9 \div 1000$
13. $6.9342 \div 1000$	14. $202.4 \div 20$	15. $403.8 \div 30$
16. $316.84 \div 40$	17. $19.2 \div 80$	18. $94.24 \div 80$
19. $12.8 \div 500$	20. $18.08 \div 400$	21. $3.64 \div 700$
22. $1.35 \div 900$	23. $650.3 \div 7000$	24. $182.5 \div 5000$

DIVISION OF A DECIMAL BY A DECIMAL

Working Rule : *In order to divide a decimal by a decimal, we take the following steps.*

Step 1 : *Convert the divisor into a whole number by multiplying the dividend and the divisor by 10 or 100 or 1000 etc. depending upon the number of decimal places in the divisor.*

Step 2 : *Now, divide the new dividend by the whole number as discussed earlier.*

19

SOLVED EXAMPLES

Example 1. *Divide* 8.64 *by* 2.4.

Solution : We have

$$8.64 \div 2.4 = \frac{8.64}{2.4} = \frac{8.64}{2.4} \times \frac{10}{10}$$

$$= \frac{86.4}{24} = 3.6$$

Hence, $8.64 \div 2.4 = 3.6$

```
          3 . 6
      ┌──────────
   2 4 ) 8 6 . 4
          7 2
        ──────
          1 4 4
          1 4 4
        ──────
              0
```

Example 2. *Divide* 2.9484 *by* 0.78.

Solution : We have

$$2.9484 \div 0.78 = \frac{2.9484}{0.78}$$

$$= \frac{2.9484}{0.78} \times \frac{100}{100}$$

$$= \frac{294.84}{78} = 3.78.$$

```
            3 . 7 8
        ┌────────────
   7 8 ) 2 9 4 . 8 4
          2 3 4
        ──────
          6 0 8
          5 4 6
        ──────
            6 2 4
            6 2 4
          ──────
                0
```

Example 3. *Divide* 11.47 *by* 0.031.

Solution : We have

$$11.47 \div 0.031 = \frac{11.47}{0.031}$$

$$= \frac{11.47}{0.031} \times \frac{1000}{1000}$$

$$= \frac{11470}{31} = 370.$$

```
            3 7 0
        ┌────────────
   3 1 ) 1 1 4 7 0
          9 3
        ──────
          2 1 7
          2 1 7
        ──────
              0
```

Example 4. *Divide* 0.00876 *by* 0.219.

Solution : We have

$$0.00876 \div 0.219 = \frac{0.00876}{0.219}$$

$$= \frac{0.00876}{0.219} \times \frac{1000}{1000}$$

$$= \frac{8.76}{219} = 0.04.$$

```
            0 . 0 4
        ┌────────────
  2 1 9 ) 8 . 7 6
            0
        ──────
          8 7 6
          8 7 6
        ──────
              0
```

Example 5. *Find the quotient :*

(*a*) 0.024 ÷ 0.4   (*b*) 0.0018 ÷ 0.09   (*c*) 0.169 ÷ 1.3

Solution : We have

(a) $0.024 \div 0.4 = \dfrac{0.024}{0.4} = \dfrac{0.024}{0.4} \times \dfrac{10}{10}$

$= \dfrac{0.24}{4} = 0.06.$

$\therefore$ Quotient = 0.06.

```
        0 . 0 6
    4 ) 0 . 2 4
        0
        ─────
        2 4
        2 4
        ─────
          0
```

(b) $0.0018 \div 0.09 = \dfrac{0.0018}{0.09} \times \dfrac{100}{100}$

$= \dfrac{0.18}{9}$

$= 0.02.$

$\therefore$ Quotient = 0.02.

```
        0 . 0 2
    9 ) 0 . 1 8
        0
        ─────
        1 8
        1 8
        ─────
          0
```

(c) $0.169 \div 1.3 = \dfrac{0.169}{1.3}$

$= \dfrac{0.169}{1.3} \times \dfrac{10}{10}$

$= \dfrac{1.69}{13} = 0.13.$

$\therefore$ Quotient = 0.13.

```
          0 . 1 3
    1 3 ) 1 . 6 9
          0
          ─────
          1 6
          1 3
          ─────
            3 9
            3 9
          ─────
              0
```

EXERCISE 48

Divide :

1. 3.24 by 0.6
2. 0.259 by 0.7
3. 0.0448 by 0.8
4. 1.305 by 0.9
5. 25.395 by 1.5
6. 2.0484 by 0.18
7. 56.192 by 3.2
8. 0.228 by 0.38
9. 0.8085 by 0.35
10. 21.976 by 1.64
11. 131.58 by 2.15
12. 0.120 by 1.5
13. 0.01365 by 0.25
14. 560.7 by 62.3
15. 37.053 by 5.37
16. 0.0108 by 0.0009
17. 0.072 by 0.08
18. 0.0028 by 0.7
19. 0.0102 by 1.7
20. 0.00216 by 0.27

21. Given that $91.78 \div 13 = 7.06$. Find the value of $917.8 \div 0.13$.

    Also find the value of $91.78 \div 1.3$.

22. *Fill in the blanks :*

    (a) $168.84 \div 14 = 1688.4 \div$ ....
    (b) $32.87 \div 1.9 = 3.287 \div$ ....
    (c) $3.288 \div 60 =$ ....$\div 5$
    (d) $36 \div 150 = 0.036 \div$ ....

DIVISION OF A WHOLE NUMBER BY A DECIMAL

Rule : *In order to divide a whole number by a decimal, we convert the divisor into a whole number by multiplying the dividend and the divisor by 10 or 100 or 1000 etc. depending upon the number of decimal places in the divisor.*

SOLVED EXAMPLES

Example 1. *Divide 24 by 0.03.*

Solution : We have

$$24 \div 0.03 = \frac{24}{0.03} = \frac{24 \times 100}{0.03 \times 100} = \frac{2400}{3} = 800.$$

Example 2. *Divide 225 by 0.25.*

Solution : We have

$$225 \div 0.25 = \frac{225}{0.25} = \frac{225 \times 100}{0.25 \times 100} = \frac{22500}{25} = 900.$$

TO CONVERT FRACTIONS INTO DECIMALS

We may convert any fraction into decimal by directly dividing its numerator by its denominator.

The following examples will make the idea more clear.

Example 3. *Convert each of the following fractions into decimal form :*

(a) $\frac{3}{4}$ (b) $\frac{5}{8}$

Solution : We have

(a) $\frac{3}{4} = 3 \div 4$ (b) $\frac{5}{8} = 5 \div 8$

```
      0.7 5
  4 ) 3.0 0
      0
      3 0
      2 8
        2 0
        2 0
          0
```

```
      0.6 2 5
  8 ) 5.0 0 0
      0
      5 0
      4 8
        2 0
        1 6
          4 0
          4 0
            0
```

$$\therefore \frac{3}{4} = 0.75$$

$$\therefore \frac{5}{8} = 0.625$$

Example 4. Convert $10\dfrac{7}{25}$ into decimal form.

Solution : We have

$$10\dfrac{7}{25} = \dfrac{10 \times 25 + 7}{25} = \dfrac{257}{25} = 257 \div 25.$$

$$\therefore\ 10\dfrac{7}{25} = 10.28$$

```
        1 0 . 2 8
 2 5 ) 2 5 7 . 0 0
        2 5
          7 0
          5 0
          2 0 0
          2 0 0
              0
```

EXERCISE 49

Find the quotient in each of the following :

1. $9 \div 0.15$
2. $88 \div 0.08$
3. $7 \div 0.014$
4. $93 \div 3.1$
5. $3 \div 2.5$
6. $42 \div 0.025$
7. $18 \div 1.2$
8. $26 \div 3.25$

Convert the following fractions into decimals :

9. $\dfrac{1}{5}$
10. $\dfrac{3}{8}$
11. $\dfrac{7}{4}$
12. $\dfrac{1}{16}$
13. $\dfrac{7}{16}$

14. $\dfrac{7}{8}$
15. $2\dfrac{3}{8}$
16. $\dfrac{21}{40}$
17. $\dfrac{17}{20}$
18. $3\dfrac{7}{20}$

19. $16\dfrac{8}{25}$
20. $8\dfrac{9}{40}$
21. $9\dfrac{9}{20}$
22. $\dfrac{15}{32}$

WORD PROBLEMS ON DIVISION OF DECIMALS

Example 1. *The total cost of 57 transistors is Rs 21982.05. What is the cost of one transistor?*

Solution : Cost of 57 transistors = Rs 21982.05

Cost of 1 transistor = Rs (21982.05 ÷ 57)

```
            3 8 5 . 6 5
 5 7 ) 2 1 9 8 2 . 0 5
        1 7 1
          4 8 8
          4 5 6
            3 2 2
            2 8 5
              3 7 0
              3 4 2
                2 8 5
                2 8 5
                    0
```

Hence, the cost of 1 transistor = Rs 385.65.

Example 2. *Mr. Soni bought some bags of cement, each weighing 49.7 kg. If the total weight of all the bags is 1143.1 kg, how many bags did he buy ?*

Solution : Total weight of all the bags = 1143.1 kg.

Weight of each bag = 49.7 kg.

Number of bags = 1143.1 ÷ 49.7

$$= \frac{1143.1}{49.7} \times \frac{10}{10}$$

$$= \frac{11431}{497} = 23.$$

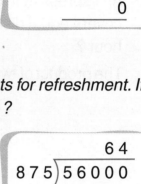

$$
\begin{array}{r}
23 \\
497\overline{)11431} \\
994 \\
\hline
1491 \\
1491 \\
\hline
0
\end{array}
$$

Hence, the number of bags bought by Mr. Soni = 23.

Example 3. *Mr. Thakural distributed Rs 560 among N.C.C. Cadets for refreshment. If each cadet received Rs 8.75, how many cadets were there ?*

Solution : Total amount distributed = Rs 560.

Amount received by each cadet = Rs 8.75.

Number of cadets $= Rs \dfrac{560}{8.75} = Rs \dfrac{560}{8.75} \times \dfrac{100}{100}$

$$= Rs \frac{56000}{875} = 64.$$

$$
\begin{array}{r}
64 \\
875\overline{)56000} \\
5250 \\
\hline
3500 \\
3500 \\
\hline
0
\end{array}
$$

Hence, the number of cadets is 64.

EXERCISE 50

1. The cost of 24 pens is Rs 375.60. What is the cost of each pen?

2. Mr. Bhatia bought 18 kg of mangoes for Rs 267.30. At what rate per kg did he buy mangoes ?

3. Mrs. Bose bought 15.5 litres of refined oil for Rs 1063.30. What is the cost of 1 litre of refined oil bought by her?

4. The weight of 37 bags of sugar is 3644.5 kg. If all the bags weigh equally, what is the weight of each bag?

5. A tin holds 16.5 litres of oil. How many such tins will be required to hold 478.5 litres of oil ?

6. If 61 buckets of equal capacity can be filled with 518.5 litres of water, what is the capacity of each bucket ?

7. A sum of Rs 2603 was equally distributed among 38 workers. How much did each worker get ?

8. If 9.75 metres of cloth costs Rs 468, what is the cost of 1 metre of cloth ?

9. 1.8 cloth is required for a shirt. How many such shirts can be made from a piece of cloth 45 m long ?

10. Mr. Bhola, the tailor stitches 24 shirts of the same size from 54 m of cloth. How much cloth is required for each shirt ?

11. Monica cuts 46 m of cloth into pieces 1.15 m each. How many pieces did she get?

12. A pile of sheets is 6. 24 cm thick. If each sheet is 0.24 cm thick, how many sheets are there in the pile ?

13. An express train covers a distance of 1073.4 km in 12 hours. Assuming that the train covers equal distances in equal periods of time, what distance does it cover in one hour ?

14. The product of two decimals is 261.36. If one of them is 17.6, find the other.

THINGS TO REMEMBER

1. The fractions in which the denominators are 10, 100, 1000 etc. are known as *decimal fractions.*

2. Numbers written in decimal form are called decimal numbers or simply decimals.

3. A decimal has two parts - whole number part and decimal part.

4. The number of digits contained in the decimal part of a decimal gives the number of its decimal places.

5. Decimals having the same number of decimal places are called like decimals, otherwise they are unlike decimals.

6. We have : 0.6 = 0.60 = 0.600 etc.

7. We may convert unlike decimals into like decimals by annexing the desired number of zeros at the end of the decimal part.

8. **Comparing Decimals :**

   Step 1 : Convert the given decimals into like decimals.

   Step 2 : First compare the whole number parts. The decimal with the greater whole number part is greater than the other.

   Step 3 : If the whole number parts are equal, compare the tenths digits. The decimal with the bigger digit in the tenths place is greater. If the tenths digits are equal, compare the hundredths digits and so on.

9. **Addition of Decimals :**

Step 1 : Convert the given decimals into like decimals.

Step 2 : Write the addends one under the other so that the decimal points of all the addends are in the same column.

Step 3 : Add as in the case of whole numbers.

Step 4 : In the sum, put the decimal point directly under the decimal points in the addends.

10. **Subtraction of Decimals :**

Step 1 : Convert the given decimals into like decimals.

Step 2 : Write the smaller number under the larger one so that their decimal points are in the same column.

Step 3 : Subtract as in the case of whole numbers.

Step 4 : In the difference, put the decimal point directly under the decimal points of the given numbers.

11. **Multiplication of a Decimal by a Whole Number :**

Step 1 : Multiply the decimal without the decimal point by the whole number.

Step 2 : Place the decimal point so as to obtain as many decimal places in the product as there are in the decimal.

12. **Multiplication of Two Decimals :**

Step 1 : Multiply the two decimals without the decimal points, just like whole numbers.

Step 2 : In the product, place the decimal point so that the number of decimal places in the product is equal to the sum of the decimal places in the given decimals.

13. **Division of a Decimal by a Whole Number :**

Step 1 : Perform the division by considering the dividend a whole number.

Step 2 : When the whole number part of the dividend is complete, put the decimal point in the quotient and proceed with the division as in case of whole numbers.

14. **Division of a Decimal by a Decimal :**

Step 1 : Convert the divisor into a whole number by multiplying the dividend and the divisor by 10, 100 or 1000 etc. depending upon the number of decimal places in the divisor.

Step 2 : Now, divide the new dividend by the whole number as discussed above.

Activity To Find the Product of Two Decimal Numbers Using Squared Paper

Take a squared paper.

Cut out a 10 × 10 grid from this paper.

Let us now find the product of two decimal numbers, say, 0.3 and 0.7.

Shade three vertical strips out of ten, using a red pen, as shown below. The shaded part represents 0.3.

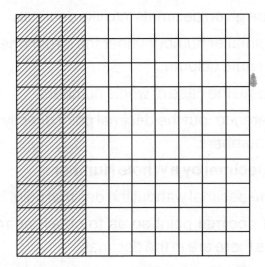

Next, shade seven horizontal strips out of ten, using a green pen, as shown below. The green shaded part represents 0.7.

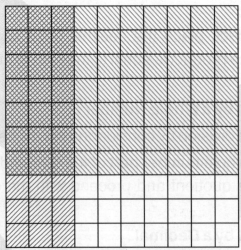

Now, observe the region shaded in both red and green.

The common shaded region has 21 squares i.e. it represents the decimal number 0.21.

Hence, 0.3 × 0.7 = 0.21.

Try finding the following products by the same method.

(a) 0.4 × 0.5   (b) 0.8 × 0.4   (c) 0.9 × 0.3

C.C.E. DRILL-9

QUESTION BAG - 1

(OBJECTIVE - TYPE QUESTIONS)

Tick (✓) the correct answer :

1. $\dfrac{15}{1000} = ?$

    (a) 0.015   (b) 0.15   (c) 0.150   (d) 0.0015

2. $2 + \dfrac{3}{10} + \dfrac{7}{100} = ?$

    (a) 2.307   (b) 2.703   (c) 2.37   (d) None of these

3. $0.4 + 0.004 + 4.4 = ?$

    (a) 4.444   (b) 5.2   (c) 4.804   (d) 5.404

4. The decimal form of $\dfrac{223}{10}$ is

    (a) 22.3   (b) 2.23   (c) 223.0   (d) 23.2

5. $7.7 + 7.77 + 7.777 = ?$

    (a) 21.777   (b) 23.247   (c) 21.427   (d) None of these

6. $0.2 \times 0.2 \times 0.2 = ?$

    (a) 0.8   (b) 0.08   (c) 0.008   (d) 0.88

7. $1.5 \times 0.9 = ?$

    (a) 0.135   (b) 1.35   (c) 0.0135   (d) 13.5

8. $18 \div 1.2 = ?$

    (a) 15   (b) 1.5   (c) 150   (d) 0.15

9. $88 \div 0.08 = ?$

    (a) 110   (b) 1100   (c) 11   (d) 1.1

10. $0.213 \div 0.00213 = ?$

    (a) 1   (b) 10   (c) 100   (d) 1000

11. $3 \times 0.3 \times 0.03 \times 30 = ?$

    (a) 0.81   (b) 0.081   (c) 0.0081   (d) 8.1

12. $\dfrac{1}{0.04} = ?$

    (a) $\dfrac{1}{40}$ (b) $\dfrac{2}{5}$ (c) 2.5   (d) 25

13. 0.04 × ? = 0.000016

    (a) 0.0004　　　　(b) 0.04　　　　(c) 4　　　　(d) None of these

14. 2.62 ÷ 131 = ?

    (a) 2　　　　(b) 20　　　　(c) 0.2　　　　(d) 0.02

15. 179.8 ÷ 2000 = ?

    (a) 0.1899　　　　(b) 8.99　　　　(c) 0.899　　　　(d) 0.0899

16. $\left(\dfrac{0.1}{0.01} + \dfrac{0.01}{0.1}\right)$ is equal to

    (a) 10.1　　　　(b) 1.01　　　　(c) 1.10　　　　(d) 10.01

17. If 4137 ÷ 1.75 = 2364, then 41.37 ÷ 17.5 is equal to

    (a) 23.64　　　　(b) 2.364　　　　(c) .2364　　　　(d) 236.4

QUESTION BAG-2

1. Which decimal number is represented by the following diagrams ?

   (a) 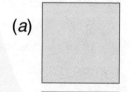 + + +

   (b) + +

   (c) + +

2. Write the next three numbers :

   (a) 1.6, 1.7, 1.8, ..., ..., ...

   (b) 9.007, 9.008, 9.009, ..., ..., ...

   (c) 6.995, 6.996, 6.997, ..., ..., ...

3. Give the decimal and fractional expansion of each of the following :

   (a) 5.729　　　　(b) 67.054　　　　(c) 875.99　　　　(d) 48.03

4. Compare and put the correct symbol > , < or = in the placeholder :

   (a) 78.9 ◯ 79.8　　　　(b) 0.99 ◯ 0.909

   (c) 5.05 ◯ 5.50　　　　(d) 9.39 ◯ 9.93

   (e) 50.94 ◯ 54.09　　　　(f) 13.67 ◯ 13.067

5. *Arrange the following in ascending order :*
   (*a*) 0.66, 0.6, 0.606, 0.666, 0.066, 0.06
   (*b*) 6.23, 6.023, 6.32, 6.203, 6.302, 6.032
   (*c*) 66.08, 60.88, 66.8, 68.66, 66.88, 68.06

6. *Compare :*
   (*a*) 4.488 + 5.564 $\bigcirc$ 9.052
   (*b*) 6 + 0.074 $\bigcirc$ 0.674
   (*c*) 3.6 + 2.03 $\bigcirc$ 5.36
   (*d*) 54.71 + 18.85 $\bigcirc$ 38.89 + 36.47

7. What should be taken away from 91 to get 36.87 ?

8. *Fill in the blanks :*
   (*a*) The place of 8 in 9.38 is ....
   (*b*) The place value of 7 in 1.76 is ....
   (*c*) When $\dfrac{17}{100}$ is written as a decimal number, it has .... decimal places.
   (*d*) Decimal fractions have denominators like ...., ..., ... etc.
   (*e*) The decimal number three-thousandths has .... decimal places .
   (*f*) $\dfrac{1}{2}$ expressed as a decimal is ....
   (*g*) The product of 48.7 and 9.643 will have .... decimal places.
   (*h*) 0.75 as a fraction in the lowest terms is ....
   (*i*) $\dfrac{1}{2} + 0.25 =$ .... (in decimals)
   (*j*) 1.64 expressed as a mixed number is ....
   (*k*) The smallest possible decimal number having three decimal places is ....

9. *State whether each of the following statements is true or false :*
   (*a*) Decimal fractions have multiples of 10 as denominators.   ....
   (*b*) Only a decimal fraction can be expressed as a decimal number.   ....
   (*c*) $\dfrac{13}{200}$ is a decimal fraction.   ....
   (*d*) Decimal numbers are actually fractional numbers.   ....
   (*e*) There are two decimal places in 63.9.   ....
   (*f*) 5 tenths = 50 hundredths.   ....
   (*g*) 2.37 + 3.8 = 5.45   ....
   (*h*) 9.42 and 2.49 are like decimals.   ....
   (*i*) In the place value chart, the place value goes on increasing from left to right.
   ....

10. Put the decimal point at the correct place in the product :
    (a) $6.5 \times 7 = 455$
    (b) $1.6 \times 1.16 = 1856$
    (c) $0.009 \times 6 = 54$
    (d) $75 \times 1.101 = 82575$

11. Fill in the placeholders :
    (a) $9.57 \times \boxed{} = 95.7$
    (b) $6.13 \times \boxed{} = 6130$
    (c) $0.368 \times \boxed{} = 36.8$
    (d) $0.007 \times \boxed{} = 0.7$
    (e) $87.78 \times \boxed{} = 87780$
    (f) $9.875 \times \boxed{} = 9875$
    (g) $8.57 \times 0 = \boxed{}$
    (h) $3.874 \times 1 = \boxed{}$
    (i) $\boxed{} \times 1000 = 93$
    (j) $\boxed{} \times 10 = 63.7$
    (k) $\boxed{} \times 1000 = 0.069$
    (l) $\boxed{} \times 100 = 0.0707$

12. Fill in the placeholders :
    (a) $0.2 \times 0.3 = \boxed{}$
    (b) $0.4 \times 0.5 = \boxed{}$
    (c) $0.7 \times 0.01 = \boxed{}$
    (d) $0.06 \times 0.08 = \boxed{}$
    (e) $15 \times 0.06 = \boxed{}$
    (f) $20 \times 0.05 = \boxed{}$
    (g) $0.009 \times 50 = \boxed{}$
    (i) $0.001 \times 0.1 = \boxed{}$

13. Divide :
    (a) $0.288 \div 2.4$
    (b) $5.94 \div 3.6$
    (c) $8.79 \div 15$
    (d) $13.03 \div 25$
    (e) $229.6 \div 2.05$
    (f) $6819.8 \div 4.3$

14. Convert the following fractions into decimals :
    (a) $\dfrac{11}{8}$
    (b) $\dfrac{36}{75}$
    (c) $\dfrac{12}{5}$

15. Solve :
    (a) $6 + \boxed{} = 8.5$
    (b) $9.5 + \boxed{} = 10.0$
    (c) $0.5 + \boxed{} = 1.25$
    (d) $1.25 + \boxed{} = 2.50$
    (e) $13.5 - \boxed{} = 12$
    (f) $1 - 0.05 = \boxed{}$
    (g) $10 - \boxed{} = 4.5$
    (h) $1.5 \times \boxed{} = 6$
    (i) $2.5 \times 4 = \boxed{}$
    (j) $0.25 \times \boxed{} = 1$
    (k) $0.5 \times 4 = \boxed{}$
    (l) $0.75 \times \boxed{} = 3$
    (m) $1.25 \times \boxed{} = 5$
    (n) $6.7 + \boxed{} = 10$

16. Fill in the placeholders :
    (a) $79 \div \boxed{} = 0.79$
    (b) $65.2 \div \boxed{} = 6.52$
    (c) $91.5 \div \boxed{} = 0.915$
    (d) $53.4 \div \boxed{} = 0.0534$
    (e) $\boxed{} \div 1000 = 0.4147$
    (f) $0.101 \div 1000 = \boxed{}$

11 ROUNDING NUMBERS

In class IV, we have learnt to round off numbers to the nearest ten, nearest hundred or nearest thousand. Let us review what we have studied before.

ROUNDING A NUMBER TO THE NEAREST TEN

Finding out the multiple of 10 which is nearest to the given number is called rounding of the given number to the nearest ten.

To round off a number to the nearest ten, we proceed stepwise as follows :

Step 1 : See the one's digit of the given number.

Step 2 : If one's digit is less than 5, replace one's digit by 0 and keep the other digits as they are.

Step 3 : If one's digit is 5 or more, increase ten's digit by 1 and replace one's digit by 0.

 SOLVED EXAMPLES

Example 1. *Round off each of the following numbers to the nearest ten:*

      (*a*) 813   (*b*) 627   (*c*) 3755   (*d*) 28572

Solution : (*a*) The given number is 813.

      Its one's digit is 3, which is less than 5.

      So, replace the one's digit by 0 and keep the other digits as they are.

      ∴   Rounded number = 810.

(*b*) The given number is 627.

      Its one's digit is 7, which is greater than 5.

      So, increase the ten's digit by 1 and replace the one's digit by 0.

      ∴   Rounded number = 630.

(*c*) The given number is 3755.

      Its one's digit is 5.

      So, increase the ten's digit by 1 and replace the one's digit by 0.

      ∴   Rounded number = 3760.

(*d*) The given number is 28572.

      Its one's digit is 2, which is less than 5.

      So, replace the one's digit by 0 and keep the other digits as they are.

      ∴   Rounded number = 28570.

Example 2. *Think of rounding numbers to the nearest ten. Write the numbers which can be rounded to 540.*

Solution : By adopting the rule for rounding numbers to the nearest ten, we find that the numbers which can be rounded to 540, are :

535, 536, 537, 538, 539, 541, 542, 543, 544.

ROUNDING A NUMBER TO THE NEAREST HUNDRED

Finding out the multiple of 100 which is nearest to the given number is called the rounding of the given number to the nearest hundred.

To round off a number to the nearest hundred, we proceed stepwise as follows :

Step 1 : See the ten's digit of the given number.

Step 2 : If ten's digit is less than 5, replace each one of ten's and one's digits by 0 and keep the other digits as they are.

Step 3 : If ten's digit is 5 or more, increase hundred's digit by 1 and replace each digit on its right by 0.

Example 3. *Round off each of the following numbers to the nearest hundred:*

    (*a*) 1928   (*b*) 6686   (*c*) 5351   (*d*) 19614

Solution :   (*a*) The given number is 1928.

        Its ten's digit is 2, which is less than 5.

        So, replace each one of ten's and one's digits by 0 and keep the other digits as they are.

        ∴   Rounded number = 1900.

  (*b*) The given number is 6686.

        Its ten's digit is 8, which is greater than 5.

        So, increase the hundred's digit by 1 and replace each one of the ten's and one's digits by 0.

        ∴   Rounded number = 6700.

  (*c*) The given number is 5351.

        Its ten's digit is 5.

        So, increase the hundred's digit by 1 and replace each one of the ten's and one's digits by 0.

        ∴   Rounded number = 5400.

  (*d*) The given number is 19614.

        Its ten's digit is 1, which is less than 5.

        So, replace each one of the ten's and one's digits by 0 and keep the other digits as they are.

        ∴   Rounded number = 19600.

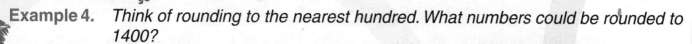

Example 4. *Think of rounding to the nearest hundred. What numbers could be rounded to 1400?*

Solution : Clearly, all the numbers from 1350 to 1449 can be rounded to 1400.

ROUNDING A NUMBER TO THE NEAREST THOUSAND

Rounding a number to the nearest thousand means finding out the multiple of 1000 which is nearest to the given number.

To round off a number to the nearest thousand, we proceed stepwise as follows:

Step 1 : See the hundred's digit of the given number.

Step 2 : If hundred's digit is less than 5, replace each one of hundred's, ten's and one's digits by 0 and keep the other digits as they are.

Step 3 : If hundred's digit is 5 or more, increase thousand's digit by 1 and replace each digit on its right by 0.

Example 5. *Round off each of the following numbers to the nearest thousand:*
    (a) 7296   (b) 10783   (c) 11520   (d) 6012

Solution : (a) The given number is 7296.

    Its hundred's digit is 2, which is less than 5.

    So, replace each one of the hundred's, ten's and one's digits by 0 and keep the other digits as they are.

    ∴ Rounded number = 7000.

(b) The given number is 10783.

    Its hundred's digit is 7, which is greater than 5.

    So, increase the thousand's digit by 1 and replace each one of the hundred's, ten's and one's digits by 0.

    ∴ Rounded number = 11000.

(c) The given number is 11520.

    Its hundred's digit is 5.

    So, increase the thousand's digit by 1 and replace each one of the hundred's, ten's and one's digits by 0.

    ∴ Rounded number = 12000.

(d) The given number is 6012.

    Its hundred's digit is 0, which is less than 5.

    So, replace each one of the hundred's, ten's and one's digits by 0 and keep the other digits as they are.

    ∴ Rounded number = 6000.

Example 6. *Think of rounding numbers to the nearest thousand. What numbers could be rounded to 15000?*

Solution : Clearly, all the numbers from 14500 to 15499 can be rounded to 15000.

ROUNDING OFF LARGE NUMBERS

Suppose the population of a city is 25,68,947. For the sake of convenience and remembrance, we may say that the population of the city is about 26 lakhs. Here we have rounded 2568947 to the nearest lakh. Thus, using the same method as above, we may round off large numbers to any place.

Example 7. *Round off each of the following numbers to the nearest ten-thousand.*

         (*a*) 573549   (*b*) 1368472

Solution : (*a*) The given number is 573549.

              Its digit at thousand's place is 3, which is less than 5.

              So, we replace each of the digits at thousand's, hundred's, ten's and one's places by 0 and keep the other digits as they are.

              ∴   Rounded number = 570000.

        (*b*) The given number is 1368472.

              Its digit at thousand's place is 8, which is greater than 5.

              So, increase the value of the digit at ten-thousand's place by 1 and replace each of the digits at thousand's, hundred's, ten's and one's places by 0.

              ∴   Rounded number = 1370000.

Example 8. *Round off each of the following numbers to the nearest lakh:*

         (*a*) 1748456   (*b*) 23674568

Solution : (*a*) The given number is 1748456.

              Its digit at ten-thousand's place is 4, which is less than 5.

              So, replace each of the digits at ten-thousand's, thousand's, hundred's, ten's and one's places by 0 and keep the other digits as they are.

              ∴   Rounded number = 1700000.

        (*b*) The given number is 23674568.

              Its digit at ten-thousand's place is 7, which is greater than 5.

              So, increase the digit at lakh's place by 1 and replace each one of the digits at ten-thousand's, hundred's, ten's and one's places by 0.

              ∴   Rounded number = 23700000.

Example 9. *Round off 134856729 to the nearest :*

         (*a*) Ten-lakh   (*b*) Crore

Solution : (*a*) 134856729 is to be rounded to the nearest ten-lakh.

              Its digit at lakh's place is 8, which is greater than 5.

              So, increase the digit at ten-lakh's place by 1 and replace each of the digits at lakh's, ten-thousand's, thousand's, hundred's, ten's and one's places by 0.

              ∴   Rounded number = 135000000.

        (*b*) 134856729 is to be rounded to the nearest crore.

              Its digit at ten-lakh's place is 4, which is less than 5.

So, replace each one of the digits at ten-lakh's, lakh's, ten-thousand's, thousand's, hundred's, ten's and one's places by 0 and keep the other digits as they are.

∴ Rounded number = 130000000.

EXERCISE 51

1. *Round off each of the following numbers to the nearest ten:*
   (a) 81　　　　　　(b) 478　　　　　(c) 875　　　　　(d) 4232
   (e) 20306　　　　(f) 34898　　　　(g) 105413　　　(h) 208979

2. *Round off each of the following numbers to the nearest hundred :*
   (a) 415　　　　　(b) 891　　　　　(c) 5650　　　　(d) 7132
   (e) 16309　　　　(f) 48768　　　　(g) 110111　　　(h) 218676

3. *Round off each of the following numbers to the nearest thousand:*
   (a) 6367　　　　　(b) 8710　　　　(c) 13492　　　(d) 26505
   (e) 218925　　　(f) 576396　　　(g) 1035608　　(h) 1867299

4. *Round off each of the following numbers to the nearest ten-thousand:*
   (a) 13670　　　　(b) 16745　　　　(c) 15892　　　(d) 21987
   (e) 347126　　　(f) 148259　　　(g) 462789　　　(h) 1570358

5. *Round off each of the following numbers to the nearest lakh:*
   (a) 138964　　　(b) 347589　　　(c) 461308　　　(d) 782615
   (e) 1054319　　(f) 1407685　　(g) 16970354　　(h) 21352419

6. *Round off each of the following numbers to the nearest ten-lakh :*
   (a) 1916423　　(b) 2347917　　(c) 7156902　　(d) 6719543
   (e) 2532104　　(f) 16380547　　(g) 36524179　　(h) 54036658

7. *Round off each of the following numbers to the nearest crore :*
   (a) 62735913　　(b) 36478609　　(c) 95632417　　(d) 70869785
   (e) 83754876　　(f) 107342310

8. *Fill in the blanks :*
   On rounding 136472508 to the nearest
   (a) ten, we get ....　　　　(b) hundred, we get ....
   (c) thousand, we get ....　(d) ten-thousand, we get ....
   (e) lakh, we get ....　　　(f) crore, we get ....

9. *The population of an Indian state is 85642574. Write the population*
   (a) to the nearest crore.　　　　(b) to the nearest lakh.
   (c) to the nearest thousand.

10. *Think of rounding to the nearest ten. What numbers could be rounded to*
    (a) 70 ?　　　(b) 140 ?　　　(c) 990 ?　　　(d) 2350 ?

11. *Think of rounding to the nearest hundred. What numbers could be rounded to*
    (a) 900 ?　　(b) 1600 ?　　(c) 5300 ?　　(d) 32500 ?

12. *Think of rounding to the nearest thousand. What numbers could be rounded to*
    (a) 9000 ?　　(b) 18000 ?　　(c) 27000 ?

ROUNDING OFF THE DECIMALS

ROUNDING A NUMBER CORRECT TO NEAREST ONE

Step 1 : Examine the digit at 1st decimal place.

Step 2 : If the digit at the 1st decimal place is less than 5, replace each digit after the decimal point to 0 and keep all the digits before the decimal point as they are.

Step 3 : If the digit at the 1st decimal place is 5 or greater than 5, increase the digit at ones place by 1 and replace each digit after the decimal point by 0.

SOLVED EXAMPLES

Example 1. *Round off each of the following decimals to the nearest one :*

    (*a*) 6.37   (*b*) 32.68   (*c*) 18.54   (*d*) 24.068

Solution: (*a*) The given decimal is 6.37.

Its digit at 1st decimal place is 3, which is less than 5.

So, replace each digit after the decimal point by 0.

∴   Rounded number = 6.00.

(*b*) The given decimal is 32.68.

Its digit at 1st decimal place is 6, which is greater than 5.

So, increase the digit at ones place by 1 and replace each digit after the decimal point by 0.

∴   Rounded number = 33.00.

(*c*) The given decimal is 18.54.

Its digit at 1st decimal place is 5.

So, increase the digit at ones place by 1 and replace each digit after the decimal point by 0.

∴   Rounded number = 19.00.

(*d*) The given decimal is 24.068.

Its digit at 1st decimal place is 0, which is less than 5.

So, replace each digit after the decimal point by 0.

∴   Rounded number = 24.000.

ROUNDING A NUMBER CORRECT TO ONE DECIMAL PLACE (OR TO THE NEAREST TENTH)

Step 1 : Examine the digit at the 2nd decimal place.

Step 2 : If the digit at the 2nd decimal place is less than 5, replace each one of the digits at the 2nd decimal place and onwards by 0.

Step 3 : If the digit at the 2nd decimal place is 5 or greater than 5, increase the digit at 1st decimal place by 1 and replace every digit after it by 0.

Example 2. *Write each of the following correct to one decimal place :*

(a) 17.73   (b) 25.625   (c) 38.19   (d) 73.452

Solution : (a) The given decimal is 17.73.

Its digit at 2nd decimal place is 3, which is less than 5.

So, we replace every digit after the 1st decimal place by 0.

∴   Rounded number = 17.70.

(b) The given decimal is 25.625.

Its digit at the 2nd decimal place is 2, which is less than 5.

So, we replace every digit after the 1st decimal place by 0.

∴   Rounded number = 25.600.

(c) The given decimal is 38.19.

Its digit at the 2nd decimal place is 9, which is greater than 5.

So, increase the digit at 1st decimal place by 1 and replace each digit after it by 0.

∴   Rounded number = 38.20.

(d) The given decimal is 73.452.

Its digit at the 2nd decimal place is 5.

So, increase the digit at 1st decimal place by 1 and replace each digit after it by 0.

∴   Rounded number = 73.500.

ROUNDING A NUMBER CORRECT TO TWO DECIMAL PLACES
(OR TO THE NEAREST HUNDREDTH)

Step 1 : Examine its digit at the 3rd decimal place.

Step 2 : If the digit at the 3rd decimal place is less than 5, replace each digit at the 3rd decimal place and onward by 0.

Step 3 : If the digit at the 3rd decimal place is 5 or greater than 5, increase the digit at the 2nd decimal place by 1 and replace each digit after it by 0.

The following example will make the ideas more clear.

Example 3. *Write each of the following decimals correct to two decimal places:*

(a) 16.783   (b) 21.736   (c) 19.405

Solution: (a) The given decimal is 16.783.

Its digit at 3rd decimal place is 3, which is less than 5.

So, replace each digit at the 3rd decimal place and onward by 0.

∴   Rounded number = 16.780.

(b) The given decimal is 21.736.

Its digit at the 3rd decimal place is 6, which is greater than 5.

So, increase the digit at the 2nd decimal place by 1 and replace every digit after it by 0.

∴   Rounded number = 21.740.

(c) The given decimal is 19.405.

Its digit at the 3rd decimal place is 5.

So, increase the digit at the 2nd decimal place by 1 and replace every digit after it by 0.

∴   Rounded number = 19.410.

ROUNDING A NUMBER CORRECT TO THREE DECIMAL PLACES (OR TO THE NEAREST THOUSANDTH)

Step 1 : Examine its digit at the 4th decimal place.

Step 2 : If the digit at the 4th decimal place is less than 5, replace each digit at the 4th decimal place and onward by 0.

Step 3 : If the digit at the 4th decimal place is 5 or greater than 5, increase the digit at the 3rd decimal place by 1 and replace each digit after it by 0.

The following example will make the ideas more clear.

Example 4. *Write each of the following decimals correct to three decimal places:*

   (a) 0.56731   (b) 16.1738   (c) 23.0345

Solution :   (a) The given decimal is 0.56731.

Its digit at 4th decimal place is 3, which is less than 5.

So, replace each digit at the 4th decimal place and onward by 0.

∴   Rounded number = 0.56700.

(b) The given decimal is 16.1738.

Its digit at the 4th decimal place is 8, which is greater than 5.

So, increase the digit at the 3rd decimal place by 1 and replace each digit after it by 0.

∴   Rounded number = 16.1740.

(c) The given decimal is 23.0345.

Its digit at the 4th decimal place is 5.

So, increase the digit at the 3rd decimal place by 1 and replace each digit after it by 0.

∴   Rounded number = 23.0350.

Example 5 . *Divide 31.27 by 19 and write the quotient correct to two decimal places.*

Solution :

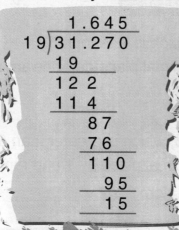

```
        1 . 6 4 5
   19 ) 3 1 . 2 7 0
        1 9
        1 2 2
        1 1 4
            8 7
            7 6
          1 1 0
            9 5
            1 5
```

Quotient = 1.645.

The digit at 3rd decimal place is 5.

So, increase the digit at 2nd decimal place by 1 and replace each digit after it by 0.

∴   Quotient (correct to 2 decimal places)

= 1.650 i.e., 1.65.

Example 6. *Express the fraction* $\frac{4}{7}$ *as a decimal correct to three decimal places.*

Solution : We have, $\frac{4}{7} = 4 \div 7$.

$$\begin{array}{r} 0.5714 \\ 7\overline{)4.0000} \\ \underline{0} \\ 4\ 0 \\ \underline{3\ 5} \\ 5\ 0 \\ \underline{4\ 9} \\ 1\ 0 \\ \underline{7} \\ 3\ 0 \\ \underline{2\ 8} \\ 2 \end{array}$$

$\therefore \ \frac{4}{7} = 0.5714$.

The digit at 4th decimal place is 4, which is less than 5.

Hence, $\frac{4}{7}$ (correct to 3 decimal places) = 0.5710.

EXERCISE 52

1. *Round off each of the following decimals to the nearest one:*
   (a) 6.3   (b) 2.7   (c) 4.5   (d) 16.8
   (e) 13.64   (f) 37.532   (g) 10.05   (h) 76.703

2. *Write each of the following decimals correct to one decimal place :*
   (a) 3.74   (b) 8.36   (c) 9.65   (d) 10.347
   (e) 24.829   (b) 32.271   (g) 86.813   (h) 102.382

3. *Write each of the following decimals correct to two decimal places :*
   (a) 0.706   (b) 5.238   (c) 11.415   (d) 17.893
   (e) 26.682   (f) 47.8491   (g) 53.1475   (h) 103.7651

4. *Write each of the following decimals correct to three decimal places :*
   (a) 0.7894   (b) 2.1635   (c) 78.4728
   (d) 19.01472   (e) 32.40361   (f) 123.00416

5. *Find the quotient correct to two decimal places in each of the following division sums :*
   (a) 2.3 ÷ 9   (b) 21.83 ÷ 16   (c) 3.7 ÷ 17
   (d) 8.283 ÷ 22   (e) 16.46 ÷ 15   (f) 101.37 ÷ 20

6. *Express each of the following fractions as a decimal correct to 3 decimal places :*
   (a) $\frac{5}{13}$ (b) $\frac{6}{7}$ (c) $\frac{5}{11}$ (d) $\frac{6}{13}$
   (e) $\frac{13}{15}$ (f) $3\frac{4}{11}$ (g) $2\frac{12}{17}$ (h) $10\frac{2}{3}$

7. *Think of rounding to the nearest one. What numbers could be rounded to?*
   (a) 11.0   (b) 17.0   (c) 20.0   (d) 46.0

C.C.E. DRILL- 10

QUESTION BAG - 1
(OBJECTIVE - TYPE QUESTIONS)

Tick (✓) the correct answer :

1. The number 6 rounded off to the nearest ten is
   (a) 6   (b) 0   (c) 10   (d) None of these

2. The number 5476 rounded off to the nearest ten is
   (a) 5470   (b) 5460   (c) 5400   (d) 5480

3. The number 3895 rounded off to the nearest ten is
   (a) 3890   (b) 3900   (c) 3800   (d) 3885

4. The number 5352 rounded off to the nearest hundred is
   (a) 5300   (b) 5350   (c) 5360   (d) 5400

5. The number 8849 rounded off to the nearest hundred is
   (a) 8850   (b) 8900   (c) 8800   (d) 8840

6. The number 10627 rounded off to the nearest thousand is
   (a) 10000   (b) 10600   (c) 11000   (d) 10700

7. The number 14510 rounded off to the nearest thousand is
   (a) 14000   (b) 15000   (c) 14500   (d) 15500

8. The number 1849678 rounded off to the nearest lakh is
   (a) 1800000   (b) 1900000   (c) 1850000   (d) 1840000

9. The number 2650123 rounded off to the nearest lakh is
   (a) 2600000   (b) 2660000   (c) 2700000   (d) 2750000

10. The number 16.53 correct to one place of decimal is
    (a) 16.50   (b) 16.60   (c) 16.00   (d) 16.03

11. The number 32.736 correct to two places of decimal is
    (a) 32.730   (b) 32.700   (c) 32.740   (d) 32.746

12. The number 16.415 correct to two places of decimal is
    (a) 16400   (b) 16.410   (c) 16.420   (d) 16.500

13. The number 8.4635 correct to three places of decimal is
    (a) 8.4630   (b) 8.4640   (c) 8.4600   (d) 8.4700

14. The number $\frac{5}{11}$ expressed as a decimal correct to three decimal places is
    (a) 0.450   (b) 0.454   (c) 0.455   (d) 0.464
15. The number $3\frac{12}{17}$ expressed as a decimal correct to two decimal places is
    (a) 3.70   (b) 3.71   (c) 3.69   (d) 3.706

QUESTION BAG - 2

1. *Fill in the blanks:*

    (a) 7 rounded off to the nearest ten is ....

    (b) 63 rounded off to the nearest ten is ....

    (c) 571 rounded off to the nearest hundred is ....

    (d) 6298 rounded off to the nearest hundred is ....

    (e) 43896 rounded off to the nearest thousand is ....

    (f) 81504 rounded off to the nearest thousand is ....

    (g) 356791 rounded off to the nearest ten-thousand is ....

    (h) 1781536 rounded off to the nearest lakh is ....

2. *State whether each of the following statements is true or false:*

    (a) 3 rounded off to the nearest ten is 0. ....

    (b) 283 rounded off to the nearest hundred is 300. ....

    (c) 6487 rounded off to the nearest thousand is 7000. ....

    (d) 10810 rounded off to the nearest ten-thousand is 10000. ....

    (e) 256340 rounded off to the nearest lakh is 200000. ....

    (f) 106 rounded off to the nearest ten is 110. ....

    (g) 23.18 correct to one decimal place is 23.2. ....

    (h) 15.783 correct to two decimal places is 15.78. ....

    (i) 19.2738 correct to three decimal places is 19.273. ....

    (j) 0.87631 correct to three decimal places is 0.876. ....

    (k) 106.478 correct to two decimal places is 106.47. ....

12 MEASURES OF LENGTH, MASS AND CAPACITY

In class IV, we studied the metric system of measurement of length, mass and capacity and the various units of these measurements. Now, we shall review what we have read earlier and study the use of decimal notation in these measurements.

MEASURES OF LENGTH

The standard or base unit of length is *metre*, denoted by *m*.

The higher units are *Kilometre (km)*, *Hectometre (hm)* and *Decametre (dam)*.

The lower units are *Decimetre (dm)*, *Centimetre (cm)* and *Millimetre (mm)*.

Thus, we have the chart as shown below :

Unit	Higher Units			Base Unit	Lower Units		
	km	hm	dam	m	dm	cm	mm
Value	1000 m	100 m	10 m	1 m	$\frac{1}{10}$ m	$\frac{1}{100}$ m	$\frac{1}{1000}$ m

We have:

$$1\text{ km} = 1000\text{ m}; 1\text{ hm} = 100\text{ m}; 1\text{ dam} = 10\text{ m}; 1\text{ dm} = \frac{1}{10}\text{ m} = 0.1\text{ m};$$

$$1\text{ cm} = \frac{1}{100}\text{ m} = 0.01\text{ m}; 1\text{ mm} = \frac{1}{1000}\text{ m} = 0.001\text{ m}.$$

CONVERSION OF HIGHER UNITS INTO LOWER UNITS

SOLVED EXAMPLES

Example 1. *Convert:*

(a) *6 km into m*   (b) *8 m into cm*

(c) *34 cm into mm*   (d) *5 m into mm*

Solution : (a) 1 km = 1000 m

∴   6 km = (6 × 1000) m = 6000 m.

(b) 1 m = 100 cm

∴   8 m = (8 × 100) cm = 800 cm.

(c) 1 cm = 10 mm

∴   34 cm = (34 × 10) mm = 340 mm.

(d) 1 m   = 100 cm = (100 × 10) mm = 1000 mm

∴   5 m   = (5 × 1000) mm = 5000 mm.

Example 2. *Convert:*

(a) *4 hm 5 dam into m*   (b) *7 dam into cm*

Solution :   We have

(a) 4 hm 5 dam   = 4 hm + 5 dam

= (4 × 100)m + (5 × 10)m

= 400 m + 50 m = 450 m.

(b)   7 dam = (7 × 10) m

= 70 m = (70 × 100) cm = 7000 cm.

Example 3. *Convert:*

(a) *3.48 km into m*   (b) *6.8 m into cm*

(c) *26.5 cm into mm*   (d) *2.3 m into mm*

Solution :   We have

(a)   1 km   = 1000 m

∴   3.48 km   = (3.48 × 1000) m = 3480 m.

(b)   1 m   = 100 cm

∴   6.8 m   = (6.8 × 100) cm = 680 cm.

(c)   1 cm   = 10 mm

∴   26.5 cm   = (26.5 × 10) mm = 265 mm.

(d)   1 m   = 100 cm = (100 × 10) mm = 1000 mm.

∴   2.3 m   = (2.3 × 1000) mm = 2300 mm.

Example 4. *Convert:*

(a) *3 km into hm*   (b) *6 hm into dam*

(c) *3.4 km into dam*   (d) *5.3 dam into dm*

Solution :   We have

(a) 1 km   = 10 hm

∴   3 km   = (3 × 10) hm = 30 hm.

(b) 1 hm   = 10 dam

∴   6 hm   = (6 × 10) dam = 60 dam.

(c)   1km   = 100 dam

∴   3.4 km   = (3.4 × 100) dam = 340 dam.

(d)   1 dam   = 10 m = (10 × 10) dm = 100 dm.

∴ 5.3 dam   = (5.3 × 100) dm = 530 dm.

Example 5. *Convert:*

    (*a*) *12 km 35 m into m*   (*b*) *9 m 15 cm into cm*

    (*c*) *8 cm 5 mm into mm*   (*d*) *2 m 8 cm into mm*

Solution : We have

    (*a*) 12 km 35 m = 12 km + 35 m

                      = (12 × 1000) m + 35 m   [∵ 1 km = 1000 m]

                      = 12000 m + 35 m = 12035 m.

    (*b*) 9 m 15 cm = 9 m + 15 cm

                      = (9 × 100) cm + 15 cm   [∵ 1 m = 100 cm]

                      = 900 cm + 15 cm = 915 cm

    (*c*) 8 cm 5 mm = 8 cm + 5 mm

                      = (8 × 10) mm + 5 mm   [∵ 1cm = 10 mm]

                      = 80 mm + 5 mm = 85 mm.

    (*d*) 2 m 8 cm = 2 m + 8 cm

                      = (2 × 100) cm + 8 cm = 200 cm + 8 cm

                      = 208 cm = (208 × 10) mm = 2080 mm.

Example 6. *Convert:*

    (*a*) *5.634 km into km and m*   (*b*) *6.32 m into m and cm*

    (*c*) *8.3 km into km and hm*   (*d*) *14.605 m into mm*

Solution : We have

    (*a*) 5.634 km = 5 km + 0.634 km

                    = 5 km + (0.634 × 1000) m

                    = 5 km + 634 m = 5 km 634 m.

    (*b*)   6.32 m = 6 m + 0.32 m

                    = 6 m + (0.32 × 100) cm

                    = 6 m + 32 cm = 6 m 32 cm.

    (*c*)   8.3 km = 8 km + 0.3 km

                    = 8 km + (0.3 × 10) hm

                    = 8 km + 3 hm = 8 km 3 hm.

    (*d*)   1 m = 100 cm = (100 × 10) mm = 1000 mm.

    ∴   14.605 m = (14.605 × 1000) mm = 14605 mm.

Example 7. *Convert 6 km 2 hm 4 dam 5 m into m.*

Solution : We have

    6 km 2 hm 4 dam 5 m = 6 km + 2 hm + 4 dam + 5 m

                          = (6 × 1000) m + (2 × 100) m + (4 × 10) m + 5 m

                          = 6000 m + 200 m + 40 m + 5 m = 6245 m.

EXERCISE 53

1. Convert:
   (a) 8 km into m
   (b) 9.4 km into m
   (c) 3.75 km into m
   (d) 16 km 24 m into m

2. Convert:
   (a) 7 km 5 hm 6 dam 4 m into m
   (b) 3 km 8 hm 4 dam into m
   (c) 6 km 6 hm into m
   (d) 4 hm 5 dam 6 m into m

3. Convert:
   (a) 9 m into cm
   (b) 7.6 m into cm
   (c) 2.36 m into cm
   (d) 8 dam into cm

4. Convert:
   (a) 6 km into hm
   (b) 5.3 km into dam
   (c) 4.63 km into dam
   (d) 2.5 dam into dm

5. Convert:
   (a) 23.4 cm into mm
   (b) 4.1 m into mm
   (c) 5.63 m into mm
   (d) 3.428 m into mm

6. Convert:
   (a) 3 km 42 m into m
   (b) 8 m 6 cm into cm
   (c) 6 cm 6 mm into mm
   (d) 4 m 4 cm into mm

7. Convert:
   (a) 5.03 km into km and m
   (b) 6.4 hm into hm and dam
   (c) 16.4 m into m and cm
   (d) 8.05 dam into m and dm

8. Convert:
   (a) 12 km 34 m into m
   (b) 50 km 9 m into m
   (c) 62 cm 5 mm into mm
   (d) 7 m 8 cm into cm

CONVERSION OF LOWER UNITS INTO HIGHER UNITS

SOLVED EXAMPLES

Example 1. Convert :
   (a) 6 mm into cm
   (b) 34 cm into m
   (c) 243 cm into m
   (c) 3640 m into km

Solution : We have

(a) $1 \text{ mm} = \dfrac{1}{10} \text{ cm}$

$\therefore$ $6 \text{ mm} = \left(6 \times \dfrac{1}{10}\right) \text{ cm} = \dfrac{6}{10} \text{ cm} = 0.6 \text{ cm}.$

(b) $1 \text{ cm} = \dfrac{1}{100} \text{ m}$

$\therefore \quad 34 \text{ cm} = \left(34 \times \dfrac{1}{100}\right) \text{m} = \dfrac{34}{100} \text{ m} = 0.34 \text{ m}.$

(c) $\quad 1 \text{ cm} = \dfrac{1}{100} \text{ m}$

$\therefore \quad 243 \text{ cm} = \left(243 \times \dfrac{1}{100}\right) \text{m} = \dfrac{243}{100} \text{ m} = 2.43 \text{ m}.$

(d) $\quad 1 \text{ m} = \dfrac{1}{1000} \text{ km}$

$\therefore \quad 3640 \text{ m} = \left(3640 \times \dfrac{1}{1000}\right) \text{km} = \dfrac{3640}{1000} \text{ km} = \dfrac{364}{100} \text{ km} = 3.64 \text{ km}.$

Example 2. *Convert :*

(a) *135 cm into hm*   (b) *560 mm into m*

Solution : We have

(a) $135 \text{ cm} = \left(135 \times \dfrac{1}{100}\right) \text{m}$ $\left[\because 1 \text{ cm} = \dfrac{1}{100} \text{ m}\right]$

$= \dfrac{135}{100} \text{ m} = 1.35 \text{ m}$

$= \left(1.35 \times \dfrac{1}{100}\right) \text{hm}$ $\left[\because 1 \text{ m} = \dfrac{1}{100} \text{ hm}\right]$

$= \dfrac{1.35}{100} \text{ hm} = 0.0135 \text{ hm}.$

(b) $560 \text{ mm} = \left(560 \times \dfrac{1}{10}\right) \text{cm}$ $\left[\because 1 \text{ mm} = \dfrac{1}{10} \text{ cm}\right]$

$= 56 \text{ cm} = \left(56 \times \dfrac{1}{100}\right) \text{m} = 0.56 \text{ m}.$ $\left[\because 1 \text{ cm} = \dfrac{1}{100} \text{ m}\right]$

Example 3. *Convert :*

(a) *7 m 60 cm into m*   (b) *2 km 3 m 5 cm into m*

Solution: We have

(a) $\quad 7 \text{ m } 60 \text{ cm} = 7 \text{ m} + 60 \text{ cm}$

$= 7 \text{ m} + \dfrac{60}{100} \text{ m}$ $\left[\because 1 \text{ cm} = \dfrac{1}{100} \text{ m}\right]$

$= 7 \text{ m} + 0.6 \text{ m} = 7.6 \text{ m}.$

(b) $\quad 2 \text{ km } 3 \text{ m } 5 \text{ cm} = 2 \text{ km} + 3 \text{ m} + 5 \text{ cm}$

$= (2 \times 1000) \text{ m} + 3 \text{ m} + \dfrac{5}{100} \text{ m}$ $\left[\because 1 \text{ cm} = \dfrac{1}{100} \text{ m}\right]$

$= 2000 \text{ m} + 3 \text{ m} + 0.05 \text{ m} = 2003.05 \text{ m}.$

Example 4. *Convert :*

   (a) *8 dam 6 cm 4 mm into m*   (b) *6 hm 6 dm 6 mm into m*

Solution: We have

   (a) 8 dam 6 cm 4 mm = 8 dam + 6 cm + 4 mm

$$= (8 \times 10)\,m + \frac{6}{100}\,m + \frac{4}{1000}\,m$$

$$\left[\therefore\ 1\,cm = \frac{1}{100}\,m\ and\ 1\,mm = \frac{1}{1000}\,m\right]$$

$$= (80\,m + 0.06\,m + 0.004\,m) = 80.064\,m.$$

   (b) 6 hm 6 dm 6 mm = 6 hm + 6 dm + 6 mm

$$= (6 \times 100)\,m + \left(6 \times \frac{1}{10}\right)m + \left(6 \times \frac{1}{1000}\right)m$$

$$\left[\because\ 1\,hm = 100\,m,\ 1\,dm = \frac{1}{10}\,m,\ 1\,mm = \frac{1}{1000}\,m\right]$$

$$= \left(600\,m + \frac{6}{10}\,m + \frac{6}{1000}\,m\right)$$

$$= (600\,m + 0.6\,m + 0.006\,m) = 600.606\,m.$$

EXERCISE 54

1.   *Convert :*
   (a) 8 mm into cm   (b) 65 cm into m
   (c) 160 cm into m   (d) 8 cm into m

2.   *Convert :*
   (a) 864 m into km   (b) 2375 m into km
   (c) 58 m into km   (d) 9 m into km

3.   *Convert :*
   (a) 5 cm 6 mm into cm   (b) 26 cm 8 mm into cm

4.   *Convert :*
   (a) 6 m 65 cm into m   (b) 35 m 28 cm into m
   (c) 8 m 5 cm into m   (d) 60 m 6 cm into m

5.   *Convert :*
   (a) 8 km 275 m into km   (b) 24 km 65 m into km
   (c) 36 km 10 m into km   (d) 6 km 5 m 4 cm into km

6.   *Convert :*
   (a) 150 cm into hm   (b) 480 mm into m

7.   Convert 9 dam 8 cm into m.

8.   Convert 8 hm 8 dm into m.

9.   Convert 4 km 9 cm 5 mm into m.

To add or subtract measures given in different units, we convert each of the given measures into the biggest given unit and then add or subtract the measures as we do in case of decimals.

SOLVED EXAMPLES

Example 1. *Add : 8 m 60 cm, 2 m 6 cm and 84 cm.*

Solution : Expressing the given measures in metres using decimal, we get:

8 m 60 cm = 8.60 m

2 m 6 cm = 2.06 m

84 cm = 0.84 m

On adding columnwise, we get:

```
    ①   ①
    8 . 6   0 m
    2 . 0   6 m
+   0 . 8   4 m
─────────────────
  1 1 . 5   0 m
```

∴ Required sum = 11.50 m = 11 m 50 cm.

Example 2. *Add: 7 km 350 m, 8 km 65 m and 3 km 8 m.*

Solution : Expressing the given measures in km using decimal, we get:

7 km 350 m = 7.350 km

8 km 65 m = 8.065 km

3 km 8 m = 3.008 km

On adding columnwise, we get:

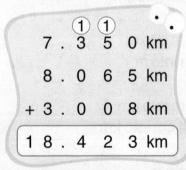

```
      ①   ①
    7 . 3   5 0 km
    8 . 0   6 5 km
+   3 . 0   0 8 km
─────────────────────
  1 8 . 4   2 3 km
```

∴ Required sum = 18.423 km = 18 km 423 m.

Example 3. *Subtract 6 km 365 m from 14 km 240 m.*

Solution : Expressing the given measures in km, using decimal, we get:

14 km 240 m = 14.240 km

6 km 365 m = 6.365 km

On subtracting columnwise, we get:

```
  1 4 . 2 4 0 km
－ 6 . 3 6 5 km
  7 . 8 7 5 km
```

∴ Required difference = 7.875 km = 7 km 875 m.

Example 4. *Subtract 9 km 75 m from 16 km 20 m.*

Solution : Expressing the given measures in km using decimal, we get:

16 km 20 m = 16.020 km and

9 km 75 m = 9.075 km

On subtracting columnwise, we get :

```
  1 6 . 0 2 0 km
－ 9 . 0 7 5 km
  6 . 9 4 5 km
```

∴ Required difference = 6.945 km.

Example 5. *Subtract 16 m 38 cm from 40 m 5 cm.*

Solution : Expressing the given measures in m using decimal, we get:

40 m 5 cm = 40.05 m

16 m 38 cm = 16.38 m

On subtracting columnwise, we get:

```
  4 0 . 0 5 m
－ 1 6 . 3 8 m
  2 3 . 6 7 m
```

∴ Required difference = 23.67 m.

Example 6. *Sunita bought 10 m cloth and used 4 m 75 cm of it for her dress. How much cloth remains unused?*

Solution : Expressing the given measures in m using decimal, we may write:

Total cloth = 10 m = 10.00 m.

Cloth used for dress = 4 m 75 cm = 4.75 m.

Length of remaining unused piece = (10.00 m – 4.75 m).

```
1 0 . 0 0 m
−  4 . 7 5 m
   5 . 2 5 m
```

∴ The length of remaining piece is 5.25 m.

MULTIPLICATION AND DIVISION OF LENGTH MEASURES

Example 7. *If 2 m 25 cm of cloth is needed for each shirt, how much cloth will be needed for 12 such shirts?*

Solution : Cloth needed for each shirt   = 2 m 25 cm = 2.25 m.

Cloth needed for 12 such shirts = (2.25 × 12) m

```
  2 . 2 5   m
×   1 2   m
2 7 . 0 0   m
```

∴ Cloth needed for 12 shirts = 27.00 m = 27 m.

Example 8. *Ravi walks 4 km 350 m every day. How much distance does he cover in a week?*

Solution : Distance covered in 1 day   = 4 km 350 m = 4.350 km.

Distance covered in 7 days = (4.350 × 7) km.

```
  4 . 3 5 0  km
×       7
3 0 . 4 5 0  km
```

∴ Total distance covered by Ravi in 1 week = 30.450 km

= 30 km 450 m.

Example 9. *A rope 18 m long is cut into 8 equal pieces. What is the length of each piece?*

Solution : Total length of the rope = 18.00 m.

Number of equal pieces = 8

Length of each piece = (18.00 ÷ 8) m

```
8)1 8.0 0(2.25
  1 6
  ──────
    2 0
    1 6
    ──────
      4 0
      4 0
      ──────
       ×
```

Hence, the length of each piece = 2.25 m

= 2 m 25 cm.

Example 10. *Sachin drives 210 km in 4 hours at a uniform speed. How much does he drive per hour?*

Solution :   Distance covered in 4 hours = 210 km = 210.000 km.

Distance covered in 1 hour = (210.000 ÷ 4) km.

```
4)210.000(52.500
  20
  ──
   10
    8
    ──
    20
    20
    ──
    000
```

Hence, Sachin drives 52.500 km = 52 km 500 m per hour.

EXERCISE 55

Add :

1. 26 km 634 m, 15 km 76 m and 8 km 708 m
2. 9 km 75 m, 12 km 165 m and 768 m
3. 8 km 8 m, 7 km 7 m and 645 m
4. 46 m 85 cm, 37 m 68 cm and 9 m 9 cm
5. 32 m 76 cm, 8 m 38 cm and 65 cm
6. 9 m 9 cm, 6 m 6 cm and 85 cm

Subtract:

7. 6 km 8 hm from 14 km
8. 18 km 675 m from 25 km 87 m
9. 34 km 68 m from 42 km 32 m
10. 10 km 9 m from 16 km 7 m
11. 46 m 85 cm from 50 m
12. 14 m 28 cm from 23 m 10 cm

13. Vinay travelled 5 km 75 m by bicycle, 18 km 356 m by bus and 1 km 872 m on foot. What is the total distance travelled by Vinay?

14. Rakesh bought 5 metres of cloth. He used 2 m 35 cm for his shirt and the rest for his trousers. How much cloth did he use for the trousers?

15. If 4 m 20 cm of cloth is needed for one frock, how much cloth will be needed for 5 such frocks?

16. A man walks at the rate of 2 km 675 m per hour, how much distance will he cover in 8 hours?

17. A 34 m long rope is divided into 10 ropes of equal size. What is the length of each small piece?

18. A man covers 255 km in 6 hours on scooter at a uniform speed. Find his speed in km per hour.

MEASURES OF MASS

The standard or base unit for measuring mass is *gram* denoted by *g*.

The other units for measuring mass are:

Kilogram (kg), *Hectogram* (hg), *Decagram* (dag),

Decigram (dg), *Centigram* (cg) and *Milligram* (mg).

All the units for measuring mass, from higher to lower level, are given in the following table:

Unit	kg	hg	dag	g	dg	cg	mg
Value	1000 g	100 g	10 g	1 g	$\frac{1}{10}$ g	$\frac{1}{100}$ g	$\frac{1}{1000}$ g

Thus, we have :

$$1 \text{ kg} = 1000 \text{ g}; \quad 1 \text{ hg} = 100 \text{ g}; \quad 1 \text{ dag} = 10 \text{ g}; \quad 1 \text{ dg} = \frac{1}{10} \text{ g} = 0.1 \text{ g};$$

$$1 \text{ cg} = \frac{1}{100} \text{ g} = 0.01 \text{ g}; \quad 1 \text{ mg} = \frac{1}{1000} \text{ g} = 0.001 \text{ g}.$$

CONVERSION OF HIGHER UNITS INTO LOWER UNITS

Example 1. *Convert:*

(a) *9 kg into g* (b) *6.5 kg into g*

(c) *7.34 kg into g* (d) *4.295 kg into g*

Solution : We have

(a) 9 kg = (9 × 1000) g = 9000 g. [∵ 1 kg = 1000 g]

(b) 6.5 kg = (6.5 × 1000) g = 6500 g. [∵ 1 kg = 1000 g]

(c) 7.34 kg = (7.34 × 1000) g = 7340 g. [∵ 1 kg = 1000 g]

(d) 4.295 kg = (4.295 × 1000) g = 4295 g. [∵ 1 kg = 1000 g]

Example 2. *Convert:*

(a) 6 kg 325 g into g (b) 3 kg 2 hg into g

(c) 6 hg 4 dag into g (d) 30 g 50 mg into mg

Solution : We have

(a) 6 kg 325 g = 6 kg + 325 g

= (6 × 1000) g + 325 g [∵ 1 kg = 1000 g]

= (6000 g + 325 g) = 6325 g.

(b) 3 kg 2 hg = 3 kg + 2 hg

= (3 × 1000) g + (2 × 100) g [∵ 1 kg = 1000 g and 1 hg = 100 g]

= (3000 g + 200 g) = 3200 g.

(c) 6 hg 4 dag = 6 hg + 4 dag

= (6 × 100) g + (4 × 10) g [∵ 1 hg = 100 g and 1 dag = 10 g]

= (600 g + 40 g) = 640 g.

(d) 30 g 50 mg = 30 g + 50 mg

= (30 × 1000) mg + 50 mg [∵ 1 g = 1000 mg]

= (30000 mg + 50 mg) = 30050 mg.

Example 3. *Convert 5 kg 3 hg 8 dag 4 g into g.*

Solution : We have

5 kg 3 hg 8 dag 4 g = 5 kg + 3 hg + 8 dag + 4 g

= (5 × 1000) g + (3 × 100) g + (8 × 10) g + 4 g

= (5000 g + 300 g + 80 g + 4 g) = 5384 g.

Example 4. *Convert:*

        (a) *6.235 kg into kg and g*   (b) *3.47 g into g and cg*

Solution : We have

      (a) 6.235 kg = 6 kg + 0.235 kg

                = 6 kg + (0.235 × 1000) g

                = 6 kg + 235 g = 6 kg 235 g.

      (b) 3.47 g = 3 g + 0.47 g

               = 3 g + (0.47 × 100) cg

               = 3 g + 47 cg = 3 g 47 cg.

CONVERSION OF LOWER UNITS INTO HIGHER UNITS

Example 5. *Convert:*

        (a) *5432 g into kg*   (b) *6580 mg into g*

        (c) *485 mg into g*   (d) *42 mg into g*

Solution : We have

      (a) $5432\,g = \left(5432 \times \dfrac{1}{1000}\right) kg$ $\left[\because\ 1\,g = \dfrac{1}{1000}\,kg\right]$

                    $= \dfrac{5432}{1000}\,kg = 5.432\,kg.$

      (b) $6580\,mg = \left(6580 \times \dfrac{1}{1000}\right) g$ $\left[\because\ 1\,mg = \dfrac{1}{1000}\,g\right]$

                    $= \dfrac{6580}{1000}\,g = \dfrac{658}{100}\,g = 6.58\,g.$

      (c) $485\,mg = \left(485 \times \dfrac{1}{1000}\right) g$ $\left[\because\ 1\,mg = \dfrac{1}{1000}\,g\right]$

                    $= \dfrac{485}{1000}\,g = 0.485\,g.$

      (d) $42\,mg = \left(42 \times \dfrac{1}{1000}\right) g$ $\left[\because\ 1\,mg = \dfrac{1}{1000}\,g\right]$

                    $= \dfrac{42}{1000}\,g = 0.042\,g$

EXERCISE 56

1. *Convert:*

    (a) 4 kg into g   (b) 8.5 kg into g

    (c) 2.84 kg into g   (d) 3.560 kg into g

2. *Convert:*

    (a) 13 kg 235 g into g   (b) 9 kg 85 g into g

    (c) 5 kg 3 hg into g   (d) 8 hg 5 dag into g

3. *Convert:*

(a) 6 kg 3 hg 4 dag 5 g into g   (b) 7 kg 6 hg 9 dag into g

(c) 5 kg 6 hg into g   (d) 8 hg 5 dag 6 g into g

4. *Convert:*

(a) 9 kg into hg   (b) 6.5 kg into dag

(c) 5.91 kg into dag   (d) 4.2 dag into dg

5. *Convert:*

(a) 2 kg 36 g into g   (b) 6 kg 8 g into g

(c) 5 kg 5 mg into mg   (d) 5 g 5 cg into mg

6. *Convert:*

(a) 6.25 kg into kg and g   (b) 7.5 hg into hg and dag

(c) 5.08 dag into g and dg   (d) 18.3 g into g and cg

7. *Convert:*

(a) 6340 g into kg   (b) 5460 mg into g

(c) 536 mg into g   (d) 23 mg into g

8. *Convert:*

(a) 4 kg 75 g into kg   (b) 7 kg 950 g into kg

(c) 9 kg 5 g into kg   (d) 16 g 65 mg into g

(e) 6 g 635 mg into g   (f) 53 g 8 mg into g

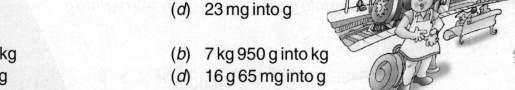

ADDITION AND SUBTRACTION OF MASS MEASURES

Example 1. *Add 8 kg 675 g, 7 kg 85 g and 13 kg 9 g.*

Solution : Expressing the given measures in kg, using decimal, we get:

8 kg 675 g = 8.675 kg

7 kg 85 g = 7.085 kg

13 kg 9 g = 13.009 kg

On adding columnwise, we get:

```
 (1)    (1)(1)
    8 . 6 7 5 kg
    7 . 0 8 5 kg
+ 1 3 . 0 0 9 kg
─────────────────
  2 8 . 7 6 9 kg
```

∴ Required sum = 28.769 kg = 28 kg 769 g.

Example 2. *Add 123 g 345 mg, 235 g 80 mg and 63 g 8 mg.*

Solution: Expressing the given measures in g using decimals, we get:

123 g 345 mg = 123.345 g

235 g 80 mg = 235.080 g

63 g 8 mg = 63.008 g

On adding columnwise, we get:

Required sum = 421.433 g = 421 g 433 mg.

```
(1)(1)  (1)(1)
  1 2 3 . 3 4 5 g
  2 3 5 . 0 8 0 g
+  6 3 . 0 0 8 g
──────────────────
  4 2 1 . 4 3 3 g
```

Example 3. *Subtract 7 kg 865 g from 10 kg.*

Solution: Expressing the given measures in kg using decimals, we get:

10 kg = 10.000 kg

7 kg 865 g = 7.865 kg

On subtracting columnwise, we get:

```
  1 0 . 0 0 0 kg
 −  7 . 8 6 5 kg
─────────────────
    2 . 1 3 5 kg
```

∴ Required difference = 2.135 kg = 2 kg 135 g.

Example 4. *Subtract 235 g 685 mg from 430 g 70 mg.*

Solution : Expressing the given measures in g using decimals, we get:

430 g 70 mg = 430.070 g

235 g 685 mg = 235.685 g

On subtracting columnwise, we get:

```
    4 3 0 . 0 7 0 g
 −  2 3 5 . 6 8 5 g
──────────────────────
    1 9 4 . 3 8 5 g
```

∴ Required difference = 194.385 g = 194 g 385 mg.

Example 5. *Asha bought 5 kg 350 g potatoes, 3 kg 725 g tomatoes and 2 kg 475 g onions. Find the total weight of vegetables bought by her.*

Solution : Expressing the given weights in kg using decimals, we get:

Weight of potatoes = 5 kg 350 g = 5.350 kg

Weight of tomatoes = 3 kg 725 g = 3.725 kg

Weight of onions = 2 kg 475 g = 2.475 kg

On adding columnwise, we get:

```
   ① ① ①
    5 . 3 5 0 kg
    3 . 7 2 5 kg
 +  2 . 4 7 5 kg
──────────────────
  1 1 . 5 5 0 kg
```

Total weight of vegetables bought by Asha = 11.550 kg
= 11 kg 550 g.

Example 6. *Kapil weighs 38 kg 450 g while Rohit weighs 43 kg 600 g. Who weighs more and by how much?*

Solution :   Clearly, Rohit weighs more.

Expressing the given weights in kg using decimals, we get:

Rohit's weight = 43 kg 600 g = 43.600 kg

Kapil's weight = 38 kg 450 g = 38.450 kg

On subtracting columnwise, we get:

$$
\begin{array}{r}
4\,3\,.\,6\,0\,0 \text{ kg} \\
-\ 3\,8\,.\,4\,5\,0 \text{ kg} \\
\hline
5\,.\,1\,5\,0 \text{ kg}
\end{array}
$$

∴ Rohit weighs more than Kapil by 5.150 kg or 5 kg 150 g.

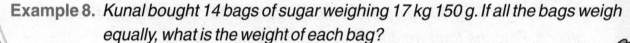

MULTIPLICATION AND DIVISION OF MASS MEASURES

Example 7. *Shalini bought 8 bags of salt, each weighing 2 kg 975 g. What is the total weight of salt bought by her?*

Solution :   Weight of 1 bag of salt = 2 kg 975 g = 2.975 kg

Weight of 8 bags of salt = (2.975 × 8) kg

= 23.800 kg.

$$
\begin{array}{r}
2\,.\,9\,7\,5 \text{ kg} \\
\times\ 8 \\
\hline
2\,3\,.\,8\,0\,0 \text{ kg}
\end{array}
$$

∴ Shalini bought 23.800 kg of salt.

Example 8. *Kunal bought 14 bags of sugar weighing 17 kg 150 g. If all the bags weigh equally, what is the weight of each bag?*

Solution :   Weight of 14 bags of sugar = 17 kg 150 g = 17.150 kg

Weight of each bag = (17.150 ÷ 14) kg

$$
\begin{array}{r}
14\,)\overline{1\,7\,.\,1\,5\,0}\,(1.225 \\
1\,4 \\
\hline
3\,1 \\
2\,8 \\
\hline
3\,5 \\
2\,8 \\
\hline
7\,0 \\
7\,0 \\
\hline
0
\end{array}
$$

∴ Weight of each bag = 1.225 kg = 1 kg 225 g.

Add:

1. 12 kg 325 g, 10 kg 265 g and 875 g
2. 9 kg 260 g, 6 kg 75 g and 3 kg 40 g
3. 15 kg 85 g, 12 kg 70 g and 625 g
4. 28 g 475 mg, 106 g 85 mg and 90 mg
5. 64 g 64 mg, 36 g 36 mg and 8 g 8 mg

Subtract:

6. 16 kg 432 g from 18 kg 320 g
7. 24 kg 75 g from 32 kg 200 g
8. 6 kg 6 g from 8 kg
9. 8 kg 25 g from 10 kg 10 g

10. Nisha bought 8 kg 260 g apples, 6 kg 325 g chikoos and 9 kg 85 g guavas. What is the total weight of fruits bought by her?

11. Ashu weighs 36 kg 540 g while his sister Nisha weighs 40 kg 125 g. Who weighs more and by how much?

12. Shashi and Sakshi together weigh 73 kg 250 g. If Shashi weighs 38 kg 675 g, what is Shakshi's weight?

13. If each bag of wheat weighs 25 kg 650 g, what is the total weight of 8 such bags?

14. The total weight of 6 bags of rice is 52 kg 500 g and all the bags weigh equally.

    Find the weight of each bag.

MEASURES OF CAPACITY

The standard or base unit for measuring capacity is *litre*, denoted by l.

The other units for measuring capacity are :

Kilolitre (kl), *Hectolitre* (hl), *Decalitre* (dal), *Decilitre* (dl), *Centilitre* (cl), *Millilitre* (ml)

All the units for measuring capacity, from higher to lower level, are given in the following table:

Unit	kl	hl	dal	l	dl	cl	ml
Value	1000 l	100 l	10 l	1 l	$\frac{1}{10}$ l	$\frac{1}{100}$ l	$\frac{1}{1000}$ l

Thus, we have :

$$1\ kl = 1000\ l;\ 1\ hl = 100\ l;\ 1\ dal = 10\ l;\ 1\ dl = \frac{1}{10}\ l = 0.1\ l ;$$

$$1\ cl = \frac{1}{100}\ l = 0.01\ l;\ 1\ ml = \frac{1}{1000}\ l = 0.001\ l.$$

CONVERSION OF HIGHER UNITS OF VOLUME INTO LOWER UNITS

Example 1. *Convert:*

(*a*) 4 l into ml
(*b*) 6 l 250 ml into ml
(*c*) 9 kl 60 l into l
(*d*) 8 dal 5 l into l

Solution : (*a*) 1 l = 1000 ml

∴ 4 l = (4 × 1000) ml = 4000 ml.

(b) $6\,l\ 250\ ml = 6\,l + 250\ ml$

$= (6 \times 1000)\ ml + 250\ ml$ $[\because 1\,l = 1000\ ml]$

$= 6000\ ml + 250\ ml = 6250\ ml.$

(c) $9\,kl\ 60\,l = 9\,kl + 60\,l$

$= (9 \times 1000)\ l + 60\ l$ $[\because 1\,kl = 1000\,l]$

$= (9000\,l + 60\,l) = 9060\,l.$

(d) $8\,dal\ 5\,l = 8\,dal + 5\,l$

$= (8 \times 10)\,l + 5\,l$ $[\because 1\,dal = 10\,l]$

$= (80\,l + 5\,l) = 85\,l.$

Example 2. *Convert:*

   (a) *5.63 kl into kl and l*   (b) *3.085 l into l and ml*

   (c) *8.940 dal into l and cl*

Solution: We have

(a) $5.63\,kl = 5\,kl + 0.63\,kl$

$= 5\,kl + (0.63 \times 1000)\,l$

$= 5\,kl + 630\,l = 5\,kl\ 630\,l.$

(b) $3.085\,l = 3\,l + 0.085\,l$

$= 3\,l + (0.085 \times 1000)\,ml$

$= 3\,l + 85\,ml = 3\,l\ 85\,ml.$

(c) $8.940\,dal = (8.940 \times 10)\,l = 89.40\,l$

$= 89\,l + 0.40\,l$

$= 89\,l + (0.40 \times 100)\,cl = 89\,l + 40\,cl = 89\,l\ 40\,cl.$

CONVERSION OF LOWER UNITS OF VOLUME TO HIGHER UNITS

Example 3. *Convert:*

   (a) *6530 ml into l*   (b) *8925 l into kl*

   (c) *5042 cl into dal*   (d) *15 l 25 cl into ml*

Solution : We have

(a) $6530\,ml = \left(6530 \times \dfrac{1}{1000}\right)l$ $\left[\because 1\,ml = \dfrac{1}{1000}\,l\right]$

$= \dfrac{6530}{1000}l = \dfrac{653}{100}l = 6.53\,l.$

(b) $8925\,l = \left(8925 \times \dfrac{1}{1000}\right)kl$ $\left[\because 1\,l = \dfrac{1}{1000}\,kl\right]$

$= \dfrac{8925}{1000}\,kl = 8.925\,kl.$

(c) $5042\ cl = \left(5042 \times \dfrac{1}{100}\right) l$ $\qquad$ $\left[\because 1\ cl = \dfrac{1}{100}\ l\right]$

$$= \frac{5042}{100} l = \left(\frac{5042}{100} \times \frac{1}{10}\right) dal \qquad \left[\because 1\ l = \frac{1}{10}\ dal\right]$$

$$= \frac{5042}{1000} dal = 5.042\ dal.$$

(d) $15\ l\ 25\ cl = 15\ l + 25\ cl$

$$= (15 \times 1000)\ ml + (25 \times 10)\ ml$$

$$= 15000\ ml + 250\ ml = 15250\ ml.$$

Example 4. *Convert:*

(a) $65\ ml$ into l $\qquad\qquad$ (b) $6\ l$ into kl

(c) $8\ l\ 500\ ml$ into l $\qquad\quad$ (d) $15\ kl\ 30\ l$ into kl

Solution : We have

(a) $1\ ml = \dfrac{1}{1000}\ l$

$\therefore 65\ ml = \left(65 \times \dfrac{1}{1000}\right) l = \dfrac{65}{1000}\ l = 0.065\ l.$

(b) $1\ l = \dfrac{1}{1000}\ kl$

$\therefore 6\ l = \left(6 \times \dfrac{1}{1000}\right) kl = \dfrac{6}{1000}\ kl = 0.065\ kl.$

(c) $8\ l\ 500\ ml = 8\ l + 500\ ml$

$$= 8\ l + \frac{500}{1000}\ l = 8\ l + 0.5\ l = 8.5\ l. \qquad \left[\because 1\ ml = \frac{1}{1000}\ l\right]$$

(d) $15\ kl\ 30\ l = 15\ kl + 30\ l$

$$= 15\ kl + \frac{30}{1000}\ kl \qquad \left[\because 1\ l = \frac{1}{1000}\ kl\right]$$

$$= 15\ kl + 0.03\ kl = 15.03\ kl.$$

EXERCISE 58

1. Convert:

(a) $8\ l$ into ml $\qquad\qquad$ (b) $3\ l\ 360\ ml$ into ml

(c) $6\ kl\ 250\ l$ into l $\qquad$ (d) $5\ dal\ 6\ l$ into l

2. Convert:

(a) $65\ kl\ 345\ l$ into l $\quad$ (b) $5\ kl\ 35\ l$ into l $\quad$ (c) $36\ kl\ 5\ l$ into l

3. Convert:

(a) $8\ l\ 375\ ml$ into ml $\quad$ (b) $37\ l\ 65\ ml$ into ml $\quad$ (c) $15\ l\ 6\ ml$ into ml

4. *Convert:*
   (*a*) 2.8 *kl* into *l*   (*b*) 6.375 *l* into *ml*   (*c*) 8.05 *l* into *ml*
5. *Convert:*
   (*a*) 6 *l* 125 *ml* into *l*   (*b*) 18 *l* 46 *ml* into *l*   (*c*) 120 *l* 8 *ml* into *l*
6. *Convert:*
   (*a*) 8 *kl* 625 *l* into *kl*   (*b*) 50 *kl* 60 *l* into *kl*   (*c*) 30 *kl* 5 *l* into *kl*
7. *Convert:*
   (*a*) 3560 *ml* into *l*   (*b*) 68 *ml* into *l*   (*c*) 9 *ml* into *l*

ADDITION AND SUBTRACTION OF CAPACITY MEASURES

SOLVED EXAMPLES

Example 1. *Add:* 9 *l* 325 *ml*, 16 *l* 85 *ml* and 28 *l* 9 *ml*.

Solution: *Expressing the given measures in l in decimal form, we get:*

9 *l* 325 *ml* = 9.325 *l*

16 *l* 85 *ml* = 16.085 *l*

28 *l* 9 *ml* = 28.009 *l*

We may add columnwise as shown.
Hence, the sum of the given measures
is 53.419 *l* = 53 *l* 419 *ml*.

```
  ②  ①  ①
  9 . 3 2 5 l
 1 6 . 0 8 5 l
+2 8 . 0 0 9 l
 5 3 . 4 1 9 l
```

Example 2. *Add:* 89 *kl* 125 *l*, 31 *kl* 84 *l* and 79 *kl* 10 *l*.

Solution : *Expressing the given measures in kl in decimal form, we get:*

89 *kl* 125 *l* = 89.125 *kl*

31 *kl* 84 *l* = 31.084 *kl*

79 *kl* 10 *l* = 79.010 *kl*

We may add columnwise as shown.
Hence, the sum of the given measures = 199.219 *kl*
= 199 *kl* 219 *l*.

```
  ①      ①
 8 9 . 1 2 5 kl
 3 1 . 0 8 4 kl
+7 9 . 0 1 0 kl
1 9 9 . 2 1 9 kl
```

Example 3. *Subtract* 89 *l* 678 *ml* from 103 *l* 250 *ml*.

Solution : Expressing the given measures in *l* using decimals,
we write:

103 *l* 250 *ml* = 103.250 *l*

89 *l* 678 *ml* = 89.678 *l*

On subtracting columnwise, we get:

```
    1 0 3 .  2 5 0 l
  -  8 9 .  6 7 8 l
  ─────────────────
     1 3 .  5 7 2 l
```

∴ Difference of given measures = 13.572 *l* = 13 *l* 572 *ml*.

Example 4. *Subtract 76 kl 675 l from 100 kl.*

Solution : Expressing the given measures in *kl* using decimals, we write:

100 *kl* = 100.000 *kl*

76 *kl* 675 *l* = 76.675 *kl*

We may subtract columnwise as shown.

```
    1 0 0 .  0 0 0 kl
  -  7 6 .  6 7 5 kl
  ──────────────────
     2 3 .  3 2 5 kl
```

∴ Difference of given measures = 23.325 *kl* = 23 *kl* 325 *l*.

Example 5. *Vidya bought 18 l 750 ml, 14 l 850 ml and 23 l 500 ml of milk from three different dairies. How much is the total milk bought by her?*

Solution : Expressing the given measures in *l* using decimals, we get:

18 *l* 750 *ml* = 18.750 *l*

14 *l* 850 *ml* = 14.850 *l*

23 *l* 500 *ml* = 23.500 *l*

We may add columnwise as shown.

```
   ① ②   ①
    1 8 .  7 5 0 l
    1 4 .  8 5 0 l
  + 2 3 .  5 0 0 l
  ──────────────────
    5 7 .  1 0 0
```

∴ Quantity of total milk bought = 57.100 *l* = 57 *l* 100 *ml*.

Example 6. *The total capacity of a water tank is 3000 l. It is filled with 1536 l 50 ml of water. Find the volume of water required to fill the tank.*

Solution : Total capacity of the tank = 3000 *l*.

Volume of water contained in it = 1536 *l* 50 *l*

= 1536.050 *l*.

```
    2 9 9 9   1 0 0 0
    3̶ 0̶ 0̶ 0̶ .  0̶ 0̶ 0̶ l
  - 1 5 3 6 .  0 5 0 l
  ──────────────────────
    1 4 6 3 .  9 5 0 l
```

Volume of water required to fill the tank

= (3000 *l*) – (1536.050)*l*

∴ Required volume of water = 1463.950 *l*

= 1463 *l* 950 *ml*.

Example 7. *If each bottle of milk contains 2 l 450 ml of milk, how much quantity of milk is there in 12 such bottles?*

Solution : Quantity of milk in each bottle = 2 l 450 ml = 2.450 l.

Quantity of milk in 12 bottles = (2.450 × 12) l

∴ Total quantity of milk in 12 bottles = 29.400 l

= 29 l 400 ml.

$$\begin{array}{r} 2.450\,l \\ \times\,1\,2 \\ \hline 2\,9\,.\,4\,0\,0\,l \end{array}$$

Example 8. *One litre of a medicine is to be packed in small bottles, each one of which can hold 125 ml of medicine. How many such bottles are needed?*

Solution : Total quantity of medicine = 1 litre = 1000 ml.

Capacity of each small bottle = 125 ml.

Number of bottles required = (1000 ÷ 125)

Hence, the number of bottles required = 8.

$$\begin{array}{r} 125\overline{)1000}(8 \\ \underline{1000} \\ \text{x} \end{array}$$

EXERCISE 59

Add:

1. 15 l 680 ml, 23 l 75 ml and 16 l 8 ml.
2. 37 l 56 ml, 40 l 67 ml and 51 l 43 ml.
3. 19 l 9 ml, 76 l 7 ml and 88 l 5 ml.
4. 86 kl 450 l, 93 kl 675 l and 3 kl 287 l.
5. 29 kl 568 l, 48 kl 39 l and 74 kl 6 l.
6. 9 kl 9 l, 8 kl 8 l and 93 l.

Subtract:

7. 68 l 590 ml from 105 l 325 ml.
8. 74 l 625 ml from 112 l.
9. 49 l 875 ml from 83 l 60 ml.
10. 56 kl 376 l from 80 kl 80 l.
11. 27 kl 89 l from 90 kl 7 l.
12. 35 kl 267 l from 50 kl.

13. Shobha bought 5 l 650 ml milk on Monday, 4 l 500 ml on Tuesday and 6 l 850 ml on Wednesday. How much milk did she buy in three days?

14. Renu bought 8 l 725 ml of milk and added 1 l 275 ml of water to it. What is the total volume of the adulterated milk ?

15. A bath tub can hold 70 l of water in it. It has 23 l 750 ml of water in it. How much more water can be poured into it ?

16. A car started out on a journey with 28 l of petrol. On reaching the destination, it was found that the car still had 12 l 365 ml of petrol. What quantity of petrol was used up in the journey?

17. The weight of Michael is 46 kg 365 g and weight of Rahul is 28 kg 975 g. What is their total weight?

Also, find the difference of their weights.

18. A bottle of syrup contains 875 ml syrup. Find in litres the quantity of syrup in 12 such bottles.

19. A can contains 2 *l* 425 *ml* of soft drink. How much soft drink will be there in 8 such bottles?

20. A leaking tap drips at the rate of 150 *ml* per hour. How many litres of water will be wasted in 10 hours?

21. 10 litres of milk is to be packed in small bottles, each one of which can hold 250 *ml*. How many such bottles are required ?

THINGS TO REMEMBER

1. (*a*) **Measures of Length**

<- Higher Units --- Base Unit --- Lower Units ->

	Kilometre	Hectometre	Decametre	Metre	Decimetre	Centimetre	Millimetre
Unit	km	hm	dam	m	dm	cm	mm
Value	1000 m	100 m	10 m	1 m	$\frac{1}{10}$ m	$\frac{1}{100}$ m	$\frac{1}{1000}$ m

(*b*) **Measures of Mass**

<- Higher Units --- Base Unit --- Lower Units ->

	Kilogram	Hectogram	Decagram	Gram	Decigram	Centigram	Milligram
Unit	kg	hg	dag	g	dg	cg	mg
Value	1000 g	100 g	10 g	1 g	$\frac{1}{10}$ g	$\frac{1}{100}$ g	$\frac{1}{1000}$ g

(*c*) **Measures of Capacity**

	Kilolitre	Hectolitre	Decalitre	Litre	Decilitre	Centilitre	Millilitre
Unit	*kl*	*hl*	*dal*	*l*	*dl*	*cl*	*ml*
Value	1000 *l*	100 *l*	10 *l*	1 *l*	$\frac{1}{10}$ *l*	$\frac{1}{100}$ *l*	$\frac{1}{1000}$ *l*

2. (*a*) To convert a higher unit to a lower unit, we multiply by 10, 100, 1000, ... according as we move 1, 2, 3, ... places towards right from higher unit in the above table.

(*b*) To convert a lower unit to a higher unit, we divide by 10, 100, 1000, ... according as we move 1, 2, 3............places towards left from lower unit in the above table.

3. (*a*) To convert a higher unit to a lower unit, we move the decimal point to the right by as many places as there are steps in going from the higher to lower unit in the above table.

(*b*) To convert a lower unit to a higher unit, we move the decimal point to the left by as many places as there are steps in going from the lower to higher unit in the above table.

QUESTION BAG - 1

(OBJECTIVE - TYPE QUESTIONS)

Tick (✓) the correct answer :

1. 12 hm 8 dam = ...m
   (a) 1208   (b) 128   (c) 1280   (d) 12080

2. 6 dm 6 mm = ...mm
   (a) 66   (b) 606   (c) 660   (d) 6006

3. 7.4 *l* = ...*l* ....*ml*
   (a) 7, 4   (b) 7, 40   (c) 7, 400   (d) 7, 4000

4. 3 km = ...cm
   (a) 3000   (b) 30000   (c) 300000   (d) 3000000

5. 76 mm= ....cm
   (a) 0.76   (b) 0.076   (c) 7.06   (d) 7.6

6. 1 *dal* 5 *dl* = ...*ml*
   (a) 1050   (b) 1500   (c) 10500   (d) 15000

7. 2 cm 2 mm = ...m
   (a) 0.022   (b) 0.202   (c) 0.0202   (d) 0.220

8. 40 g 40 mg = ...mg
   (a) 4004   (b) 4040   (c) 40004   (d) 40040

9. 6.75 cm = ...km
   (a) 0.675   (b) 0.0675   (c) 0.00675   (d) 0.000675

10. Sumit can ride 16 km 350 m in an hour. How many kilometres can he ride in 7 hours?
    (a) 112. 245   (b) 114. 135   (c) 114. 45   (d) None of these

11. 56 *kl* 650 *ml* = ...*ml*
    (a) 56650   (b) 560650   (c) 5600650   (d) 56000650

12. One egg has a mass of about 65 g. What is the mass of 2 dozen eggs?
    (a) 1.56 kg   (b) 1.344 kg   (c) 1.3 kg   (d) 1.04 kg

13. A man carried with him 3 soap bars weighing 125 g each and 4 detergent cakes weighing 275 g each. The total weight carried by him was
    (a) 1 kg 200 g   (b) 1 kg 325 g   (c) 1 kg 475 g   (d) 1 kg 600 g

QUESTION BAG - 2

1. *Fill in the placeholders:*

   (a) 1 *hl* = [   ] *l*   (b) 1 km = [   ] dam

   (c) 1 cm = [   ] mm   (d) 1 hg = [   ] dag

   (e) 1 dm = [   ] cm   (f) 1 *dl* = [   ] *ml*

   (g) 1 *kl* = [   ] *ml*   (h) 1 hm = [   ] cm

   (i) 1 cg = [   ] mg   (j) 1 hm = [   ] dm

2. *Fill in the placeholders:*

(a) 1 ml = [ ] l (b) 1 mm = [ ] dm

(c) 1 mg = [ ] cg   (d) 1 m = [ ] hm

(e) 1 l = [ ] dal (f) 1 dal = [ ] kl

(g) 1 hm = [ ] km   (h) 1 g = [ ] dag

(i) 1 l = [ ] kl (j) 1 dm = [ ] hm

(k) 10 mg = [ ] g   (l) 10 m = [ ] km

3. *Fill in the placeholders:*

(a) 6.86 hl = [ ] ml (b) 0.375 km = [ ] dam

(c) 63 m = [ ] km   (d) 79 cm = [ ] m

(e) 93.78 hm = [ ] dm   (f) 0.1 g = [ ] kg

(g) 3.33 m = [ ] mm   (h) 6.05 l = [ ] ml

(i) 380 cm = [ ] hm   (j) 960 ml = [ ] kl

(k) 860 cg = [ ] g   (l) 356 dl = [ ] kl

(m) 5.55 dal = [ ] cl (n) 3.7 cm = [ ] dam

4. *Fill in the placeholders:*

(a) 5 cm 7mm = [ ] cm   (b) 9 m 5 cm = [ ] m

(c) 10 kg 84 g= [ ] kg   (d) 20 g 20 mg = [ ] g

(e) 7 kl 96 l = [ ] kl (f) 15 km 64 m = [ ] km

(g) 4 hm 60 m = [ ] m   (h) 96 hl 80 l = [ ] dal

(i) 160 g 16 mg = [ ] g

5. *Subract :*

(a) 7 cm 6 mm – 6 cm 7 mm   (b) 8 km – 3 km 456 m

(c) 13 m 22 cm – 5 m 58 cm   (d) 6 g – 625 mg

(e) 32 kg 112 g – 23 kg 248 g   (f) 50 l – 26 l 725 ml

6. *State whether each of the following statements is true of false :*

(a) To convert dam into dm, we divide. ....

(b) To convert ml into dl, we multiply. ....

(c) To convert hl into cl, we multiply. ....

(d) To convert kg into dag, we multiply by 100.........................

(e) To convert cl into l, we divide by 1000. ....

7. *Express each of the following in km :*

(a) 2 hm 3 dam 4 cm   (b) 483 hm   (c) 396 mm   (d) 63 cm   (e) 7035. 9 cm

8. *Express each of the following in grams :*

(a) 384 cg   (b) 3 dg 4 cg 5 mg   (c) 466 dg

9. From 7.11 l syrup, how many small bottles of 45 ml each can be filled?

AVERAGE

13

INTRODUCTION

Suppose a car covers a distance of 324 km in 6 hours.

Then, we calculate the average speed of the car as:

$$\text{Average speed} = \frac{\text{Total distance covered in km}}{\text{Number of hours taken}} = \frac{324}{6} \text{ km/hr} = 54 \text{ km/hr.}$$

We say that the average speed of the car is 54 km/hr.

In general, for a given number of observations, we define:

$$\textit{Average} = \frac{\textit{Sum of all the given observations}}{\textit{Number of these observations}}.$$

SOLVED EXAMPLES

Example 1. *In a test, the marks obtained by Kamal are given below:*

Mathematics	English	Hindi	Science	Social Studies
96	84	75	90	70

Find his average marks per subject.

Solution : Sum of all the marks obtained = (96 + 84 + 75 + 90 + 70) = 415.

Number of subjects = 5.

Average marks per subject = $\frac{415}{5}$ = 83.

Hence, Kamal's average marks per subject are 83.

Example 2. *The daily earnings of a rickshaw puller during a week are:*

Rs 127, Rs 132, Rs 110, Rs 96, Rs 130, Rs 85, Rs 104

Find his average daily earning.

Solution: Total earning of the rickshaw puller in 7 days

= Rs (127 + 132 + 110 + 96 + 130 + 85 + 104) = Rs 784.

Average earning per day = $\dfrac{\text{Total earning in Rs}}{\text{Number of days}}$

$= \dfrac{784}{7}$ = Rs 112.

Hence, his average daily earning is Rs 112.

Example 3. *The weights of six boys in a group are:*

34 kg 300 g; 31 kg 600 g; 32 kg 400 g; 35 kg 450 g; 32 kg 800 g and 33 kg 250 g.

Find the average weight per boy.

Solution : Sum of the weights of all the 6 boys = 199.800 kg

$$\text{Average weight per boy} = \frac{\text{Sum of their weights}}{\text{Number of boys}}$$

$$= \frac{199.800}{6} \text{ kg}$$

$$= 33.300 \text{ kg}$$

Hence, the average weight per boy is 33 kg 300 g.

```
    3 4 . 3 0  0 kg
    3 1 . 6 0  0 kg
    3 2 . 4 0  0 kg
    3 5 . 4 5  0 kg
    3 2 . 8 0  0 kg
 +  3 3 . 2 5  0 kg
 ─────────────────
    1 9 9 . 8 0  0 kg
```

Average of Numbers

We define the average of some given numbers as:

$$\textbf{Average} = \frac{\textbf{Sum of given numbers}}{\textbf{Number of these numbers}}.$$

Example 4. *Find the average of the numbers:*

(*a*) 2, 3, 5, 7, 11 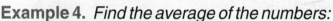 (*b*) $5\frac{1}{3}$, $3\frac{1}{2}$, $4\frac{1}{2}$, 4

Solution: (*a*) Sum of the given numbers = (2 + 3 + 5 + 7 + 11) = 28.

Number of these numbers = 5.

$$\text{Average of the given numbers} = \frac{\text{Sum of given numbers}}{\text{Number of these numbers}}$$

$$= \frac{28}{5} = 5.6.$$

Hence, the average of the given numbers is 5.6.

(*b*) The given numbers are $\frac{16}{3}$, $\frac{7}{2}$, $\frac{9}{2}$ and 4.

$$\text{Sum of the given numbers} = \left(\frac{16}{3} + \frac{7}{2} + \frac{9}{2} + \frac{4}{1} \right)$$

$$= \frac{(32 + 21 + 27 + 24)}{6} = \frac{104}{6} = \frac{52}{3}.$$

Number of these numbers = 4.

$$\text{Average of the given numbers} = \left(\frac{52}{3} \div 4 \right) = \left(\frac{52}{3} \times \frac{1}{4} \right) = \frac{13}{3} = 4\frac{1}{3}.$$

Hence, the average of the given numbers is $4\frac{1}{3}$.

Example 5. *Find the average of all odd numbers between 20 and 30.*

Solution: All odd numbers between 20 and 30 are:

21, 23, 25, 27 and 29.

Sum of given numbers = (21 + 23 + 25 + 27 + 29) = 125.

Number of these numbers = 5.

Average of the given numbers = $\dfrac{\text{Sum of the given numbers}}{\text{Number of these numbers}}$

$= \dfrac{125}{5} = 25.$

Hence, the average of all odd numbers between 20 and 30 is 25.

EXERCISE 60

1. Find the average of 9, 11, 13, 15 and 17.
2. Find the average of 9.3, 6.7, 7.4 and 8.2.
3. Find the average of $6\dfrac{2}{5}$, $5\dfrac{3}{10}$, $4\dfrac{1}{5}$ and $7\dfrac{7}{10}$.
4. Find the average of first nine counting numbers.
5. Find the average of all odd numbers between 50 and 60.
6. Find the average of all even numbers between 7 and 17.
7. Find the average of all prime numbers between 20 and 40.
8. Find the average of first six multiples of 3.
9. In a Cricket Test Series of 6 matches Hemant scored 102, 56, 230, 40, 180 and 124 runs. Find his average score per match.
10. The prices of six chairs are Rs 732, Rs 750, Rs 690, Rs 793, Rs 700 and Rs 745. Find the average price per chair.
11. During five successive hours a car covered 65 km, 72 km, 68 km, 70 km and 55 km. Find the average speed of the car per hour.
12. The ages of five girls in a group are: 16 years 4 months; 15 years 8 months; 14 years 9 months; 15 years 3 months and 14 years 8 months. Find the average age per girl in the group.
13. The lengths of 4 pieces of wire are: 16 m 80 cm, 17 m 25 cm, 13 m 75 cm and 12 m 20 cm. Find the average length per piece.
14. A man earned Rs 8500 per month during first 4 months and Rs 10000 per month during next 2 months. Find his average earning per month during this period.

THINGS TO REMEMBER

1. Average = $\dfrac{\text{Sum of given observations}}{\text{Number of observations}}$

2. Average of given numbers = $\dfrac{\text{Sum of the given numbers}}{\text{Number of these numbers}}$

14 PERCENTAGE

INTRODUCTION

The term *per cent* comes from two Latin words **per centum** which means **'out of 100'**.

Thus, 5 percent means 5 out of 100 $= \dfrac{5}{100} = 5$ hundredths

12 percent means 12 out of 100 $= \dfrac{12}{100} = 12$ hundredths

Thus, we define the term percent as under:

PER CENT: *By a certain per cent we mean that many hundredths.*

The symbol for per cent is %.

Examples: (*i*) $8\% = 8$ hundredths $= \dfrac{8}{100}$.

(*ii*) $23\% = 23$ hundredths $= \dfrac{23}{100}$.

CONVERTING A PERCENTAGE INTO A FRACTION OR A DECIMAL

Rule: *To convert a certain percent into an equivalent fraction, the percentage numeral is divided by 100.*

SOLVED EXAMPLES

Example 1. *Express each of the following as a numeral:*

(*a*) 25%   (*b*) 40%   (*c*) $6\dfrac{1}{4}\%$ (*d*) 12.5%

Solution : We have

(*a*) $25\% = \dfrac{25}{100} = \dfrac{1}{4}$.   (*b*) $40\% = \dfrac{40}{100} = \dfrac{2}{5}$.

(*c*) $6\dfrac{1}{4}\% = \dfrac{25}{4}\% = \left(\dfrac{\overset{1}{\cancel{25}}}{4} \times \dfrac{1}{\underset{4}{\cancel{100}}}\right) = \dfrac{1}{16}$.

(*d*) $12.5\% = \dfrac{12.5}{100} = \dfrac{\overset{1}{\cancel{125}}}{\underset{8}{\cancel{1000}}} = \dfrac{1}{8}$.

Example 2. *Express each of the following as a decimal:*

(*a*) 63%   (*b*) 9%   (*c*) 7.5%

Solution: (*a*) $63\% = \dfrac{63}{100} = 0.63$.   (*b*) $9\% = \dfrac{9}{100} = 0.09$.

(*c*) $7.5\% = \dfrac{7.5}{100} = \dfrac{75}{1000} = 0.075$.

Rule: *To convert a fraction or a decimal into a percentage, multiply by 100.*

Example 3. *Convert each of the following fractions into a percentage:*

(a) $\dfrac{9}{25}$ 　　　　 (b) $\dfrac{3}{4}$ 　　　　 (c) $2\dfrac{3}{5}$

Solution : We have

(a) $\dfrac{9}{25} = \left(\dfrac{9}{25} \times 100 \right) \% = 36\%.$ 　 (b) $\dfrac{3}{4} = \left(\dfrac{3}{4} \times 100 \right) \% = 75\%.$

(c) $2\dfrac{3}{5} = \left(\dfrac{13}{5} \times 100 \right) \% = 260\%.$

Example 4. *Convert each of the following decimals into a percentage:*

(a) 0.6 　　　 (b) 0.75 　　　 (c) 0.08 　　　 (d) 2.5

Solution : We have

(a) $0.6 = (0.6 \times 100)\% = \left(\dfrac{6}{10} \times 100 \right) \% = 60\%.$

(b) $0.75 = (0.75 \times 100)\% = \left(\dfrac{75}{100} \times 100 \right) \% = 75\%.$

(c) $0.08 = (0.08 \times 100)\% = \left(\dfrac{8}{100} \times 100 \right) \% = 8\%.$

(d) $2.5 = (2.5 \times 100)\% = \left(\dfrac{25}{10} \times 100 \right) \% = 250\%.$

Example 5. *Find :*

(a) 16 % of 125 　　　 (b) 6% of Rs 225 　　　 (c) 8% of 160 km

Solution : We have

(a) $16 \% \text{ of } 125 = \left(\dfrac{16}{100} \text{ of } 125 \right) = \left(\overset{5}{\cancel{125}} \times \dfrac{\overset{4}{\cancel{16}}}{\underset{1}{\cancel{100}}} \right) = 20.$

(b) $6 \% \text{ of Rs } 225 = \left(\dfrac{6}{100} \text{ of Rs } 225 \right) = \text{Rs} \left(\overset{9}{\cancel{225}} \times \dfrac{\overset{3}{\cancel{6}}}{\underset{4\ 2}{\cancel{100}}} \right) = \text{Rs} \dfrac{27}{2} = \text{Rs } 13.50.$

(c) $8 \% \text{ of } 160 \text{ km} = \left(\dfrac{8}{100} \text{ of } 160 \text{ km} \right) = \left(\overset{8}{\cancel{160}} \times \dfrac{8}{\underset{5}{\cancel{100}}} \right) \text{km} = \dfrac{64}{5} \text{ km} = 12.8 \text{ km}.$

Example 6. *What percent of 85 is 17?*

Solution : $\text{Required } \% = \left(\dfrac{\overset{1}{\cancel{17}}}{\underset{5}{\cancel{85}}_1} \times \overset{20}{\cancel{100}} \right) \% = 20\%.$

Example 7. *What percent of 65 is 104?*

Solution : $\text{Required } \% = \left(\dfrac{\overset{8}{\cancel{104}}}{\underset{5}{\cancel{65}}_1} \times \overset{20}{\cancel{100}} \right) \% = 160\%.$

Example 8. *What is the number whose 12% is 54?*

Solution : We have

12 % of the required number = 54.

$\therefore \dfrac{12}{100} \times$ (Required number) = 54

$\therefore$ Required number $= \left(\overset{9}{\cancel{54}} \times \dfrac{\overset{50}{\cancel{100}}}{\underset{2}{\cancel{12}}} \right) = 450$.

Hence, 450 is the number whose 12% is 54.

Example 9. *Write 35 paise as a percentage of a rupee.*

Solution : 35 paise $= \dfrac{35}{100}$ of a rupee

$= \left(\dfrac{35}{100} \times 100 \right)$ % of a rupee

$= 35\%$ of a rupee.

Example 10. *Write 15 mm as a percentage of a cm.*

Solution : 15 mm $= \dfrac{15}{10}$ of a cm

$= \left(\dfrac{15}{10} \times 100 \right)$ % of a cm

$= 150\%$ of a cm.

Example 11. *Write 20 m as a percentage of a km.*

Solution : 20 m $= \dfrac{20}{1000}$ of a km

$= \left(\dfrac{20}{1000} \times 100 \right)$ % of a km

$= 2\%$ of a km.

Example 12. *What percent is 7 m 80 cm of 65 m?*

Solution : 7 m 80 cm $= (7 \times 100)$ cm $+ 80$ cm $= 780$ cm.

65 m $= (65 \times 100)$ cm $= 6500$ cm.

Required % $= \left(\dfrac{\overset{12}{\cancel{780}}}{\underset{1}{\cancel{6500}}} \times \cancel{100} \right) \% = 12\%$.

Example 13. *What percent is 1 min 48 seconds of 1 hour?*

Solution : 1 min 48 sec $= (1 \times 60)$ sec $+ 48$ sec $= (60 + 48)$ sec $= 108$ sec.

1 hour $= 60$ min $= (60 \times 60)$ sec $= 3600$ sec.

Required % $= \left(\dfrac{\overset{3}{\cancel{108}}}{\underset{1}{\cancel{3600}}} \times \cancel{100} \right) \% = 3\%$.

Example 14. A group of 80 students went on a picnic. 15% of them were girls. How many girls were there in the group? How many were boys?

Solution: Total number of students = 80.

Percentage of girls = 15%.

Number of girls = (15% of 80) = $\left(\dfrac{\overset{3}{\cancel{15}}}{\underset{5}{\cancel{100}}} \times \overset{4}{\cancel{80}}^{1} \right)$ = 12.

Number of boys = (80 – 12) = 68.

EXERCISE 61

1. Express each of the following as a fraction in its lowest terms:

   (a) 35%
   (b) 48%
   (c) 72%
   (d) 84%

   (e) $7\dfrac{1}{2}\%$
   (f) $8\dfrac{1}{3}\%$
   (g) $16\dfrac{2}{3}\%$
   (h) 37.5%

   (i) 135%
   (j) 225%
   (k) 2%
   (l) 9.6%

2. Express each of the following as a decimal:

   (a) 23%
   (b) 72%
   (c) 6%
   (d) 10%

   (e) 35.6%
   (f) 104%
   (g) 180%
   (h) 235%

   (i) 4.5%
   (j) 6.25%
   (k) 0.3%
   (l) 0.25%

3. Convert each of the following fractions into a percentage:

   (a) $\dfrac{23}{100}$
   (b) $\dfrac{9}{100}$
   (c) $\dfrac{7}{10}$
   (d) $\dfrac{1}{4}$

   (e) $\dfrac{1}{8}$
   (f) $\dfrac{2}{5}$
   (g) $\dfrac{3}{20}$
   (h) $\dfrac{9}{20}$

   (i) $\dfrac{18}{25}$
   (j) $\dfrac{27}{50}$
   (k) $\dfrac{9}{16}$
   (l) $\dfrac{37}{40}$

   (m) $\dfrac{2}{3}$
   (n) $2\dfrac{1}{5}$
   (o) $3\dfrac{1}{4}$
   (p) $2\dfrac{7}{10}$

4. Convert each of the following decimals into a percentage:

   (a) 0.8
   (b) 0.25
   (c) 0.76
   (d) 0.06

   (e) 0.325
   (f) 0.004
   (g) 1.05
   (h) 4.2

5. Find the value of:

   (a) 24% of 175
   (b) 8% of 225
   (c) 70% of 80

   (d) 120% of 45
   (e) 16% of 550
   (f) 6.4% of 750

   (g) 9% of 70
   (h) 5% of 12.6
   (i) 15% of 15

6. *Find the value of:*

   (a) 20% of Rs 70
   (b) 70% of 40 kg
   (c) 14% of 750 g

   (d) 6% of Rs 125
   (e) 60% of 1 year
   (f) 5% of a metre

   (g) 8% of a litre
   (h) 8% of 2 kg
   (i) 10% of a litre

7. (a) What per cent of 72 is 18?
   (b) What per cent of 70 is 14?

   (c) What per cent of 30 is 24?
   (d) What per cent of 65 is 104?

   (e) What per cent of 42 is 29.4?
   (f) What per cent of 63 is 31.5?

8. (a) What per cent is 45 P of Re 1?
   (b) What per cent is 34 P of Rs 1.70?

   (c) What per cent is 400 m of 1 km?
   (d) What per cent is 15 cm of 1 m?

   (e) What per cent is 3 mm of 1 cm?
   (f) What per cent is 225 g of 2.5 kg?

9. Find the number whose 8% is 14.

10. Find the number whose 6% is 8.1.

11. Find the number whose 12.5% is 3.5.

12. Find the amount whose 12% is Rs 15.

13. Find the length whose 18% is 27 cm.

14. Find the weight whose 20% is 250 gm.

15. In a class of 40 pupils, 35% are girls. How many girls are there in the class? How many of the pupils are boys?

16. A man earns Rs 10800 per month. He spends 75% of his income and the rest he saves. How much does he save every month?

17. In an examination, Nisha obtained 312 marks out of 650. What percentage of marks did she get?

18. A metal contains 36% zinc and the rest is copper. Find the quantity of zinc and copper in 325 g of this metal.

THINGS TO REMEMBER

1. By a certain per cent we mean that many hundredths.

   Thus, $8\% = 8$ hundredths $= \dfrac{8}{100} = \dfrac{2}{25}$.

2. To convert a certain per cent into a fraction, the percentage numeral is divided by 100.

3. To convert a fraction into a percentage, multiply the given fraction by 100.

4. To convert a decimal into a percentage, multiply the given decimal by 100.

TIME

Till now, we have learnt to read time from a clock and conversion of days into hours and hours into minutes.

We shall now extend these ideas further.

THE 24-HOUR CLOCK

We normally use the 12-hour clock to measure time. However, *Air Services, Railways, Shipping Lines, Defence Forces and Television Networks throughout the world use the 24-hour clock.*

A 24-hour clock dial may be visualised as the one given below.

Under this system, **4 digits** are used to indicate the time.

The first two digits show the hours and the last two digits the minutes.

The day starts at 12 mid-night and is written as 0000 hours.

The following table shows the 12-hour clock time and the corresponding 24-hour clock time.

12-hour clock time	24-hour clock time
12 mid-night	0000 hours or 2400 hours
0 : 10 a.m.	0010 hours
0 : 59 a.m.	0059 hours
1 a.m.	0100 hours
2 a.m.	0200 hours
5 : 30 a.m.	0530 hours
11 : 15 a.m.	1115 hours
12 noon	1200 hours

12-hour clock time	24-hour clock time
12 : 01 p.m.	1201 hours
12 : 59 p.m.	1259 hours
1 p.m.	1300 hours
2 p.m.	1400 hours
5 : 20 p.m.	1720 hours
9 : 45 p.m.	2145 hours
11 : 30 p.m.	2330 hours
11 : 59 p.m.	2359 hours
12 mid-night	2400 hours

To Convert 24-hour Clock Time to 12-hour Clock Time

Rule 1 : *Time from Mid-night 0000 hours to 1200 noon: If the number formed by the first two digits from the left of a 24-hour clock time is less than 12, then it denotes the number of hours before noon and so **a.m.** is to be used with it.*

Examples :
(a) **0535 hours** denotes **5 : 35 a.m.**
(b) **0920 hours** denotes **9 : 20 a.m.**
(c) **1159 hours** denotes **11 : 59 a.m.**

Rule 2 : *1200 hours denotes 12 : 00 p.m.*

Rule 3 : *Time from 1201 to 1259 hours : If the number formed by the first two digits from the left of a 24-hour clock time is 12, other than 1200 then p.m. is to be used with it.*

Examples :
(a) **1201 hours** denotes **12 : 01 p.m.**
(b) **1245 hours** denotes **12 : 45 p.m.**
(c) **1259 hours** denotes **12 : 59 p.m.**

Rule 4 : *Time from 1300 hours to 2400 hours: If the number formed by the first two digits from the left of a 24-hour clock time is 13 or more, then the difference between the number and 12 gives the number of hours and **p.m.** is to be used with it.*

Examples :
(a) **1300 hours** denotes **1 : 00 p.m.**
(b) **1745 hours** denotes **5 : 45 p.m.**
(c) **2359 hours** denotes **11 : 59 p.m.**
(d) **2400 hours** denotes **12 : 00 a.m.**

Example : Write the following in terms of a.m. or p.m. or noon or mid-night.

(*a*) 1320 hours   (*b*) 0805 hours   (*c*) 1200 hours

(*d*) 1608 hours   (*e*) 2400 hours   (*f*) 0025 hours

Solution : Using the rules for converting 24-hour clock time to 12-hour clock time, we have :

(*a*) 1320 hours = 1 : 20 p.m.   (*b*) 0805 hours = 8 : 05 a.m.

(*c*) 1200 hours = 12 noon   (*d*) 1608 hours = 4 : 08 p.m.

(*e*) 2400 hours = 12 mid-night   (*f*) 0025 hours = 0 : 25 a.m.

EXERCISE 62

1. Write the time using a.m. or p.m. or noon or mid-night :

(*a*) 0640 hours   (*b*) 0130 hours   (*c*) 0020 hours   (*d*) 1206 hours

(*e*) 1256 hours   (*f*) 1438 hours   (*g*) 1624 hours   (*h*) 0000 hours

(*i*) 2347 hours   (*j*) 2139 hours   (*k*) 1354 hours   (*l*) 2000 hours

2. Convert the following into 24-hour clock time :

(*a*) 4 : 05 a.m.   (*b*) 11 : 32 a.m.   (*c*) 0 : 08 a.m.   (*d*) 0 : 46 a.m.

(*e*) 12 : 15 p.m.   (*f*) 2 : 18 p.m.   (*g*) 10 : 00 p.m.   (*h*) 0 : 58 a.m.

(*i*) 12 : 58 p.m.   (*j*) 1 : 10 a.m.   (*k*) 2 : 30 a.m.   (*l*) 9 : 30 p.m.

3. Given below is an extract from an Airline Time-table.

	Plane A	Plane B	Plane C
DELHI	0005	1210	1835
LUCKNOW	0045	1305	1915
PATNA	0125	1350	2000

This table shows the departure times of three planes from Delhi and Lucknow and arrival time at Patna.

Read it carefully and answer the following questions. Express them in a.m. or p.m.

(*a*) When does the plane B leave Delhi ?

(*b*) When does the plane A leave Lucknow ?

(*c*) When does the plane C reach Patna ?

4. Given below is an extract from a Railway Time-table. Study the table carefully and answer the questions given below. State the time in terms of a.m. or p.m.

Stations		Kalka-Mail	Purva-Express	Rajdhani-Express
Delhi	a	0730		
	d	0800		
New Delhi	a	—	1430	2140
	d		1610	2210
Kanpur	a	1450	2305	0020
	d	1505	2325	0100
Asansol	a	0046	0850	0730
	d	0130	0905	0800
Howrah	a	0700	1450	1205
	d	—	—	—

Here *a* stands for arrival and *d* stands for departure.

(*a*) When does the Purva-Express leave New-Delhi ?

(*b*) At what time the Kalka-Mail reaches Asansol ?

(*c*) At what time the Rajdhani-Express reaches Howrah ?

(*d*) At what time the Purva-Express reaches Kanpur ?

CLOCKS WITH THREE HANDS

In some clocks, apart from the hour hand and the minute hand, there is a third hand, called **seconds hand.**

The seconds hand makes a full round in 1 *minute and the time in which it moves between two successive small divisions is called* 1 *second.*

Thus, **60** *seconds* **= 1** *minute.*

CONVERSION OF TIME

We know that :

1 hour	=	60 minutes.
1 minute	=	60 seconds.
1 day	=	24 hours.
1 week	=	7 days.
1 fortnight	=	2 weeks = 14 days
1 year	=	12 months.
1 year	=	365 days.
1 leap year	=	366 days.

SOLVED EXAMPLES

Example 1. *Convert :*

(a) 3 days into hours.   (b) 5 days 18 hours into hours.

Solution : (a) 1 day = 24 hours.

∴ 3 days = (3 × 24) hours = 72 hours.

(b) 5 days 18 hours

= 5 days + 18 hours

= (5 × 24) hours + 18 hours   [∵ 1 day = 24 hours]

= (120 hours + 18 hours) = 138 hours.

Example 2. *Convert :*

(a) 14 hours into minutes.   (b) 5 hours 42 minutes into minutes.

(c) 2 days 16 hours 30 minutes into minutes.

Solution : We have

(a) 1 hour = 60 minutes.

∴ 14 hours = (14 × 60) minutes = 840 minutes.

(b) 5 hours 42 minutes

= 5 hours + 42 minutes

= (5 × 60) minutes + 42 minutes [∵ 1 hour = 60 minutes]

= (300 minutes + 42 minutes) = 342 minutes

(c) 2 days 16 hours 30 minutes

= 2 days + 16 hours + 30 minutes

= (2 × 24) hours + 16 hours + 30 minutes   [∵ 1 day = 24 hours]

= (48 hours + 16 hours) + 30 minutes

= 64 hours + 30 minutes

```
    6 4
  × 6 0
  ------
  3 8 4 0
```

= (64 × 60) minutes + 30 minutes [∵ 1 hour = 60 minutes]

= 3840 minutes + 30 minutes

= 3870 minutes.

Example 3 : *Convert :*

(a) 16 minutes into seconds.

(b) 8 minutes 24 seconds into seconds

(c) 2 hours 36 minutes 18 seconds into seconds .

Solution :

(a) 1 minute = 60 seconds.

∴ 16 minutes = (16 × 60) seconds = 960 seconds.

(b) 8 minutes 24 seconds = 8 minutes + 24 seconds

= (8 × 60) seconds + 24 seconds

[∵ 1 minute = 60 seconds

= 480 seconds + 24 seconds = 504 seconds.

(c) 2 hours 36 minutes 18 seconds

= 2 hours + 36 minutes + 18 seconds

= (2 × 60) minutes + 36 minutes + 18 seconds

[∵ 1 hour = 60 minutes]

= (120 minutes + 36 minutes) + 18 seconds

= 156 minutes + 18 seconds

= (156 × 60) seconds + 18 seconds

[∵ 1 minute = 60 seconds]

= 9360 seconds + 18 seconds = 9378 seconds.

$$\begin{array}{r} 1\,5\,6 \\ \times\,6\,0 \\ \hline 9\,3\,6\,0 \end{array}$$

Example 4.   *Convert:*

(a) 3 years 8 months into months.

(b) 4 weeks 5 days into days.

Solution :   We have

(a) 3 years 8 months

= 3 years + 8 months

= (3 × 12) months + 8 months   [∵ 1 year = 12 months]

= 36 months + 8 months = 44 months.

(b) 4 weeks 5 days

= 4 weeks + 5 days

= (4 × 7) days + 5 days   [∵ 1 week = 7 days]

= (28 days + 5 days) = 33 days.

CONVERTING LOWER UNITS INTO HIGHER UNITS

Example 5.   *Convert 754 minutes into hours and minutes.*

Solution :   60 minutes = 1 hour.

∴ 754 minutes = (754 ÷ 60) hours

$$\begin{array}{r} 60\,\overline{)7\,5\,4}\,(12 \\ \underline{6\,0} \\ 1\,5\,4 \\ \underline{1\,2\,0} \\ 3\,4 \end{array}$$

So, 754 minutes = 12 hours 34 minutes.

Example 6. *Convert 2146 seconds into minutes and seconds.*

Solution : We know that 60 seconds = 1 minute.

∴ 2146 seconds = (2146 ÷ 60) seconds

```
60)2146(35
    180
    ─────
     346
     300
    ─────
      46
```

So, 2146 seconds = 35 minutes 46 seconds.

Example 7. *Convert 664 hours into days and hours.*

Solution : We know that 24 hours =1 day.

∴ 664 hours = (664 ÷ 24) days

```
24)664(27
   48
   ─────
   184
   168
   ─────
    16
```

So, 664 hours = 27 days 16 hours.

Example 8. *Convert 365 days into weeks and days.*

Solution : We know that 7 days = 1 week.

∴ 365 days = (365 ÷ 7) weeks.

```
7)365(52
  35
  ─────
   15
   14
  ─────
    1
```

So, 365 days = 52 weeks 1 day.

EXERCISE 63

1. *Convert :*

(*a*) 8 days into hours   (*b*) 17 days into hours

(*c*) 6 days 19 hours into hours   (*d*) 14 days 6 hours into hours

(*e*) 11 days 11 hours into hours

2. *Convert :*

(*a*) 10 hours into minutes   (*b*) 8 hours 56 minutes into minutes

(*c*) 16 hours 43 minutes into minutes   (*d*) 3 days 12 hours 25 minutes into minutes

(*e*) 2 days into minutes

3. *Convert :*

(*a*) 9 minutes into seconds.

(*b*) 6 minutes 54 seconds into seconds

(*c*) 13 minutes 36 seconds into seconds

(*d*) 3 hours 25 minutes 16 seconds into seconds

(*e*) 5 hours 5 minutes 5 seconds into seconds

4. *Convert:*

    (*a*) 4 years into months   (*b*) 5 years 10 months into months

    (*c*) 14 years 8 months into months.

5. *Convert :*

    (*a*) 5 weeks 6 days into days   (*b*) 8 weeks 4 days into days

    (*c*) 43 weeks 1 day into days   (*d*) 2 years into days

    (*e*) 3 years 120 days into days

6. *Convert :*

    (*a*) 137 minutes into hours and minutes

    (*b*) 385 minutes into hours and minutes

    (*c*) 1023 minutes into hours and minutes

    (*d*) 2006 minutes into hours and minutes

7. *Convert :*

    (*a*) 1354 seconds into minutes and seconds

    (*b*) 2105 seconds into minutes and seconds

    (*c*) 3268 seconds into minutes and seconds

8. *Convert :*

    (*a*) 73 hours into days and hours   (*b*) 200 hours into days and hours

    (*c*) 529 hours into days and hours   (*d*) 1016 hours into days and hours

9. *Convert :*

    (*a*) 230 days into weeks and days   (*b*) 341 days into weeks and days

    (*c*) 400 days into weeks and days

ADDITION AND SUBTRACTION OF TIME

SOLVED EXAMPLES

Example 1.   *Add 3 hours 23 minutes and 5 hours 27 minutes.*

Solution :

hours	minutes
3	2 3
+ 5	2 7
8	5 0

Step 1.   *Adding minutes :*
23 minutes + 27 minutes = 50 minutes.
Write 50 under minutes column.

Step 2.   *Adding hours :*
3 hours + 5 hours = 8 hours.
Write 8 under hours column.

∴ (3 hours 23 minutes) + (5 hours 27 minutes) = 8 hours 50 minutes.

Example 2.   *Add 6 hours 36 minutes and 9 hours 48 minutes.*

Solution :

hours	minutes
①	
6	3 6
+ 9	4 8
1 6	2 4

Step 1.   *Adding minutes :*
36 minutes + 48 minutes
= 84 minutes
= 60 minutes + 24 minutes
= 1 hour + 24 minutes
Write 24 under minutes column.
Carry over 1 to hours column.

Step 2.   *Adding hours :*
1 hour (carried over) + 6 hours + 9 hours
= 16 hours.
Write 16 under hours column.

∴ (6 hours 36 minutes) + (9 hours 48 minutes) = 16 hours 24 minutes.

Example 3.   *Add 26 minutes 48 seconds and 12 minutes 46 seconds.*

Solution :

minutes	seconds
①	
2 6	4 8
+ 1 2	4 6
3 9	3 4

Step 1.   *Adding seconds:*
48 seconds + 46 seconds
= 94 seconds
= 60 seconds + 34 seconds
= 1 minute + 34 seconds.
Write 34 under seconds column.
Carry over 1 to minutes column.

Step 2.   *Adding minutes :*
1 minute (carried over) + 26 minutes
+ 12 minutes = 39 minutes.
Write 39 under minutes column.

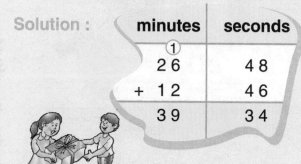

∴ (26 minutes 48 seconds) + (12 minutes 46 seconds)

= 39 minutes 34 seconds.

Example 4.   *Add 7 weeks 5 days and 9 weeks 4 days.*

Solution :   Adding Days:
5 days + 4 days = 9 days = 7 days + 2 days
= 1 week + 2 days
Write 2 under days column and carry over
1 to weeks column.

Weeks	Days
①	
7	5
+ 9	4
17	2

Adding Weeks:
1 week (carried over) + 7 weeks + 9 weeks = 17 weeks.
Write 17 under weeks column.

∴ 7 weeks 5 days + 9 weeks 4 days = 17 weeks 2 days.

Example 5. Subtract 3 hours 34 minutes from 5 hours 50 minutes.

Solution :

hours	minutes
5	5 0
− 3	3 4
2	1 6

Step 1. *Subtracting minutes:*
50 minutes − 34 minutes = 16 minutes.
Write 16 under minutes column.

Step 2. *Subtracting hours :*
5 hours − 3 hours = 2 hours.
Write 2 under hours column.

∴ (5 hours 50 minutes) − (3 hours 34 minutes) = 2 hours 16 minutes.

Example 6. Subtract 8 hours 56 minutes from 12 hours 24 minutes.

Solution :

ours	minutes
⑪ 1̶2̶	㊙8 4̶ 2̶4̶
− 8	5 6
3	2 8

h

Step 1. *Subtracting minutes:*
We cannot subtract 56 minutes from
24 minutes. So we borrow 1 hour, leaving
behind 11 hours.
Now, 60 minutes + 24 minutes
                        = 84 minutes
∴ 84 minutes − 56 minutes = 28 minutes.
Write 28 under minutes column.

Step 2. *Subtracting hours :*
11 hours − 8 hours = 3 hours.
Write 3 under hours column.

∴ (12 hours 24 minutes) − (8 hours 56 minutes) = 3 hours 28 minutes.

Example 7. Subtract 34 minutes 45 seconds from 43 minutes 10 seconds.

Solution :

minutes	seconds
㊷4 2 4̶3̶	㊲7 0 1̶0̶
− 3 4	2 4
8	4 6

Step 1. *Subtracting seconds:*
We cannot subtract 24 seconds from
10 seconds. So, we borrow 1 minute,
leaving behind 42 minutes.
Now, 60 seconds + 10 seconds
                        = 70 seconds
∴ 70 seconds − 24 seconds = 46 seconds.

Step 2. *Subtracting minutes :*
42 minutes − 34 minutes = 8 minutes.

∴ (43 minutes 10 seconds) − (34 minutes 24 seconds) = 8 minutes 46 seconds.

Example 8. What time will it be 4 hours 40 minutes after 6 : 30 p.m.?

Solution : **Step 1 :** Convert 6 : 30 p.m. into hours.

We know that 6 : 30 p.m. means 1830 hours = 18 hours 30 minutes.

Step 2 : Add 4 hours 40 minutes to 18 hours 30 minutes.

Adding minutes:
30 minutes + 40 minutes
                = 70 minutes
                = 60 minutes
                = 1 hour + 10 minutes.

hours	minutes
①	
1 8	3 0
+ 4	4 0
2 3	1 0

COMPOSITE MATHEMATICS – 5

Write 10 under minutes column. Carry over 1 to hours column.

Adding hours:

1 hour (carried over) + 18 hours + 4 hours = 23 hours.

Write 23 under hours column.

∴ Required time = 23 hours 10 minutes = 2310 hours = 11.10 p.m.

Hence the time 4 hours 40 minutes after 6 : 30 p.m. is 11 : 10 p.m.

Example 9. *What time was it 8 hours 30 minutes before 5 : 20 p.m. ?*

Solution : **Step 1 :** *Convert 5 : 20 p.m. into hours.*

We know that :

5 : 20 p.m. means 1720 hours = 17 hours 20 minutes.

Step 2 : *Subtract 8 hours 30 minutes from 17 hours 20 minutes.*

hours	minutes
⑯	⑧⓪
~~17~~	~~20~~
− 8	30
8	50

Subtracting minutes :

We cannot subtract 30 minutes from 20 minutes.

So, we borrow 1 hour, leaving behind 16 hours.

Now, 1 hour + 20 minutes = 60 minutes + 20 minutes = 80 minutes.

And, 80 minutes − 30 minutes = 50 minutes.

Write 50 under minutes column.

Subtracting hours :

16 hours − 8 hours = 8 hours.

Write 8 under hours column.

∴ Required time = 8 hours 50 minutes = 0850 hours = 8 : 50 a.m.

Hence, the time 8 hours 30 minutes before 5 : 20 p.m. is 8 : 50 a.m.

Example 10. *Find the interval between 8 : 45 a.m. and 2 : 20 p.m.*

Solution : **Step 1 :** *Convert 2 : 20 p.m. into hours.*

2 : 20 p.m. means 1420 hours

= 14 hours 20 minutes

Step 2 : *Convert 8 : 45 a.m. into hours.*

8 : 45 a.m. means 0845 hours

= 8 hours 45 minutes.

Step 3 : *Subtract 8 hours 45 minutes from 14 hours 20 minutes.*

Subtracting minutes :

We cannot subtract 45 minutes from 20 minutes.

So, we borrow 1 hour, leaving behind 13 hours.

Now, 1 hour + 20 minutes

= 60 minutes + 20 minutes = 80 minutes.

And, 80 minutes – 45 minutes

= 35 minutes.

Write 35 under minutes column.

hours	minutes
⑬	⑧⓪
1̶4̶	2̶0̶
– 8	4 5
5	3 5

Subtracting hours :

13 hours – 8 hours = 5 hours.

Write 5 under hours column.

Hence, the required time is 5 hours 35 minutes.

Example 11. *Subtract 17 years 8 months from 21 years.*

Solution : *Subtracting Months :*

We cannot subtract 8 months from 0 month.

So, we borrow 1 year, leaving behind 20 years.

Now, 1 year 0 month = 12 months.

And, 12 months – 8 months = 4 months.

Write 4 under months column.

Years	Months
⑳	⑫
2̶1̶	0̶
– 1 7	8
3	4

Subtracting Years :

20 years – 17 years = 3 years.

Write 3 under years column.

∴ 21 years – 17 years 8 months = 3 years 4 months.

EXERCISE 64

1. Add the following :

   (a) 2 days 18 hours and 3 days 12 hours   (b) 14 days 16 hours and 6 days 8 hours

   (b) 5 weeks 4 days and 4 weeks 5 days

2. Add the following :

   (a) 5 hours 35 minutes and 4 hours 15 minutes

   (b) 8 hours 46 minutes and 6 hours 54 minutes

   (c) 17 hours 8 minutes and 7 hours 52 minutes

   (d) 2 hours 30 minutes, 4 hours 50 minutes and 5 hours 40 minutes

3. Add the following :

   (a) 8 minutes 28 seconds and 6 minutes 17 seconds

   (b) 13 minutes 32 seconds and 8 minutes 53 seconds

   (c) 17 minutes 46 seconds and 18 minutes 14 seconds

   (d) 9 minutes 45 seconds, 6 minutes 24 seconds and 8 minutes 16 seconds

4. **Subtract:**

   (a) 3 days 12 hours from 5 days 20 hours

   (b) 8 days 18 hours from 12 days 10 hours

   (c) 7 days 6 hours from 10 days

   (d) 3 weeks 5 days from 5 weeks 2 days

5. **Subtract:**

   (a) 6 hours 25 minutes from 8 hours 40 minutes

   (b) 8 hours 46 minutes from 11 hours 30 minutes

   (c) 16 hours 34 minutes from 23 hours 26 minutes

   (d) 9 hours 40 minutes from 24 hours

6. **Subtract:**

   (a) 8 minutes 32 seconds from 12 minutes 40 seconds

   (b) 24 minutes 54 seconds from 36 minutes 23 seconds

   (c) 41 minutes 37 seconds from 54 minutes 25 seconds

   (d) 10 minutes 48 seconds from 13 minutes

7. Subtract 14 years 9 months from 20 years.

8. What time will it be 3 hours 50 minutes after 7 : 30 p.m. ?

9. What time will it be 6 hours 30 minutes after 9 : 40 p.m. ?

10. What time was it 3 hours before 1 : 30 p.m. ?

11. What time was it 6 hours 25 minutes before 4 : 15 p.m. ?

12. Find the interval between 7 : 25 a.m. and 3 : 10 p.m.

DURATION OF AN ACTIVITY

SOLVED EXAMPLES

Example 1. *Nidhi's school starts at 7 : 30 a.m. and closes at 2 : 15 p.m. Find the working hours of the school.*

Solution : Closing time of the school = 2 : 15 p.m. = 14 : 15 hours.

Opening time of the school = 7 : 30 a.m. = 7 : 30 hours.

Working hours of the school = (14 : 15 hours) − (7 : 30 hours)

Hours	Min
~~14~~ ⑬	~~15~~ ⑦⑤
− 7	3 0
6	4 5

∴ Working hours of the school are 6 hrs 45 min.

Example 2. *A bus leaves Delhi at 7 : 50 p.m. and reaches Lucknow at 5 : 30 a.m. the next day. Find the duration of the journey.*

Solution : Departure time of the bus = 7 : 50 p.m. = 19 : 50 hours.

Time interval from 7 : 50 p.m. to 12 midnight

= (24 : 00 hours) – (19 : 50 hours)

Hours	Min
(23)	(60)
2 4	0 0
– 1 9	5 0
4	1 0

∴ Time interval from 7 : 50 p.m. to 12 midnight is 4 hrs 10 min.

Time interval from 12 mid night to 5 : 30 a.m. the next day

= 5 hrs 30 min

∴ Total time taken = (4 hrs 10 min) + (5 hrs 30 min)

= 9 hrs 40 min.

Hours	Min
4	1 0
+ 5	3 0
9	4 0

Example 3. *A train started from Delhi at 6 : 30 a.m. on Monday and reached Cochin on Thursday at 8 : 10 a.m . Find the total duration of time taken by the train from Delhi to Cochin.*

Solution : Duration from 6 : 30 a.m. on Monday to 6 : 30 a.m. on Thursday

= 3 days = (3 × 24) hours = 72 hours.

Duration from 6 : 30 a.m. to 8 : 10 a.m. on Thursday

= 1 hour 40 min.

Total time taken = 72 hours + (1 hour 40 min)

= 73 hours 40 minutes.

Hours	Min
(7)	(70)
8	1 0
– 6	3 0
1	4 0

Example 4. *Devesh joined Delhi Public School on 20th September 2007 and left it on 4th April, 2010. How long did he study in that school?*

Solution : Period from 20th September 2007 to 19th September 2009 = 2 years.

Period from 20th September 2009 to 19th March 2010 = 6 months.

Period from 20th March 2010 to 3rd April 2010

= (12 + 3) days = 15 days.

Total period for which Devesh studied in that school

= 2 years 6 months 15 days.

Month	March		April
Days	12	+	3

Example 5. *Sudhir was born on 4th May 2006 and his sister Seema was born on 2nd August 2010. Who is elder and by how much?*

Solution : Clearly, 4th May 2006 comes earlier than 2nd August 2010.

So, Sudhir was born earlier than his sister Seema.

∴ Sudhir is elder to Seema.

Period from 4th May 2006 to 3rd May 2010 = 4 years.

Period from 4th May 2010 to 3rd July 2010 = 2 months.

Period from 4th July 2010 to 1st August 2010

= (28 + 1) days = 29 days.

Total period by which Sudhir is elder

= 4 years 2 months 29 days.

Month	July	Aug
Days	28 +	1

EXERCISE 65

1. Reetu's school starts at 8 : 15 a.m. and closes at 3 : 40 p.m. Find the working hours of her school.

2. A stationery shop opens at 9 : 30 a.m. and closes at 8 : 00 p.m. How long does the shop remain open?

3. A bus leaves the bus stop at 6 : 50 p.m. and reaches its destination at 6 : 30 a.m. the next day. Find the duration of the journey.

4. A train left Delhi at 5 : 40 p.m. on Sunday and reached Bengaluru on Wednesday at 12 : 30 p.m. Find the total duration of the journey.

5. Naresh joined a company on 8th August 2005 and left it on 3rd January 2010. How long did he work for the company ?

6. Neera's winter vacations were from 5th December, 2009 to 12th February, 2010. For how many days her school was closed ?

7. I started teaching at the age of 22 years 7 months. I am now 50 years 2 months old. How long have I been teaching ?

8. Punam was born on 7th April 2004 and her brother Amit was born on 2nd March 2009. Who is younger and by how much ?

THINGS TO REMEMBER

1. A day begins at 12 mid-night and ends at 12 mid-night on the following day.

2. Time between 12 mid-night and 12 noon is denoted by *a.m.*

3. Time between 12 noon and 12 mid-night is denoted by *p.m.*

4. In 24-hour clock system four digits are used to indicate time. The first two digits show the hours and the last two digits the minutes.

5. The day starts at 12 mid-night and the time is 0000 hours.

6. *To convert 24-hour clock time to 12-hour clock time :*

   Rule 1. If the number formed by the first two digits of a 24-hour clock time is less than 12, it denotes the number of hours before noon and so *a.m.* is to be used with it.

   Rule 2. If the number formed by the first two digits of a 24-hour clock time is more than 12, the difference between the number and 12 gives the number of hours after noon and so *p.m.* is to be used with it.

   Rule 3. If the number formed by the first two digits of a 24-hour clock time is 12 (other than 1200), *p.m.* is to be used with it.

7. 1 day = 24 hours; 1 hour = 60 minutes and 1 minute = 60 seconds.

8. There are 7 days in a week, 2 weeks in a fortnight and 12 months or 365 days in a year.

C.C.E. DRILL - 12

QUESTION BAG - 1

(OBJECTIVE - TYPE QUESTIONS)

Tick (✓) the correct answer :

1. A dance show began at 6 : 35 p.m. and it lasted for 35 minutes. At what time did the dance show end?

   (a) 7 : 00 p.m.　　　　(b) 7 : 05 p.m.　　　　(c) 7 : 10 p.m.　　　　(d) 7 : 15 p.m.

2. Soumya went to sleep at 9 : 25 p.m. and woke up at 5 : 10 a.m. For how long did she sleep?

   (a) 7 hours 15 minutes　　　　　　(b) 7 hours 35 minutes

   (c) 7 hours 45 minutes　　　　　　(d) 8 hours 15 minutes

3. 9 : 15 p.m. in 24 hours clock is

   (a) 1815 hours　　(b) 2015 hours　　(c) 2115 hours　　(d) 2315 hours

4. The time $3\frac{1}{2}$ hours before 2 : 20 p.m. is

   (a) 10 : 30 a.m.　　(b) 10 : 40 a.m.　　(c) 10 : 50 p.m.　　(d) 10 : 50 a.m.

5. The sum of 6 years 8 months and 8 years 6 months is

   (a) 15 years 4 months　　　　　　(b) 15 years 2 months

   (c) 14 years 8 months　　　　　　(d) 14 years 4 months

6. 1 century = ...years

   (a) 10　　　　(b) 50　　　　(c) 100　　　　(d) 1000

7. The difference between 9 hours 25 minutes and 3 hours 45 minutes is

   (a) 3 hours 40 minutes　　　　　　(b) 3 hours 35 minutes

   (c) 4 hours 15 minutes　　　　　　(d) 4 hours 45 minutes

8. A fair started on January 12, 2008 and ended on March 12, 2008. How long did the fair last?

   (a) 59 days　　(b) 60 days　　(c) 61 days　　(d) 62 days

9. If 1st of March is Friday then the number of Sundays in the month of March of that year is

   (a) 3　　　　(b) 4　　　　(c) 5　　　　(d) 6

10. The number of complete weeks in a leap year is

    (a) 50　　(b) 51　　(c) 52　　(d) 53

11. How many seconds are there in a year?

    (a) 365 × 60 × 60　　(b) 365 × 24 × 60　　(c) 365 × 24 × 360　　(d) 365 × 24 × 3600

QUESTION BAG - 2

1. *What time will it be*

   (a) 2 hours 35 minutes after 10 : 35 a.m.?　　(b) 8 hours 50 minutes after 6 : 45 p.m.?

   (c) 5 hours 15 minutes after 2250 hours?　　(d) 1 hour 45 minutes before 3 : 10 p.m.?

   (e) 4 hours 25 minutes before 2 : 05 a.m.?　　(f) 7 hours 30 minutes before 1220 hours?

2. Complete the following table:

	12-hour clock	24-hour clock		12-hour clock	24-hour clock
(a)	6 : 22 p.m.	....	(b)	1 : 10 p.m.	....
(c)	....	0052 hours	(d)	....	2316 hours
(e)	7 : 05 a.m.	....	(f)	12 : 33 p.m.	....
(g)	....	2125 hours	(h)	....	1818 hours

3. A book fair began on 26th December. It lasted for 18 days. When will be the last day of the fair?

4. Ashish began studying at 5 : 20 p.m. He studied for 1 hour 50 minutes. At what time did he finish his studies ?

5. A train leaves the station at 10 : 30 a.m. and reaches its destination at 5 : 45 a.m. the next day. Find the duration of the journey.

6. *Solve :*

(a)
hr	min
4 2	2 4
− 2 4	4 2

(b)
hr	min	sec
2 0	4 3	5 0
+ 4	2 7	5 0

(c)
hr	min	sec
5	3 5	3 2
+ 7	4 8	5 5

(d)
hr	min	sec
8	1 8	2 0
− 4	2 0	3 6

7. *Add :*

(a) 7 years 8 months and 8 years 9 months (b) 24 days 19 hours and 26 days 18 hours

8. *Subtract :*

(a) 6 min 36 sec from 14 min 22 sec   (b) 12 days 16 hours from 22 days 8 hours
(c) 23 years 7 months from 50 years 3 months

9. *Fill in the placeholders:*

(a) 468 hours = ☐ days ☐ hours

(b) 101 days = ☐ weeks ☐ days

(c) 567 months = ☐ years ☐ months

(d) 735 minutes = ☐ hours ☐ minutes

(e) 867 seconds = ☐ minutes ☐ seconds

(f) 3 hours 35 minutes = ☐ minutes

(g) 9 minutes 29 seconds = ☐ seconds

(h) 6 hours 36 minutes = ☐ seconds

(i) 5 days 15 hours = ☐ hours

(j) 7 years 7 months = ☐ months

(k) 5 weeks 4 days = ☐ days

16 MONEY

INTRODUCTION

We know that 1 rupee is written as Re 1.

The plural of rupee is rupees.

$$Re\ 1 = 1\ rupee = 100\ paise$$

and $1\ paisa = Re\ \dfrac{1}{100} = Re\ 0.01$

Examples: We write:

(a) 18 rupees 45 paise as Rs 18.45

(b) 9 rupee 9 paise as Rs 9.09

(c) 1 rupee 5 paise as Rs 1.05

(d) 74 paise as Re 0.74

(e) 6 paise as Re 0.06

(f) 1 paisa as Re 0.01

CONVERSION OF RUPEES INTO PAISE

Rule: *In order to convert rupees into paise, we multiply by 100.*

Example 1. *Convert into paise:*

(a) Rs 53.65   (b) Rs 108.06   (c) Rs 4.80

(d) Re 0.83   (e) Re 0.08   (f) Rs $56\dfrac{1}{4}$

Solution: We have

(a) Rs 53.65 $= (53.65 \times 100)$ paise $= 5365$ paise.

(b) Rs 108.06 $= (108.06 \times 100)$ paise $= 10806$ paise.

(c) Rs 4.80 $= (4.80 \times 100)$ paise $= 480$ paise.

(d) Re 0.83 $= (0.83 \times 100)$ paise $= 83$ paise.

(e) Re 0.08 $= (0.08 \times 100)$ paise $= 8$ paise.

(f) Rs $56\dfrac{1}{4}$ $= Rs\ 56 + Re\ \dfrac{1}{4}$

$= (56 \times 100)\ paise + \left(\dfrac{1}{4} \times 100\right) paise$

$= 5600\ Paise + 25\ paise = 5625\ paise.$

CONVERSION OF PAISE INTO RUPEES

Rule: *In order to convert paise into rupees, we divide by 100.*

Example 2. *Convert into rupees:*

       (*a*) 3625 paise   (*b*) 850 paise   (*c*) 53 paise   (*d*) 4 paise

Solution: We have :

    (*a*) 3625 paise $= Rs \dfrac{3625}{100} = Rs\ 36.25.$

    (*b*) 850 paise $\ = Rs \dfrac{850}{100} = Rs\ 8.50.$

    (*c*) 53 paise $\ \ = Re \dfrac{53}{100} = Re\ 0.53.$

    (*d*) 4 paise $\ \ \ = Re \dfrac{4}{100} = Re\ 0.04.$

EXERCISE 66

1. *Convert into paise:*

    (*a*) Rs 8.56   (*b*) Rs 92.67   (*c*) Rs 123.05   (*d*) Rs 70.70

    (*e*) Re 0.84   (*f*) Re 0.03   (*g*) Re 0.10   (*h*) Re 0.09

2. *Convert into paise:*

    (*a*) 36 rupees 85 paise   (*b*) 6 rupees 6 paise   (*c*) Rs $37\dfrac{1}{2}$

    (*d*) Rs $19\dfrac{1}{4}$ (*d*) Rs $23\dfrac{3}{4}$

3. *Convert into rupees:*

    (*a*) 8365 paise   (*b*) 7000 paise   (*c*) 874 paise   (*d*) 708 paise

    (*e*) 104 paise   (*f*) 92 paise   (*g*) 16 paise   (*h*) 9 paise

    (*i*) 2 paise

ADDITION OF MONEY

Example 1. *Add Rs 29.75 and Rs 36.48.*

Solution :   Adding columnwise, we get:

$$
\begin{array}{r}
① ① ① \\
Rs\ 2\,9\ .7\ 5 \\
+\ Rs\ 3\,6\ .4\ 8 \\
\hline
Rs\ 6\,6\ .2\ 3 \\
\hline
\end{array}
$$

     $\therefore$ Rs 29.75 + Rs 36.48 = Rs 66.23 .

Example 2. *Add 56 rupees 87 paise and 78 rupees 59 paise.*

Solution :   We have

       56 rupees 87 paise = Rs 56.87

       78 rupees 59 paise = Rs 78. 59

$$
\begin{array}{r}
① ① ① \\
Rs\ 5\,6\ .8\ 7 \\
+\ Rs\ 7\,8\ .5\ 9 \\
\hline
Rs\ 1\,3\,5\ .4\ 6 \\
\hline
\end{array}
$$

Putting them in column form and adding columnwise, we get:

56 rupees 87 paise + 78 rupees 59 paise = 135 rupees 46 paise.

Examples 3.   Namita bought the following items from a stationery shop:

A pen for Rs 26.35; a note book for Rs 47.85; a pencil for Rs 6.20 and an eraser for Rs 4.05

Find the amount to be paid by her to the shopkeeper.

Solution: We have

		② ① ①
Cost of a pen	=	Rs 2 6 . 3 5
Cost of a note-book	=	Rs 4 7 . 8 5
Cost of a pencil	=	Rs 6 . 2 0
Cost of a eraser	=	+ Rs 4 . 0 5
Total amount	=	Rs 8 4 . 4 5

Hence, the total amount to be paid by Namita is Rs 84.45.

SUBTRACTION OF MONEY

Example 4.   *Subtract Rs 29.75 from Rs 43.20.*

Solution :   We have

$$
\begin{array}{r}
Rs\ 4\ 3\ .\ 2\ 0 \\
-\ Rs\ 2\ 9\ .\ 7\ 5 \\
\hline
Rs\ 1\ 3\ .\ 4\ 5
\end{array}
$$

∴ Rs 43.20 – Rs 29.75 = Rs 13.45.

Example 5.   *Subtract Rs 321.87 from Rs 601.05.*

Solution: We have

$$
\begin{array}{r}
Rs\ 6\ 0\ 1\ .\ 0\ 5 \\
-\ Rs\ 3\ 2\ 1\ .\ 8\ 7 \\
\hline
Rs\ 2\ 7\ 9\ .\ 1\ 8
\end{array}
$$

∴ Rs 601.05 – Rs 321.87 = Rs 279.18.

Example 6.   *Reenu bought a book for Rs 325.65 and gave a 500 rupee note to the shopkeeper. What amount did she get back?*

Solution:

Total amount paid	=	Rs 5 0 0 . 0 0
Cost of the book	=	– Rs 3 2 5 . 6 5
Balance	=	Rs 1 7 4 . 3 5

Hence, Reenu got back Rs 174.35.

EXERCISE 67

Add:

1. Rs 54.65 and Rs 27.85
2. Rs 73.84 and Rs 39.76
3. Rs 61.83, Rs 38.67 and Rs 8.95
4. Rs 107.40, Rs 245.80 and Rs 68.90
5. Rs 372.56, Rs 168.68 and Rs 37.86

Subtract:

6. Rs 97.68 from Rs 114.36
7. Rs 174.54 from Rs 200.60
8. Rs 29.87 from Rs 37.05
9. Rs 147.85 from Rs 203.00
10. Rohan bought a book for Rs 126.50, a note book for Rs 35.80, a geometry box for Rs 28.65 and a pencil sharpener for Rs 6.05. What is the total amount paid by Rohan?
11. Sajal bought oranges for Rs 132.80; apples for Rs 87.95 and guavas for Rs 73.40. What is the total amount paid by Sajal?
12. A shopkeeper purchased a bat for Rs 163.25 and sold it for Rs 205.00. How much money did he earn?
13. Manisha bought stationery worth of Rs 685.65 and gave a 1000 rupee note to the shopkeeper. How much money did she get back?

MULTIPLICATION OF MONEY

SOLVED EXAMPLES

Example 1. *Multiply Rs 48.53 by 8.*

Solution: We have

$$\begin{array}{r} \text{Rs } 4\,8\,.\,5\,3 \\ \times\ \ \ \ 8 \\ \hline \text{Rs } 3\,8\,8\,.\,2\,4 \end{array}$$

∴ Rs 48.53 × 8 = Rs 388.24.

Example 2. *If the cost of 1 metre of cloth is Rs 58.65, find the cost of 12 metres of cloth.*

Solution: Cost of 1 metre of cloth = Rs 58.65
Cost of 12 metres of cloth = Rs (58.65 × 12)

$$\begin{array}{r} \text{Rs } 5\,8\,.\,6\,5 \\ \times\,1\,2 \\ \hline \text{Rs } 7\,0\,3\,.\,8\,0 \end{array}$$

Hence, the cost of 12 metres of cloth is Rs 703.80.

Example 3. *If a worker is paid Rs 367.50 per day, how much will he earn in a week?*

Solution: Worker's earning in 1 day = Rs 367.50
Worker's earning in 7 days = Rs (367.50 × 7)

$$\begin{array}{r} \text{Rs } 3\,6\,7\,.\,5\,0 \\ \times\ \ \ \ 7 \\ \hline \text{Rs } 2\,5\,7\,2\,.\,5\,0 \end{array}$$

Hence the worker will earn Rs 2572.50 in a week.

SOLVED EXAMPLES

Example 4. *Divide Rs 266.85 by 9.*

Solution: We have

```
      2 6 6.8 5 ( 2 9.6 5
9 )
      1 8
      ─────
        8 6
        8 1
      ─────
          5 8
          5 4
        ─────
            4 5
            4 5
          ─────
              0
```

∴   Rs 266.85 ÷ 9 = Rs 29.65.

Example 5. *The cost of 9 school bags is Rs 2949.75. Find the cost of each bag.*

Solution: Cost of 9 bags = Rs 2949.75

Cost of 1 bag   = Rs 2949.75 ÷ 9

```
      2 9 4 9.7 5 ( 3 2 7.7 5
9 )
      2 7
      ─────
        2 4
        1 8
      ─────
          6 9
          6 3
        ─────
            6 7
            6 3
          ─────
              4 5
              4 5
            ─────
                0
```

Hence, the cost of each bag is Rs 327.75.

Example 6. *The cost of 16 kg of potatoes is Rs 205.60. Find the cost of potatoes per kg.*

Solution : Cost of 16 kg of potatoes = Rs 205.60

Cost of 1 kg of potatoes = Rs 205.60 ÷ 16

```
16 ) 2 0 5.6 0 ( 1 2 .8 5
      1 6
      ‾‾‾
      4 5
      3 2
      ‾‾‾
      1 3 6
      1 2 8
      ‾‾‾‾‾
          8 0
          8 0
          ‾‾‾
            0
```

Hence, the cost of potatoes per kg = Rs 12.85.

EXERCISE 68

Multiply:

1. Rs 14.45 by 8
2. Rs 86.38 by 15
3. Rs 137.96 by 12
4. Rs 305.05 by 16
5. Rs 268.54 by 18
6. Rs 410.37 by 20

Divide:

7. Rs 63.50 by 5
8. Rs 283.25 by 11
9. Rs 658.70 by 14
10. Rs 260.00 by 16

11. If the cost of each packet of biscuits is Rs 23.85, find the cost of 16 such packets.

12. The cost of 1 chair is Rs 247.60. Find the cost of 15 such chairs.

13. The cost of 1 kg of sugar is Rs 35.80. Find the cost of 18 kg of sugar.

14. The cost of 14 kg of tomatoes is Rs 231.00. Find the cost of 1 kg of tomatoes.

15. The cost of 17 jam bottles is Rs 901.85. Find the cost of each jam bottle.

16. The cost of 16 kg rice is Rs 616.00. Find the cost of rice per kg.

THINGS TO REMEMBER

1. Re 1 = 1 rupee = 100 paise

   1 paisa = Re $\frac{1}{100}$ = Re 0.01.

BASIC GEOMETRICAL CONCEPTS

PLANE

We come across a lot of flat surfaces in our everyday life. The top of a table, the surface of a wall, the surface of a paper, the face of a blackboard are all flat surfaces.

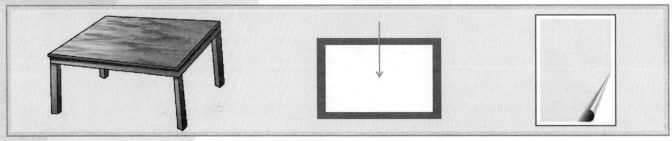

In mathematics, *a smooth flat surface which extends endlessly in all the directions is called a* **plane.**

A plane has no boundary.

We draw figures such as triangle, rectangle, circle etc. in a plane.

We call them as **plane figures.**

POINT

A **point** *is a mark of position.*

Usually, a fine dot marked with a sharp-edged pencil, represents a point.

In the given figure, A is a point.

A point has no length, breadth or thickness.

$\dot{A}$

LINE SEGMENT

Let A and B be two points on the plane of a paper. *The straight path from A to B is called the* **line segment AB.** This is denoted by $\overline{AB}$. We may also call it line segment $\overline{BA}$, denoted by $\overline{BA}$.

A •————— Line segment —————• B

The points A and B are called the **end points of $\overline{AB}$.**

The distance between the points A and B is called the **length of $\overline{AB}$.**

Thus, a line segment has a definite length, which can be measured.

The edges of a table, the edges of a ruler etc. are examples of line segments.

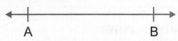

LINE

*A line segment extended endlessly on both sides is called a **line**.*

Thus, a line segment AB extended on both sides and marked by arrow marks at the two ends represents a line, denoted by $\overleftrightarrow{AB}$ or $\overleftrightarrow{BA}$.

A ←——|————————————|——→ B
　　　A　　　　　　　　　B

Arrows in opposite directions indicate that the line is endless.

Sometimes a line is represented by a small letter *l, m, n* etc.

In the adjoining figure, *l* is a line.

←————————————————→ *l*

A line has no end points.

A line does not have a definite length.

Since the line is endless, it cannot be drawn on a paper. We can simply represent a line, as done above.

An infinite number of lines can be drawn through a given point.

However, only one line can be drawn through two given points A and B i.e. line $\overleftrightarrow{AB}$.

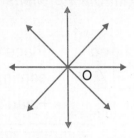

←——|————————————|——→
　　A　　　　　　　　　B

RAY

Have you ever observed a narrow beam of light emerging from a torch or the light rays from the sun? These light beams emerge from the light source and go on endlessly in one direction. This is the basic concept of a ray.

*A line segment extended endlessly in one direction, is called a **ray**.*

Thus, a line segment AB extended in the direction from A to B and marked by an arrow mark at B, represents a ray AB, denoted by $\overrightarrow{AB}$.

•——————|————→
A　　　　　B

Clearly, a ray $\overrightarrow{AB}$ has one end point, namely A. This end point A of ray $\overrightarrow{AB}$ called its **initial point**.

Since a ray is endless in one direction, it cannot be drawn on a paper.

We can simply represent a ray, as done above.

Clearly, a ray has no definite length.

$\overrightarrow{AB}$ is a ray with initial point A and extending endlessly in the direction from A to B represented by

•——————|————→
A　　　　B

$\overrightarrow{BA}$ is a ray with initial point B and extending endlessly in the direction from B to A, represented by

B •―――――|――――→ A

Clearly, ray $\overrightarrow{AB}$ and ray $\overrightarrow{BA}$ are two different rays.

Measuring Line Segments

To measure a line segment we need a **ruler**.

One edge of a ruler is marked in centimetres (cm).

Each centimetre is divided into 10 equal small divisions.

Each small division is called a millimetre (mm).

Example 1. *Measure the length of a given line segment $\overline{AB}$.*

A――――――――――――――― B

Method : Place the edge of the ruler along line segment AB, keeping the zero centimetre mark of the ruler at the point A.

Read the mark on the ruler at the point B.

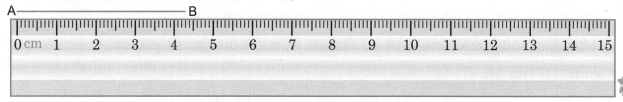

We observe that the end point B is 3 small divisions ahead of 4 cm mark.

So, the length of $\overline{AB}$ is 4 cm 3 mm or 4.3 cm.

To Draw a Line Segment of a Given Length

Example 2. *Draw a line segment of length 9 cm.*

Method : Place the ruler on the plane of the paper and hold it firmly.

Mark a point with a fine pencil against the zero centimetre mark of the ruler. Name it point A.

By sliding the pencil gently along the edge of the ruler draw a line segment upto the 9 cm mark on the ruler. Name the point against 9 cm mark as B.

A――――――――――――――――――――――――――――――― B

Then, $\overline{AB}$ = 9 cm.

Distinction Between a Line Segment, a Line and a Ray:

A Line Segment	A Line	A Ray
1. A line segment has two end points.	1. A line has no end points.	1. A ray has only end point.
2. A line segment has a definite length.	2. A line does not have a definite length.	2. A ray does not have a definite length.
3. A line segment can be drawn on a paper.	3. A line cannot be drawn on a paper. We can simply represent a line by a diagram.	3. A ray cannot be drawn on a paper. We can simply represent a ray by a diagram.
4. A ———— B is a line segment AB.	4. Line $\overleftrightarrow{AB}$ is represented by A B	4. Ray $\overrightarrow{AB}$ is represented by A B

EXERCISE 69

1. Which of the following has two end points ?

   (*a*) a line   (*b*) a ray   (*c*) a line segment   (*d*) a plane

2. Which of the following has no end point ?

   (*a*) a line segment   (*b*) a ray   (*c*) a line   (*d*) a plane

3. Which of the following has no end points ?

   (*a*) a line   (*b*) a ray   (*c*) a line segment   (*d*) a plane

4. Which of the following has a definite length ?

   (*a*) a line   (*b*) a line segment   (*c*) a ray   (*d*) a plane

5. Which of the following can be drawn on a piece of paper ?

   (*a*) a line   (*b*) a line segment   (*c*) a ray   (*d*) a plane

6. *Draw a line segment of length:*

   (*a*) 5 cm   (*b*) 6.3 cm   (*c*) 7.5 cm

7. *Match the entries in Column I and Column II :*

Column I	Column II
1. A ray has	(A) a definite length
2. A line has	(B) no definite length
3. A line cannot	(C) only one end point
4. A line segment has	(D) two end points
5. A line segment has	(E) represents the part of a plane
6. The face of the blackboard	(F) be drawn on a paper

8. *Fill in the blanks :*

(*a*) A ray has ....end point.

(*b*) A line has .... end points.

(*c*) A line .... be drawn on a paper.

(*d*) A ray has no .... length.

(*e*) A line segment has a .... length.

9. *Identify and name the line segments and rays in the following figures :*

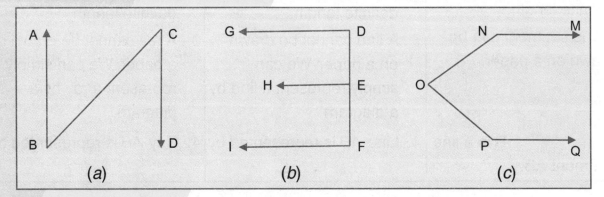

(*a*) (*b*) (*c*)

10. *Mark suitable points and draw a diagram of each of the following :*

(*a*) A ray QP

(*b*) A line XY

(*c*) A line segment CD

(*d*) A ray MN

THINGS TO REMEMBER

1. A smooth flat surface which extends endlessly in all the directions, is called a plane.

2. A point is an exact location.

3. Let A and B be two given points. Then, the straight path between A and B is called the line segment $\overline{AB}$.

4. $\overline{AB}$ extended endlessly in both the directions is called a line $\overleftrightarrow{AB}$.

5. $\overline{AB}$ extended endlessly in the direction from A to B is called a ray $\overrightarrow{AB}$.

6. (*a*) A line segment has two end points.   (*b*) A ray has one end point.

   (*c*) A line has no end point.

7. (*a*) A line segment has a definite length.

   (*b*) A line as well as a ray has no definite length.

18 CONCEPT OF ANGLES

Observe the hands of a clock. The two hands are at different positions at different points of time, as they move along the dial constantly. The two hands represent two rays meeting at a point. The concept of angle came into existence with the need to measure the amount of rotation of the rays.

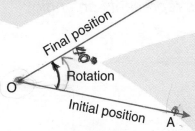

Suppose that a ray $\overrightarrow{OA}$ starts rotating about its end point O. Then, its initial position is OA. It keeps rotating about O, till it reaches the final position OB. Then, the two positions OA and OB form an angle, denoted by ∠AOB, where the symbol ∠ stands for angle.

Geometrically, we define an angle as given below.

ANGLE : *Two rays having a common end point form an* **angle.**

The two rays forming an angle are called the **arms** of the angle.

The common end point is called the **vertex** of the angle.

To name an angle, we name any point on one ray, then the vertex and then any point on the other ray.

In the above figure, the rays $\overrightarrow{OA}$ and $\overrightarrow{OB}$ form an angle at O, to be denoted by ∠AOB or ∠BOA.

$\overrightarrow{OA}$ and $\overrightarrow{OB}$ are the **arms** and O is the **vertex** of this angle.

Sometimes, we name this angle by vertex as ∠O.

Sometimes an angle is named by some natural number such as ∠1 etc. or a small letter such as ∠a etc.

Interior and Exterior of an Angle :

Consider an angle ∠CAB.
Let us take a point P on ray $\overrightarrow{AB}$ and a point Q on ray $\overrightarrow{AC}$.
We say that the points P and Q lie on ∠CAB.
Mark a point R inside ∠CAB and a point S
outside ∠CAB. We say that R lies in the interior
of ∠CAB and S lies in the exterior of ∠CAB.
The shaded region is the interior of ∠CAB.

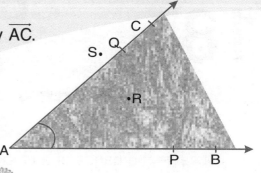

EXERCISE 70

1. Which of the following figures represents an angle?

(a)   (b)   (c)   (d)

2. Name the angles in each of the following figures. Also, name the vertex and the arms in each case:

(a)

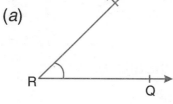

(b)

 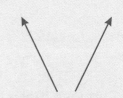

(c)

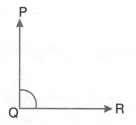

(d)

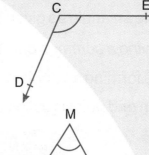 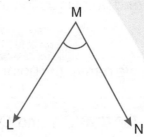

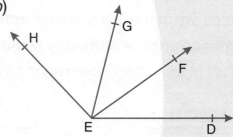

3. How many angles are formed in each of the following figures? Name them.

(a)

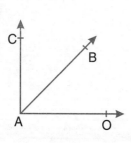

(b)

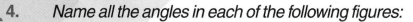

4. Name all the angles in each of the following figures:

(*a*)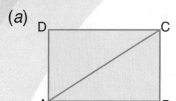

(*b*)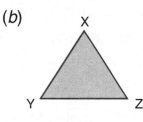

(*c*)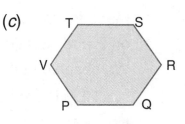

5. In the adjoining figure, name the points:

(*a*) on the angle ;

(*b*) in the interior of the angle;

(*c*) in the exterior of the angle.

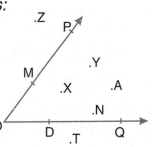

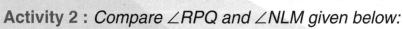

COMPARISON OF ANGLES

The size of an angle is measured by how much the arms are opened out and not by how long the arms appear to be.

Activity 1 : *Compare ∠CAB and ∠ FDE given below:*

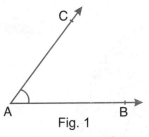

Fig. 1

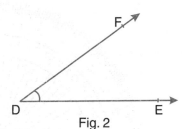

Fig. 2

Method : Trace ∠FDE on a paper.

Place the tracing of ∠FDE on ∠CAB such that D falls on A and $\overrightarrow{DE}$ falls along $\overrightarrow{AB}$. (see figure 3)

We observe that F lies in the interior of ∠CAB.

∴ ∠FDE is smaller than ∠CAB.

Fig. 3

Activity 2 : *Compare ∠RPQ and ∠NLM given below:*

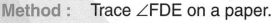

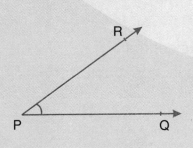

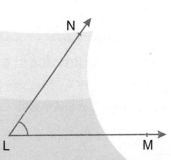

Method :   Trace ∠NLM on a paper.

Place the tracing of ∠NLM on ∠RPQ such that L falls on P and $\overrightarrow{LM}$ falls on $\overrightarrow{PQ}$. (see adjoining figure)

We observe that N lies in the exterior of ∠RPQ.

∴ ∠NLM is greater than ∠RPQ.

However, this method of tracing angles to compare them, is practically difficult. To overcome this difficulty, we need to measure am angle exactly

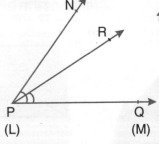

MEASURING ANGLES

We measure angles in *degrees*.

A complete turn around a point is divided into 360 equal parts.

Each of these parts is called a degree, to be denoted by 1°.

Thus, a complete turn around a point is equal to 360°.

PROTRACTOR

An instrument called *protractor* is used to measure an angle.

You can find it in your geometry box.

The diagram of a protractor is shown below.

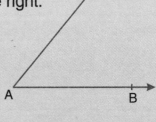

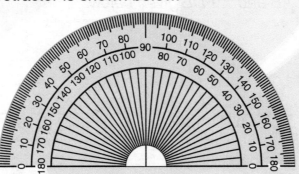

It is in the shape of a semi-circle.

The mid-point of its horizontal edge is called its central point.

The angle at the centre is divided into 180 equal small divisions, each measuring 1°.

A protractor has two scales – inner and outer.

One scale begins with 0° on the right and runs to 180° on the left.

The other scale begins with 0° on the left and runs to 180° on the right.

Example 1. *Find the measure of ∠CAB shown here:*

Method   : Place the protractor in such a way that its central point lies on A, the vertex of ∠CAB and its horizontal edge lies on arm AB.

Now, note the mark on the rim of the protractor through which arm AC passes. Taking the scale whose 0° mark lies on AB, we find that AC passes through 50° mark.

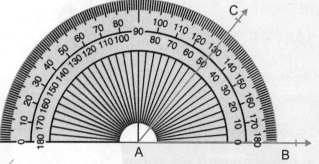

∴ The measure of ∠CAB is 50° and we write, m ∠CAB = 50°.

We may also write : ∠CAB = 50°.

Example 2. *Find the measure of ∠LMN given below:*

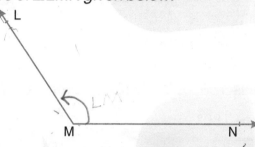

Method : Place the protractor in such a way that its central point lies on M, the vertex of ∠LMN and its horizontal edge along the arm MN.

Now, note the mark on the rim of the protractor, through which arm ML passes.

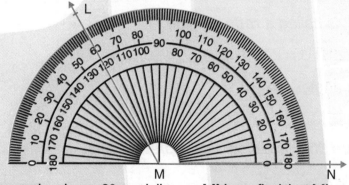

Taking the scale whose 0° mark lies on MN, we find that ML passes through 120° mark.

∴ ∠LMN = 120°.

CLASSIFICATION OF ANGLES

I. ACUTE ANGLE

An angle whose measure is more than 0°
*and less than 90°, is called an **acute angle**.*

In the given figure, ∠ABC = 50°< 90°.

∴ ∠ABC is an acute angle.

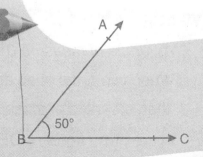

II. RIGHT ANGLE

An angle whose measure is more 90°,

is called a **right angle**.

In the given figure, ∠LMN = 90°.

∴ ∠LMN is a right angle.

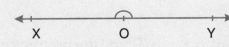

III. OBTUSE ANGLE

An angle whose measure is more than 90°.

and less than 180°, is called an **obtuse angle.**

In the given figure, ∠PQR = 120°.

Clearly, it is more than 90° but less than 180°.

∴ ∠PQR is an obtuse angle.

IV. STRAIGHT ANGLE:

An angle whose measure is 180° is called a **straight angle.**

In the given figure, ∠XOY = 180°.

∴ ∠XOY is a straight angle.

V. REFLEX ANGLE:

An angle whose measure is more than 180°

and less than 360°, is called a **reflex angle.**

In the given figure, ∠STU = 240°.

∴ ∠STU is a reflex angle.

VI. COMPLETE ANGLE

An angle of measure 360° is called a **complete angle.**

In the given figure, ∠XYZ = 360°.

∴ ∠XYZ is a complete angle.

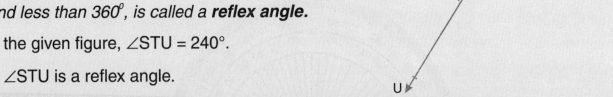

VII. ZERO ANGLE

An angle of measure 0° is called a **zero angle.**

When two arms of an angle overlap each other,

then an angle of measure 0° is formed.

In the given figure, ∠DEF = 0°.

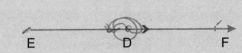

COMPLEMENTARY ANGLES

Two angles are said to be **complementary**, *if the sum of their measures is 90°.*

And, each one of these angles is called the **complement** of the other.

Consider the angles ∠ABC and ∠DEF given below:

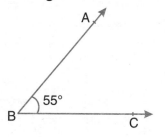
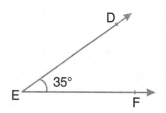

Here, ∠ABC = 55° and ∠DEF= 35°.

∴ ∠ABC + ∠DEF = (55° + 35°) = 90°.

Thus, ∠ABC and ∠DEF are complementary angles. In other words, we can say that:

∠ABC and ∠DEF are complements of each other.

Example 3. *Find the complement of an angle of 36°.*

Solution : Complement of 36° = (90° − 36°) = 54°.

Hence, the complement of 36° is 54°.

SUPPLEMENTARY ANGLES

Two angles are said to be **supplementary,** *if the sum of their measures is 180°.*

And, each one of these angles is called the **supplement** of the other.

Consider the angles ∠PQR and ∠XYZ given below.

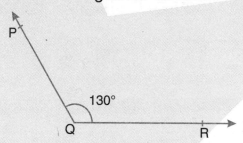
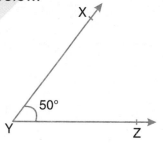

Here, ∠PQR = 130° and ∠XYZ = 50°.

∴ ∠PQR + ∠XYZ = (130°+ 50°) = 180°.

Thus, ∠PQR and ∠XYZ are supplementary angles. In other words, we can say that :

∠PQR and ∠XYZ are supplement of each other.

Example 4. *Find the supplement of an angle of 62°.*

Solution : Supplement of 62° = (180° − 62°) = 118°.

Hence, the supplement of 62° is 118°.

EXERCISE 71

1. Measure the following angles using a protractor and fill in the blanks :

(a)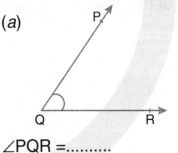

∠PQR =..........

(b)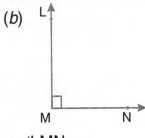

∠LMN =..........

(c)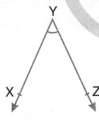

∠XYZ =..........

(d)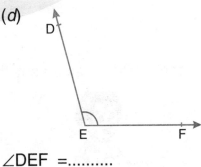

∠DEF =..........

(e)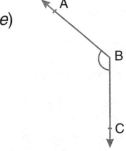

∠ABC =..........

(f)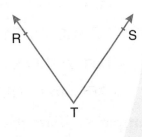

∠RTS =..........

2. Measure each of the following angles and mention whether it is acute, obtuse or right angle:

(a)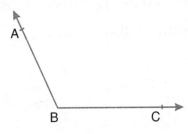

(b)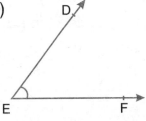

(c)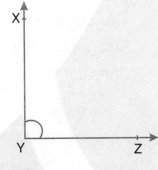

(d)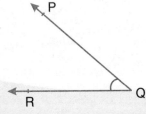

(e)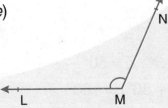

(f)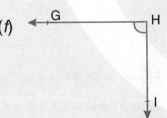

3. Classify each of the following angles as acute, obtuse or right angle :

(a) 46°   (b) 90°   (c) 102°   (d) 88°

(e) 128°   (f) 92°   (g) 176°   (h) 10°

4. Which of the following pairs of angles are complementary?

   (a) 50°, 130°   (b) 42°, 48°   (c) 36°, 64°   (d) 20°, 70°

   (e) 65°, 35°   (f) 115°, 65°   (g) 10°, 80°   (h) 0°, 90°

5. Which of the following pairs of angles are supplementary?

   (a) 54°, 36°   (b) 72°, 108°   (c) 130°, 70°   (d) 15°, 75°

   (e) 80°, 100°   (f) 20°, 70°   (g) 40°, 140°   (h) 0°, 180°

6. Write the complement of each of the following angles:

   (a) 43°   (b) 56°   (c) 72°   (d) 19°

   (e) 27°   (f) 80°   (g) 45°   (h) 85°

7. Write the supplement of each of the following angles:

   (a) 30°   (b) 47°   (c) 70°   (d) 15°

   (e) 90°   (f) 103°   (g) 84°   (h) 137°

8. Fill in the blanks :

   (a) When two rays form an angle, their common end point is called the .... of the angle.

   (b) Angles are measured in ....

   (c) Angles are measured with the help of a ....

   (d) The measure of a right angle is ....

   (e) The measure of a .... angle is 180°.

DRAWING ANGLES USING A PROTRACTOR

Example : *Draw an angle of 75° using ruler and protractor .*

Method :

Step 1. Draw a ray $\overrightarrow{AB}$.

Step 2. Place the protractor in such a way that its central point lies on A and its horizontal edge lies along AB.

Step 3. Run your eyes along the scale whose 0° mark lies on AB until you find the 75° mark on the rim.

Step 4. On that mark put a dot with a fine pencil and name it C.

Step 5. Remove the protractor and draw ray $\overrightarrow{AC}$.

Then, ∠CAB is the required angle such that ∠CAB = 75°.

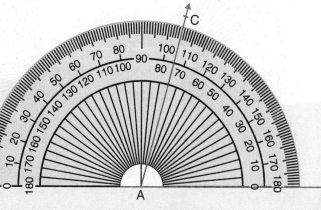

REMARK: Sometimes a ray is given and we have to construct an angle of a given measure on it. The ray may be given in any of the positions given below:

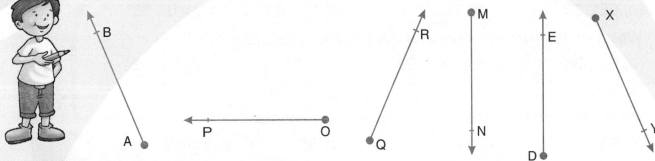

For this, always remember two things :

(*a*) Place the protractor with its central point on the initial point of the ray.

(*b*) Always start reading from the 0 mark on the protractor on the side towards which the arrow mark of the ray points.

Thus, in the above positions, the protractor shall be placed and readings taken in the direction as shown.

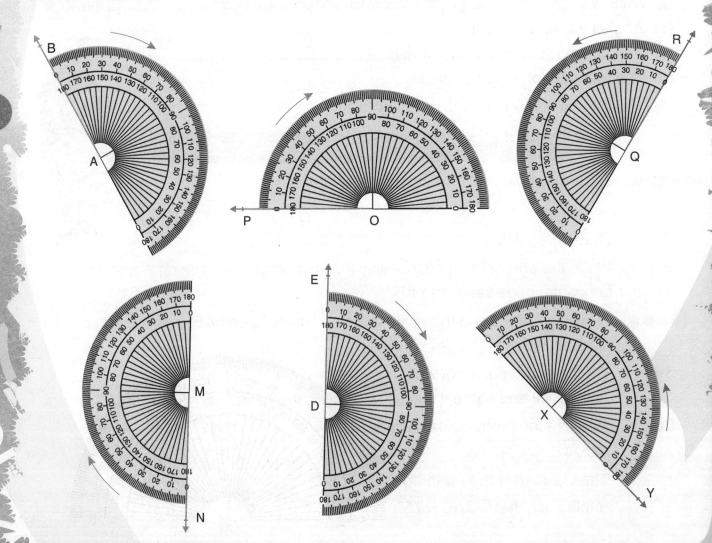

1. *Use protractor and scale to construct the following angles :*
   - (*a*) 80°
   - (*b*) 65°
   - (*c*) 45°
   - (*d*) 90°
   - (*e*) 130°
   - (*f*) 145°
   - (*g*) 125°
   - (*h*) 180°

2. A ray OP is given below. Copy it on your notebook and construct an ∠POQ of measure 150°.

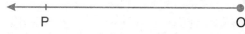

   P   O

3. A ray AB is given below. Copy it on your notebook and construct an ∠CAB of measure 65°.

   B

   A

THINGS TO REMEMBER

1. Two rays having a common end point form an angle. The two rays forming an angle are called the arms of the angle.

   The common end point of the two rays forming an angle is called the vertex of the angle. We denote an angle by ∠.

2. We measure angles in degrees, using a protractor.

3. A complete turn around a point is equal to 360°.

4. (*a*) An angle whose measure is greater than 0° and less than 90°, is called an **acute angle.**

   (*b*) An angle whose measure is 90°, is called a **right angle.**

   (*c*) An angle whose measure is greater than 90° and less than 180°, is called an **obtuse angle.**

   (*d*) An angle whose measure is 180°, is called a **straight angle.**

5. (*a*) Two angles, the sum of whose measures is 90°, are called **complementary angles.**

   (*b*) Two angles, the sum of whose measures is 180°, are called **supplementary angles.**

QUESTION BAG - 1

(OBJECTIVE - TYPE QUESTIONS)

Tick (✓) the correct answer:

1. How many different angles can you count in the given figure?
   (*a*) 3   (*b*) 4
   (*c*) 5   (*d*) 6

2. Which of the following contains the types of angles in correct ascending order of their measures?
   (*a*) Acute, Obtuse, Right, Straight, Reflex
   (*b*) Acute, Right, Obtuse, Reflex, Straight
   (*c*) Acute, Right, Obtuse, Straight, Reflex
   (*d*) Acute, Obtuse, Straight, Right, Reflex

3. The rays forming ∠ABC are
   (*a*) $\overrightarrow{AB}$ and $\overrightarrow{BC}$ (*b*) $\overrightarrow{AB}$ and $\overrightarrow{CB}$ (*c*) $\overrightarrow{BA}$ and $\overrightarrow{BC}$ (*d*) $\overrightarrow{BA}$ and $\overrightarrow{CB}$

4. How many degrees does the minute hand of a clock turn through in one hour?
   (*a*) 90°   (*b*) 180°   (*c*) 270°   (*d*) 360°

5. The complement of an angle of 65° is
   (*a*) 15°   (*b*) 25°   (*c*) 30°   (*d*) 35°

6. The supplement of an angle of 85° is
   (*a*) 80°   (*b*) 90°   (*c*) 95°   (*d*) 105°

7. By what angle does a soldier turn when he takes an "about turn"?
   (a) 90°   (b) 180°   (c) 360°   (d) None of these

8. If two complementary angles are equal what is the size of each?
   (*a*) 30°   (*b*) 45°   (*c*) 60°   (*d*) 90°

9. If two supplementary angles are equal what is the size of each?
   (*a*) 60°   (*b*) 80°   (*c*) 90°   (*d*) 120°

10. Through what angle must the aerial turn to be vertical?
    (*a*) 44°   (*b*) 48°   (*c*) 54°   (*d*) 60°

11. Which type of angle has a measure that is smaller than a right angle?
    (*a*) Acute   (*b*) Obtuse   (*c*) Straight   (*c*) Reflex

12. Each of the following is smaller than a straight angle, except
    (*a*) Acute angle   (*b*) Obtuse angle   (*c*) Reflex angle   (*d*) Right angle

13. Which type of angle best describes angle Q?

    (a) Acute   (b) Right

    (c) Obtuse   (d) None of these

14. If $\angle 1$ measures $125°$, then $\angle 2$ measures

    (a) $45°$ (b) $55°$

    (c) $65°$ (d) $75°$

QUESTION BAG - 2

1. *Fill in the blanks:*

    (a) Two rays with a .... end point form an angle.

    (b) While naming an angle, the middle letter is always its ....

    (c) The unit for measuring an angle is ....

    (d) A straight angle is equal to .... right angles.

    (e) The measure of .... angle is less than $90°$.

    (f) Angle of measure $270°$ is called a ....angle.

    (g) An angle of measure $360°$ is called a .... angle.

    (h) A reflex angle is always greater than $180°$ but less than ....

2. *State whether each of the following statements is true or false:*

    (a) A straight angle is equal to $180°$.   ....

    (b) An obtuse angle is greater than $180°$.   ....

    (c) A reflex angle is always greater than a straight angle.   ....

    (d) Reflex angle of $90°$ is $180°$.   ....

    (e) The inner and outer scales of a protractor read the same measurement at $90°$.   ....

    (f) The measures on the outer scale of the protractor increase from left to right.   ....

3. *Answer the following questions:*   ....

    (a) Can two acute angles be put together to make a straight angle?   ....

    (b) Can three acute angles be put together to make a reflex angle?   ....

    (c) Can an obtuse angle and a reflex angle together make a complete angle?   ....

4. *List the following angles in increasing order of their sizes:*

5. *Look at the given figure and then complete the table given below it:*

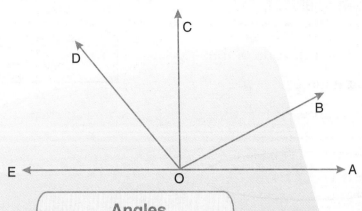

Angles	Types of Angles
(a) ∠AOB	
(b) ∠AOC	
(c) ∠DOE	
(d) ∠AOE	
(e) ∠AOD	
(f) Pair of angles ∠AOB and ∠BOC	
(g) Pair of angles ∠AOB and ∠BOE	

6. In the above figure which angle is the complement of ∠DOE?

7. In the above figure which angle is the supplement of ∠AOD?

8. *Calculate the reflex angle of the given angles:*

    (a) 75°   (b) 160°   (c) 35°   (d) 90°   (e) 145°

9. *Fill in the blanks:*

    (a) The complement of an angle of 50° is ....

    (b) The complement of an angle of 75° is ....

    (c) The supplement of an angle of 135° is ....

    (d) The supplement of an angle of 65° is ....

PARALLEL AND PERPENDICULAR LINES

INTERSECTING LINES

Look at the lines AB and CD shown herewith.

If we extend them on both sides, we find that they meet at a point O.

We say that the lines AB and CD intersect at the point O.

Thus, $\overleftrightarrow{AB}$ and $\overleftrightarrow{CD}$ are the intersecting lines.

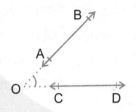

PARALLEL LINES

Consider the two lines $\overleftrightarrow{EF}$ and $\overleftrightarrow{GH}$, shown below.

If we extend these lines on both sides, we find that they do not intersect, even when we extend them to any extent.

Such lines are called parallel lines.

The distance between such lines always remains the same.

Thus, we define parallel lines as under:

*The lines which lie in the same plane and do not intersect, are known as **parallel lines.***

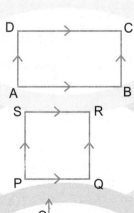

If $\overleftrightarrow{AB}$ is parallel to $\overleftrightarrow{CD}$, we write, $\overleftrightarrow{AB} \parallel \overleftrightarrow{CD}$.

The opposite edges of a ruler; the opposite edges of a table;

the opposite edges of a book; the opposite edges of a black board are all examples of parallel lines.

The opposite sides of a rectangle are parallel.

In given rectangle ABCD, we have:

$\overleftrightarrow{AB} \parallel \overleftrightarrow{DC}$ and $\overleftrightarrow{AD} \parallel \overleftrightarrow{BC}$.

The opposite sides of a square are parallel.

In given square PQRS, we have

$\overleftrightarrow{PQ} \parallel \overleftrightarrow{SR}$ and $\overleftrightarrow{PS} \parallel \overleftrightarrow{QR}$.

PERPENDICULAR LINES

*When two lines intersect and make an angle of 90°, we say that the given lines are **perpendicular** to each other.*

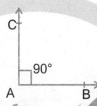

In the given figure, $\overleftrightarrow{AC}$ is perpendicular to $\overleftrightarrow{AB}$ and we write, $\overleftrightarrow{AC} \perp \overleftrightarrow{AB}$.

Examples :   (i)   The adjacent edges of a table top are perpendicular to each other.

                 (ii)   The adjacent edges of a book are perpendicular to each other.

SET SQUARES

Two triangular objects (shown in figure given below) contained in your geometry box are called **Set Squares.**

The angles of one of the set squares are 90°, 30° and 60°.

The angles of another set square are 90°, 45° and 45°.

We shall now discuss the use of set squares to draw a line parallel or perpendicular to a given line.

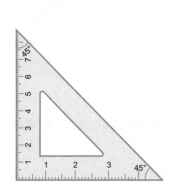

To Draw a Line Parallel To a Given Line and Passing Through a Given Point

Example 1 .   *Let AB be a given line and P be a point outside it.*

•P

$\xleftrightarrow{\hspace{1cm} A \hspace{3cm} B \hspace{1cm}}$

Draw a line parallel to $\overleftrightarrow{AB}$ and passing through P using a ruler and a set square.

Method :

Step 1:   Take a set square and place its one perpendicular edge along AB as shown in figure 1.

Step 2:   Place a ruler along the non-perpendicular edge of the set square as shown in figure 1.

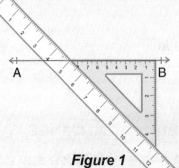

Figure 1

Step 3 : Now hold the ruler firmly and slide the set square upwards along the ruler till its edge previously falling along AB, now touches the point P.

Step 4 : Draw a line CD along this edge of the set square, passing through the point P as shown in figure 2.

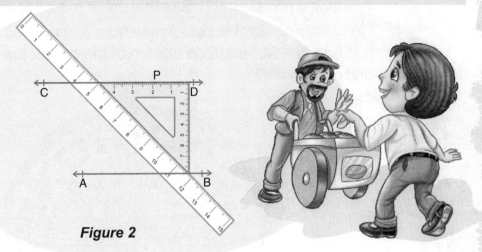

Figure 2

Thus, CD is a line passing through the point P and is parallel to AB.

To Draw a Line Perpendicular to a Given Line

Example 2 . *Let AB be a given line and L be a point on it.*

Draw a line perpendicular to AB at L using a set square.

Method : Place a set square such that one of its edges forming a right angle falls along the line AB and the vertex at which the right angle is formed falls on L. Fix the set square firmly and draw a ray LM along the edge of the set square perpendicular to that lying along AB.

Now remove the set square.

Then, LM is the required line perpendicular to AB at L.

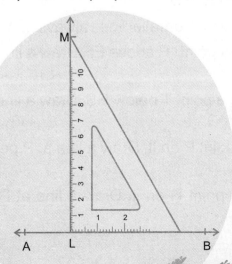

Example 3 . *Let XY be a given line and P be a point on it.*

X   P   Y

Draw a line perpendicular to XY at P using protractor.

Method : Place a protractor in such a way that its horizontal edge lies along line XY and the central point lies at P. See that the 0° mark lies on XY.

Read the protractor anticlockwise from 0° mark and mark point Q with the pencil just near the 90° mark on the rim of the protractor. Now remove the protractor and draw ray $\overrightarrow{PQ}$.

Then, PQ ⊥ XY.

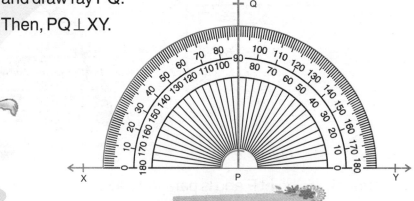

EXERCISE 73

1. The adjoining figure shows a cuboid.

   (*a*) How many sets of parallel line segments can you find? Name them.

   (*b*) How many sets of perpendicular line segments can you find?

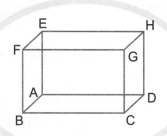

2. *Fill in the blanks :*

   (*a*) Two parallel lines do not .... when produced.

   (*b*) When two lines intersect and make a .... they are said to be perpendicular to each other.

   (*c*) The distance between two parallel lines always ....

3. Draw a line EF and take a point P above EF. Draw a line GH passing through P such that GH ∥ EF.

4. Draw a line RS and take a point T below RS. Draw a line PQ passing through T such that PQ ∥ RS.

5. Draw a line AB. Mark a point P on it. Draw a line at P perpendicular to AB, using set-squares.

6. Draw a line PQ. Mark a point R on it. Draw a line at R perpendicular to PQ, using protractor.

7. Draw a line segment CD = 5 cm. Mark a point E on CD such that CE = 2 cm. At E draw EF ⊥ CD by using protractor.

8. Draw a line segment LM = 5.4 cm. Mark a point N on LM such that LN = 2.3 cm. At N draw NP ⊥ LM draw by using set-squares.

THINGS TO REMEMBER

1. Two lines in a plane which meet in a point are called intersecting lines.

2. The lines which lie in the same plane and do not intersect are known as parallel lines.

3. The distance between two parallel lines always remains the same.

4. Two lines in a plane are either parallel or they intersect each other.

5. When two lines intersect and make an angle of 90°, they are said to be perpendicular to each other.

ACTIVITY TIME

Activity 1.

I. To make a perpendicular line from a point on the given line, by paper folding.

Step 1. Take a sheet of plain paper. Measure and draw a line segment AB of length 5 cm.

Step 2. Mark any point P on the line segment AB.

Step 3. Fold the paper along a line passing through the point P such that the part of the line segment AB that lies on one side of the line of fold falls on the other part. Make a crease and unfold the paper.

Step 4. Draw a line XY along the crease as shown in fig. 1. Then, line XY is perpendicular to the given line segment at the given point P.

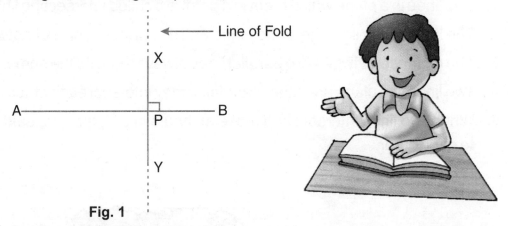

Fig. 1

II. To make a line intersecting a given line at a given point, by paper folding.

Step 1. Take a sheet of plain paper. Measure and draw a line segment AB of length 5 cm.

Step 2. Mark any point P on this line segment.

Step 3. Fold the paper along a line passing through the point P. Make a crease and unfold the paper.

Step 4. Draw a line XY along the crease as shown in fig. 2.
Then, line XY is a line intersecting the given line at a given point P.

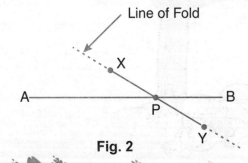

Fig. 2

III.   To make a line parallel to the given line by paper folding.

Step 1.   Take a sheet of plain paper. Measure and draw a line segment AB of length 5 cm.

Step 2.   Mark any point P on this line segment.

Step 3.   Fold the paper along a line passing through the point P such that the part of the line AB that lies on one side of the line of fold falls over the other part. Make a crease and unfold the paper.

Step 4.   Draw a line XY along the crease as shown in fig. 3.

Step 5.   Mark a point Q on the line XY.

Step 6.   Fold the paper along a line passing through the point Q such that the part of the line XY that lies on one side of the line of fold falls over the other part. Make a crease and unfold the paper.

Step 7.   Draw a line CD along the crease as shown in fig. 3.
Then, line CD is a line parallel to the given line AB.

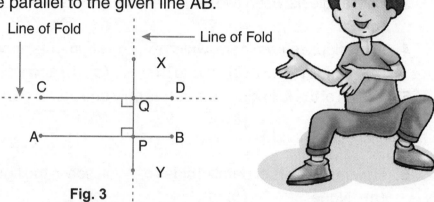

Fig. 3

Activity 2.

Write all the letters of the English alphabet which are formed by straight lines, as shown below:

A E F H I K L M
N T V W X Y Z

In each letter, identify and find the parallel and perpendicular line segments.

Answer the following questions:

1. Which of the letters above have parallel line segments? How many such letters are there?

2. Which of the letters above have perpendicular line segments? How many such letters are there?

3. Which of the letters have neither parallel nor perpendicular line segments? How many such letters are there?

QUESTION BAG - 1

(OBJECTIVE - TYPE QUESTIONS)

Tick(✓) the correct answer:

1. Which of the following sets of lines are not perpendicular?

   (*a*)   (*b*)   (*c*)   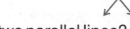   (*d*)

2. Which of the following statements best describes two parallel lines?

   (*a*) They meet at exactly one point.   (*b*) They meet at exactly two points.
   (*c*) They are always the same distance apart.   (*d*) They form a right angle.

3. The angle between two perpendicular lines is

   (*a*) 30°   (*b*) 60°   (*c*) 90°   (*d*) 180°

4. In the figure shown here, which two line segments appear to be parallel?

   (*a*) I and IV   (*b*) II and III   (*c*) III and V   (*d*) IV and V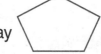

5. Which of the following figures has only one pair of parallel lines?

   (*a*)   (*b*)   (*c*)    (*d*)

6. How many pairs of parallel sides can you see in the figure shown here?

   (*a*) None   (*b*) 1   (*c*) 2   (*d*) Can't say

7. How many pairs of parallel lines are there in a rectangle?

   (*a*) 1   (*b*) 2   (*c*) 4   (*d*) None of these

QUESTION BAG - 2

1. *Fill in the blanks:*

   (*a*) The walls of a room are .... to the floor.
   (*b*) A lamp-post is placed .... to the street.
   (*c*) A railway track is laid .... to the ground.
   (*d*) A long corridor can be represented by .... lines.
   (*e*) A T-junction of two straight roads is an example of .... lines.

2. *State whether each of the following statements is true or false:*

   (*a*) When two lines intersect each other, they may or may not be perpendicular.
   (*b*) Railway track is a perfect example of parallel lines.
   (*c*) Two lines in a plane are either intersecting or parallel.

3. *In the adjacent figure name :*

   (*a*) the pairs of perpendicular line segments;
   (*b*) the pairs of parallel line segments.

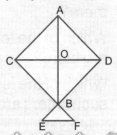

20 TRIANGLES

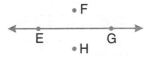

COLLINEAR AND NON-COLLINEAR POINTS

COLLINEAR POINTS:

The points which lie on the same straight line are called **collinear points.**

In the given figure, all the four points A, B, C, D lie on the same straight line.

Hence, the points A, B, C, D are collinear.

NON-COLLINEAR POINTS:

The points which do not lie on the same straight line are called **non-collinear points.** In the given figure, it is clear that the points E, F, G, H do not lie on the same straight line.

So, these points are non-collinear.

TRIANGLE

A closed figure bounded by three line segments is called a **triangle.**

We denote a triangle by the symbol △.

Let A, B, C be three non-collinear points. If we join them in pairs, we get a closed figure bounded by three line segments namely AB, BC and CA.

This closed figure is the triangle ABC, denoted by △ ABC.

A △ ABC has:

(i)   three **vertices**, namely **A**, **B** and **C**.

(ii) three **sides**, namely **AB**, **BC** and **CA**.

(iii) three **angles**, namely ∠**A**, ∠**B** and ∠**C**.

We may denote these angles by ∠BAC, ∠ABC and ∠ACB respectively.

We may note here that:

The angle opposite to the side BC is ∠A.

The angle opposite to the side AC is ∠B.

The angle opposite to the side AB is ∠C.

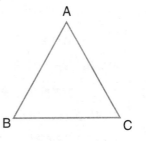

PARTS OF A TRIANGLE:

A triangle has six parts, namely three sides and three angles.

CLASSIFICATION OF TRIANGLES ACCORDING TO SIDES

1. **ISOSCELES TRIANGLE:**

   If only two sides of a triangle are equal, then it is called an **isosceles triangle**.

   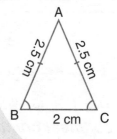

   In the given figure, in △ ABC we have AB = AC and BC is different.

   ∴ △ ABC is an isosceles triangle.

   Measure ∠B and ∠C. You will find that ∠B = ∠C.

   Thus, we have an important result given below.

   The angles opposite to the equal sides of an isosceles triangle are equal.

2. **EQUILATERAL TRIANGLE:**

   If all the three sides a triangle are equal, then it is called an **equilateral triangle**.

   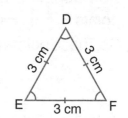

   In the given figure, in △ DEF, we have DE = EF = DF.

   ∴△DEF is an equilateral triangle.

   Measure ∠D, ∠E and ∠F.

   You will find that ∠D = ∠E = ∠F = 60°.

   Thus, we have an important result given below:

   All angles of an equilateral triangle are equal, each measuring 60°.

3. **SCALENE TRIANGLE:**

   If all the three sides of a triangle are of different lengths, then it is called a **scalene triangle.**

   In the given figure, in △PQR, we have
   PQ = 2.5 cm, QR = 4 cm and PR = 3 cm.
   ∴PQ ≠ QR ≠ PR.

   ∴ △PQR is a scalene triangle.

   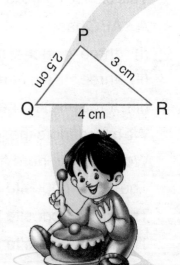

   Measure the angles ∠P, ∠Q and ∠R.

   You will find that ∠P ≠ ∠Q ≠ ∠R.

   Thus, we have the important result given below.

   All the angles of a scalene triangle are different.

AN IMPORTANT RESULT

The sum of the lengths of any two sides of a triangle is always greater than the length of the third side.

VERIFICATION:

Three triangles are given below. Measure the sides of each one of them and fill in the blanks in the table given below.

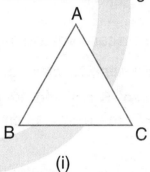

(i)

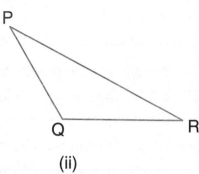

(ii)

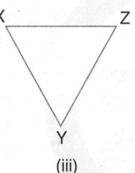

(iii)

Name of the Triangle	Measure of its sides	Sum of the measures of sides taken two at a time	Fill in the blanks with > or < or =
(i) ΔABC	AB = ...cm	AB + BC = ...cm	AB + BC ....CA
	BC = ...cm	BC + CA = ...cm	BC + CA ....AB
	CA = ...cm	AB + CA = ...cm	AB + CA ....BC
(ii) ΔPQR	PQ = ...cm	PQ + QR = ...cm	PQ + QR ....PR
	QR = ...cm	QR + PR = ...cm	QR + PR ....PQ
	PR = ...cm	PQ + PR = ...cm	PQ + PR ....QR
(iii) ΔXYZ	XY = ...cm	XY + YZ = ...cm	XY + YZ ....XZ
	YZ = ...cm	YZ + XZ = ...cm	YZ + XZ ....XY
	XZ = ...cm	XY + XZ = ...cm	XY + XZ ....YZ

Thus, we conclude:

The sum of the lengths of any two sides of a triangle is always greater than the length of the third side.

POSSIBILITY OF FORMING A TRIANGLE WITH SIDES OF GIVEN LENGTHS

Suppose we are given three line segments of given lengths. With these line segments, we can form a triangle only when *the sum of the lengths of two smaller line segments is greater than the length of the longest one.*

SOLVED EXAMPLES

Example 1. *Can we form a triangle with line segments of lengths 7cm, 8 cm and 13 cm?*

Solution : The sum of the lengths of two smaller line segments = 7 cm + 8 cm = 15 cm.

The length of the longest line segment = 13 cm.

Thus, the sum of the lengths of two smaller line segments is greater than the length of the longest line segment.

Hence, the line segments of lengths 7 cm, 8 cm and 13 cm can form a triangle.

Example 2. *Is it possible to form a triangle whose sides are 5 cm, 6 cm and 12 cm long?*

Solution : Let us consider three line segments of lengths 5 cm, 6 cm and 12 cm. The sum of the lengths of two smaller line segments = 5 cm + 6 cm = 11 cm.

The length of the longest line segment = 12 cm.

Thus, the sum of the lengths of two smaller line segments is not greater than the length of the longest line segment.

So, it is not possible to form a triangle by the three line segments of lengths 5 cm, 6 cm and 12 cm.

EXERCISE 74

1. In the given figure, name
   (a) the vertices of the triangle;
   (b) the sides of the triangle;
   (c) the angles of the triangle;

2. Classify the following triangles with respect to their sides:

(a)
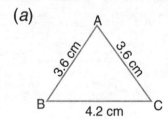

(b)
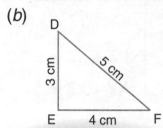

(c)
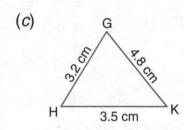

(d)
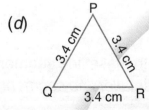

(e)
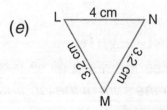

(f)
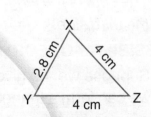

3. Measure the sides of each one of the triangles given below. Verify in each case that the sum of the lengths of any two sides is greater than the length of the third side.

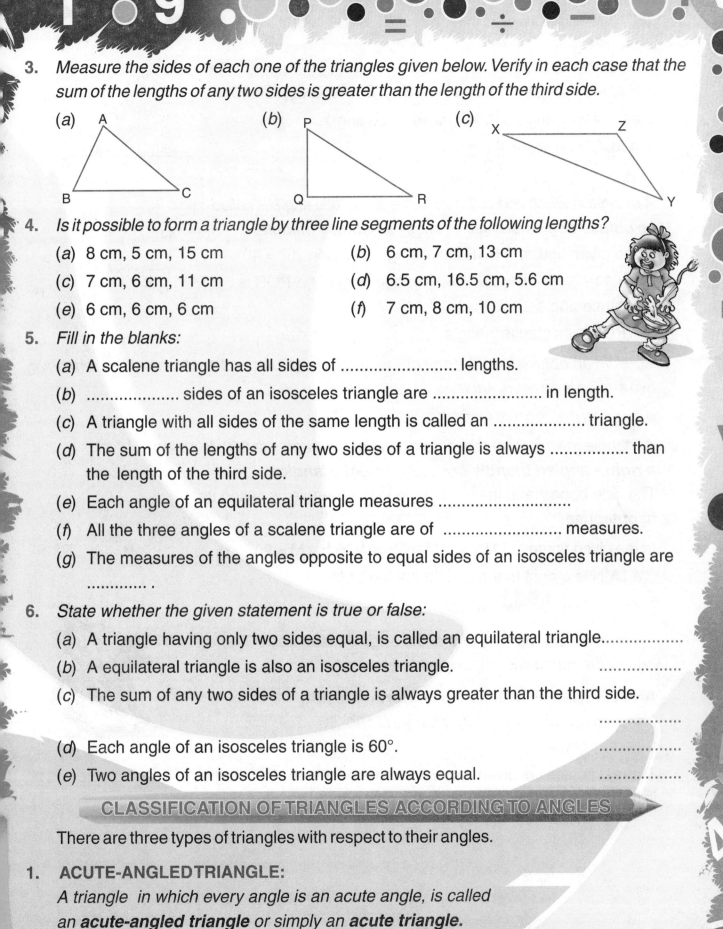

(a)   A, B, C

(b)   P, Q, R

(c)   X, Z, Y

4. Is it possible to form a triangle by three line segments of the following lengths?

(a) 8 cm, 5 cm, 15 cm   (b) 6 cm, 7 cm, 13 cm

(c) 7 cm, 6 cm, 11 cm   (d) 6.5 cm, 16.5 cm, 5.6 cm

(e) 6 cm, 6 cm, 6 cm   (f) 7 cm, 8 cm, 10 cm

5. Fill in the blanks:

(a) A scalene triangle has all sides of .... lengths.

(b) .... sides of an isosceles triangle are .... in length.

(c) A triangle with all sides of the same length is called an .... triangle.

(d) The sum of the lengths of any two sides of a triangle is always .... than the length of the third side.

(e) Each angle of an equilateral triangle measures ....

(f) All the three angles of a scalene triangle are of .... measures.

(g) The measures of the angles opposite to equal sides of an isosceles triangle are ....

6. State whether the given statement is true or false:

(a) A triangle having only two sides equal, is called an equilateral triangle.................

(b) A equilateral triangle is also an isosceles triangle.   ....

(c) The sum of any two sides of a triangle is always greater than the third side.   ....

(d) Each angle of an isosceles triangle is 60°.   ....

(e) Two angles of an isosceles triangle are always equal.   ....

CLASSIFICATION OF TRIANGLES ACCORDING TO ANGLES

There are three types of triangles with respect to their angles.

1. ACUTE-ANGLED TRIANGLE:

A triangle in which every angle is an acute angle, is called an **acute-angled triangle** or simply an **acute triangle.**

In the given figure,

$\triangle ABC$ is a triangle in which $\angle A = 75°$, $\angle B = 60°$ and $\angle C = 45°$.

Clearly, every angle of $\triangle ABC$ is an acute angle.

$\therefore$ $\triangle ABC$ is an acute triangle.

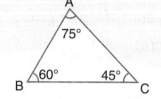

2. OBTUSE-ANGLED TRIANGLE:

*A triangle in which one of the angles is an obtuse angle is called an **obtuse-angled triangle** or simply an **obtuse triangle.***

In the given figure, $\triangle PQR$ is a triangle in which $\angle P = 40°$, $\angle Q = 110°$ and $\angle R = 30°$. Clearly, one angle of $\triangle PQR$ is an obtuse angle.

$\therefore$ $\triangle PQR$ is an obtuse triangle.

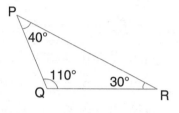

Note: *In an obtuse triangle, one of the angles is obtuse and each one of the remaining two angles is an acute angle.*

3. RIGHT - ANGLED TRIANGLE:

*A triangle in which the measure of one of the angles is 90°, is called a **right - angled triangle** or simply a **right triangle**.*

The side opposite to the right angle in the triangle, is called its **hypotenuse**.

In the given figure, $\triangle LMN$ is a triangle in which $\angle M = 90°$.

$\therefore \triangle LMN$ is a right triangle, right angled at M.

Clearly, LN is the hypotenuse of $\triangle LMN$.

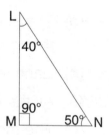

Note: *In a right triangle, one of the angles measures 90° and each one of the remaining two angles is acute.*

ANGLE SUM PROPERTY (An Important result)
The sum of all the angles of a triangle is 180°.

VERIFICATION:

Three triangles are given below. Measure each one of the angles of each triangle and fill in the blanks in the table given on the next page:

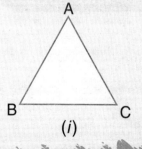
(i)

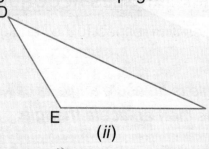
(ii)

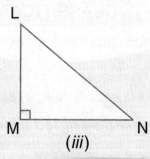
(iii)

Name of the Triangle	Measure of its angles	Sum of the measures of the angles of the triangle
(i) ΔABC	∠A = ... ∠B = ... ∠C = ...	∠A + ∠B + ∠C =
(ii) ΔDEF	∠D = ... ∠E = ... ∠F = ...	∠D + ∠E + ∠F =
(iii) ΔLMN	∠L = ... ∠M = ... ∠N = ...	∠L + ∠M + ∠N =

In each triangle, you will find that the sum of its angles is 180°.

Thus, we have the following property of a triangle.

The sum of all the angles of a triangle is 180°.

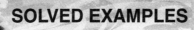

SOLVED EXAMPLES

Example 1. In △ABC, it is given that ∠A = 65° and ∠B = 70°. Find ∠C.

Solution : We know that the sum of all the angles of a triangle is 180°.

∴ ∠A + ∠B + ∠C = 180°.

Also ∠A + ∠B = (65° + 70°) = 135°.

∴ ∠C = (180° − 135°) = 45°.

Hence, ∠C = 45°.

Example 2. Which of the following cannot be the measures of the three angles of a triangle?

(a) ∠A = 80°, ∠B = 55° and ∠C = 45°.

(b) ∠P = 75°, ∠Q = 60° and ∠R = 50°.

(c) ∠X = 80°, ∠Y = 40° and ∠Z = 45°.

Solution : We have:

(a) ∠A + ∠B + ∠C = (80° + 55° + 45°) = 180°.

∴ The sum of the three angles is 180°.

Hence, the given angles are the angles of △ABC.

(b) $\angle P + \angle Q + \angle R = (75° + 60° + 50°) = 185° > 180°$.

∴ Given measures cannot be the measures of the angles of a triangle.

(c) $\angle X + \angle Y + \angle Z = (80° + 40° + 45°) = 165° < 180°$.

∴ Given measures cannot be the measures of the angles of a triangle.

Example 3. *One of the two equal angles of an isosceles triangle measures 55°. Find all the angles of the triangle.*

Solution : The sum of two equal angles of the triangle = $(55° + 55°) = 110°$.

Sum of all the three angles of the triangle = $180°$.

∴ Third angle = $(180° - 110°) = 70°$.

Hence, the angles of the given triangle are 55°, 55° and 70°.

EXERCISE 75

1. *Classify the following triangles with respect to their angles.*

(a)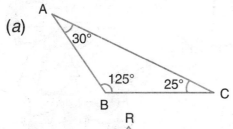

(b)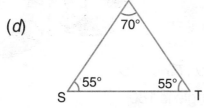

(c)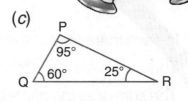

(d)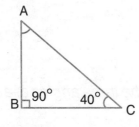

(e)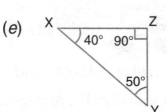

(f)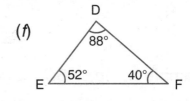

2. *Find the third angle in each of the following triangles:*

(a)

(b)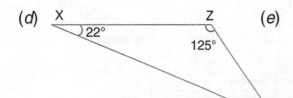

(c)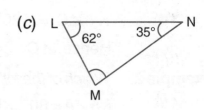

(d)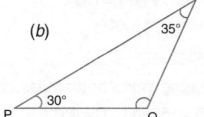

(e)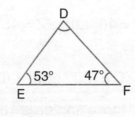

(f)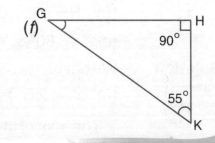

COMPOSITE MATHEMATICS – 5

3. In △ABC, if ∠B = 46° and ∠C = 54°, find ∠A.
4. In △PQR, if ∠P = 35° and ∠Q = 62°, find ∠R.
5. In △XYZ, if ∠X = 105° and ∠Z = 35°, find ∠Y.
6. In a right-angled triangle, one angle measures 35°. Find each of the remaining two angles.
7. If all the angles of a triangle are equal, find the measure of each one of them.
8. One of the two equal angles of an isosceles triangle is 64°. Find the measure of each angle of the triangle.
9. Find the measure of each of the two equal angles of an isosceles right triangle.
10. Find each of the two equal angles of an isosceles triangle whose third angle is 80°.
11. *Fill in the blanks with equilateral, isosceles or scalene:*
    (a) In △ABC, if ∠A = 55° and ∠C = 45°, then △ABC is ....
    (b) In △PQR, if ∠P = 90° and ∠Q = 45°, then △PQR is ....
    (c) In △XYZ, if ∠X = ∠Y = 60°, then △XYZ is ....
12. *Fill in the blanks with acute-angled, right-angled or obtuse-angled:*
    (a) In △ABC, if ∠B = 56° and ∠C = 40°, then △ABC is ....
    (b) In △PQR, if ∠P = ∠Q = 40°, then △PQR is ....
    (c) In △XYZ, if ∠X = ∠Y = 45°, then △XYZ is ....
    (d) In △LMN, if ∠L = 46° and ∠M = 34°, then △LMN is ....
13. *Answer the following:*
    (a) How many acute angles can a triangle have?
    (b) How many right angles can a triangle have?
    (c) How many obtuse angles can a triangle have?
14. *Which of the following cannot be the measures of all the three angles of a triangle?*
    (a) ∠A = 110°, ∠B = 25° and ∠C = 35°
    (b) ∠D = 63°, ∠E = 37° and ∠F = 80°
    (c) ∠X = 72°, ∠Y = 32° and ∠Z = 76°
    (d) ∠P = 70°, ∠Q = 70° and ∠R = 50°

THINGS TO REMEMBER

1. A closed figure bounded by three line segments is called a triangle, denoted by △.
2. In the given figure, △ABC is given. It has:
    (a) three vertices, namely A, B and C
    (b) three sides, namely AB, BC and CA
    (c) three angles, namely ∠A, ∠B and ∠C or ∠BAC, ∠ABC and ∠BCA
3. (a) If all the three sides of a triangle are of different lengths, then the triangle is called a **scalene triangle**.
    (b) A triangle with two sides of equal length is called an **isosceles triangle**.
    (c) A triangle with all the three sides of equal lengths is called an **equilateral triangle**.

4. The sum of the lengths of any two sides of a triangle is always greater than the length of the third side.

5. (a) A triangle, one of whose angles is a right angle, is called a **right-angled triangle**.

   (b) A triangle with one obtuse angle is called an **obtuse-angled triangle**.

   (c) A triangle with all the three angles acute is called an **acute-angled triangle**.

6. The sum of all the three angles of a triangle is 180°.

ACTIVITY TIME

On a dot grid as shown below, join the dots in maximum possible ways to form different shapes of triangles. Carefully observe these triangles and classify them as scalene, isosceles and equilateral triangles. Is there any type of triangle which you cannot form by joining the dots on the dot-grid? State.

C.C.E. DRILL - 15

QUESTION BAG - 1

(OBJECTIVE - TYPE QUESTIONS)

1. How many parts does a triangle have?
    (a) 9   (c) 3   (b) 6   (d) 4

2. In the adjoining figure, the point P lies
    (a) in the interior of △ABC   (c) in the exterior of △ABC
    (c) on △ABC   (d) outside △ABC

3. The triangular pieces in an instrument box are called
    (a) protractors   (b) scales   (c) compasses   (d) set-squares

4. A triangle having all sides of different lengths is called
    (a) an equilateral triangle   (b) an isosceles triangle
    (c) a scalene triangle   (d) a right triangle

5. The sum of the lengths of any two sides of a triangle is
    (a) always equal to the length of the third side
    (b) always greater than the length of the third side
    (c) always less than the length of the third side

6. In an equilateral triangle
    (a) all sides are equal   (b) all angles are equal
    (c) Both (a) and (b)   (d) None of these

7. Which of the following cannot be the lengths of three sides of a triangle?
    (a) 6 cm, 7 cm, 12 cm   (b) 5 cm, 6 cm, 11 cm   (c) 4 cm, 5 cm, 7 cm

8. The measure of each angle of an equilateral triangle is
    (a) 30°   (b) 45°   (c) 60°   (d) 50°

9. Two angles of a triangle are 40° and 25° respectively. The third angle is :
    (a) 35°   (b) 25°   (c) 65°   (d) 115°

10. One of the base angles of an isosceles triangle is 70°. The vertical angle of the triangle is:
    (a) 70°   (b) 60°   (c) 40°   (d) 30°

11. Which of the following can be the angles of a triangle?
    (a) 30°, 50°, 80°   (b) 40°, 75°, 65°   (c) 50°, 40°, 70°   (d) 62°, 38°, 90°

12. The sum of all the three angles of a triangle is:
    (a) 90°   (b) 100°   (c) 120°   (d) 180°

13. In a △ABC, if ∠A = 90° then the hypotenuse is
    (a) AB   (b) BC   (c) CA   (d) Any of these

14. The angles in a right-angled isosceles triangle are
    (a) 90°, 30°, 60°   (b) 90°, 40°, 50°   (c) 90°, 45°, 45°   (d) 90°, 70°, 20°

15. Two angles of a triangle are given as $98\frac{1}{2}°$ and $33\frac{1}{2}°$. Then the measure of third angle is
    (a) 48°   (b) 58°   (c) 63°   (d) 72°

16. If 4 cm and 7 cm are the lengths of two sides of a triangle, then the length of the third side may be
    (a) 3 cm   (b) 6 cm   (c) 11 cm   (d) 12 cm

17. Number of triangles in the given figure is
    (a) 12   (b) 14   (c) 16   (d) 20

QUESTION BAG-2

1. *Can a triangle have*
   (a) two right angles?   (b) two obtuse angles?   (c) two acute angles?

2. *Can a triangle have*
   (a) each angle greater than 60° ?   (b) each angle less than 60° ?
   (c) each angle equal to 60° ?

3. *Fill in the blanks:*
   (a) A triangle is formed by joining three .... points.
   (b) A triangle has .... sides and .... angles.
   (c) The sides of a scalene triangle are of .... lengths.
   (d) The sum of any two sides of a triangle is .... than the third side.
   (e) The sum of the angles of a triangle is ....
   (f) One angle of a right triangle measures ....
   (g) If one angle of a triangle measures 120°, it is....................................

4. *State whether each of the following statements is true or false:*
   (a) In a right-angled triangle, the right angle is the greatest angle of the triangle.
   (b) An equilateral triangle is also equiangular.   ....
   (c) A triangle can be both right-angled and isosceles.   ....
   (d) An equilateral triangle is always acute-angled.   ....
   (e) A right triangle can be equilateral.   ....
   (f) In a right-angled triangle, the side opposite to the right angle is the
       longest.   ....
   (g) If one angle of a triangle is obtuse, the other two angles must be
       acute.   ....

5. *Fill in the blanks:*

   (*a*) One acute angle of a right triangle is 35°. The other acute angle is ....

   (*b*) Two angles of a triangle are 35° and 65°. The third angle is ....

   (*c*) Two sides of a triangle are 6 cm and 8 cm. The length of the third side is .... 14 cm.

   (*d*) In ΔABC, it is given that AB = AC, then ∠B = ...

6. *Which can be the sides of the given triangle?*

   (*a*) In ΔABC, AB = 6 cm, BC = 5 cm and AC = 11 cm.

   (*b*) In ΔDEF, DE = 5 cm, EF = 9 cm and DF = 4 cm.

   (*c*) In ΔPQR, PQ = 4 cm, QR = 8 cm and PR = 3 cm.

   (*d*) In ΔXYZ, XY = 2.3 cm, YZ = 3.1 cm, and XZ = 5.3 cm.

7. The sum of two angles of a triangle is 135°. Find the measure of the third angle.

8. *Find the unknown angle in each of the triangles given below:*

   (*a*) 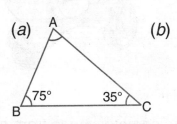 (*b*) 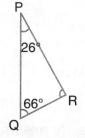 (*c*) 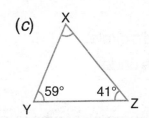 (*d*)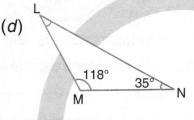

9. *Is it possible to have a triangle with the following sides and angles?*

   (*a*) 7.5 cm, 3.5 cm, 4 cm   (*b*) 80°, 35°, 65°

   (*c*) 110°, 60°, 30°   (*d*) 70°, 70°, 70°

   (*e*) 50°, 50°, 90°   (*f*) 10 cm, 12 cm, 8 cm

10. *The measures of two angles of a triangle are given below. Classify each of these triangles as acute-angled, obtuse-angled and right-angled:*

    (*a*) 60°, 60°   (*b*) 45°, 45°   (*c*) 70°, 70°

    (*d*) 30°, 30°   (*e*) 60°, 30°   (*f*) 45°, 35°

CIRCLES

INTRODUCTION

If we put a bangle or a one-rupee coin on the plane of the paper and move our pencil around it, we obtain a closed curve shown below:

 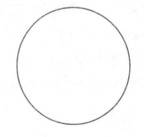

Such a closed curve is called a circle.

Actually, we define a circle as under.

CIRCLE:

*A **circle** is a simple closed curve all of whose points are at the same distance from a fixed point inside it.*

The fixed point is called the **centre** of the circle.

The constant distance between the centre of a circle and any point on the circle, is called its **radius**.

In the given figure, O is the **centre** of a circle and OA is its **radius**.

TO DRAW A CIRCLE WITH THE HELP OF A COMPASS

Draw a circle of radius 3 cm.

CONSTRUCTION : We draw the circle in following steps.

Step 1 : Fix a sharp pencil in the pencil holding arm of the compass firmly.

Step 2 : Fix the metal tip of the compass on the ruler at 0 and open out the compass in such a way that its pencil tip rests on 3 cm mark on the ruler.

Step 3 : Take a point O on the plane of the paper. Rest the metal tip of the compass firmly at O.

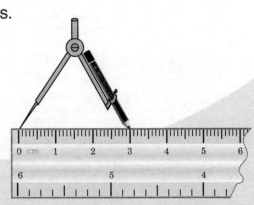

Step 4 : Now hold the head of the compass firmly and move the pencil point around to trace a circle of radius 3 cm.

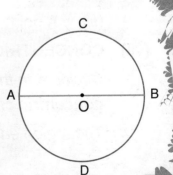

TEMRS RELATED TO CIRCLES

(i) DIAMETER OF A CIRCLE:

*The line segment having its end points on the circle and passing through the centre is called its **diameter**.*

In the given figure, O is the centre of a circle and AB is a diameter.

Clearly, AB = (OA + OB) = 2 × OA   [∵ OA = OB = radius]

∴ **Diameter = 2 × (Radius)**

(ii) CHORD OF A CIRCLE:

*A line segment whose end points lie on the circle, is called a **chord**.*

In the given figure, O is the centre of the circle.

In this circle, each of the line segments CD, EF, AB is a chord.

In fact, **the diameter is the longest chord in a circle.**

(iii) ARC OF A CIRCLE:

*Any part of a circle is called an **arc** of the circle.*

Usually, we name an arc by three points, out of which two are the end points of the arc and third one lies in between them.

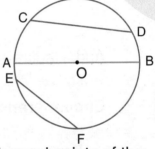

In the given figure, ACB is an arc of the given circle, to be denoted by A͡CB.

MINOR ARC AND MAJOR ARC:

Points A and B divide the circle into two unequal arcs.

The shorter arc A͡CB is called the **Minor Arc** and the longer arc B͡DA is called the **Major Arc**.

(iv) SEMI-CIRCLE:

*Half of a circle is called a **Semi-Circle**.*

In the given figure, ACB is a semi-circle and ADB is also a semi-circle.

Note that a semi-circle is also an arc of the circle.

(v) CIRCUMFERENCE OF A CIRCLE:

*The perimeter of a circle is called its **circumference.***

Measuring The Circumference Of A Given Circle Using Thread

Suppose a circle is given with centre O. Mark a point A on the circle. Keep one end of a thread at A. Spread the thread along the boundary of the circle. Mark the point on the thread which again falls on A. Measure the length of the thread upto this point. This length gives the circumference of the circle.

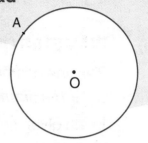

Note: If we draw several circles and measure the circumference and diameter of each, we shall find in each case that

$$\frac{\text{Circumference}}{\text{Diameter}} = \frac{22}{7} \text{ or } 3.14$$

This value is denoted by π (called Pie). Thus, $\pi = \frac{22}{7}$ or $\pi = 3.14$.

$\therefore$ Circumference $= \pi \times$ (diameter of the circle)

$\qquad\qquad\quad = 2\pi \times$ (radius of the circle)

And, Radius $\quad = $ (circumference) $\div\ 2\pi$

Circumference of a circle = 2 × π × radius, where $\pi = \dfrac{22}{7}$

Radius of a circle = $\dfrac{\text{Circumference}}{2\ \pi}$.

(vi) INTERIOR AND EXTERIOR OF A CIRCLE:

Consider a circle with centre O and take a point A on the circle . Join OA. It is clear that:

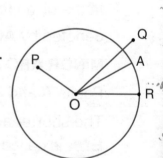

(*i*)   A point P lies in the interior of the circle, if OP < OA.

(*ii*)   A point Q lies in the exterior of the circle, if OQ > OA.

(*iii*)   A point R lies on the circle, if OR = OA.

(vii) CONCENTRIC CIRCLES:

*Circles with the same centre and different radii are called **concentric circles.***

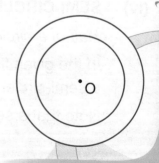

*The region enclosed by two concentric circles is called a **ring.***

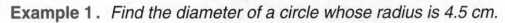

SOLVED EXAMPLES

Example 1. *Find the diameter of a circle whose radius is 4.5 cm.*

Solution : Radius of the given circle = 4.5 cm

Diameter of the given circle = 2 × (Radius)

= (2 × 4.5) cm = 9 cm.

Hence, the diameter of the given circle is 9 cm.

Example 2. *Find the radius of a circle whose diameter is 7 cm.*

Solution : Diameter of the given circle = 7 cm.

Radius of the given circle $= \dfrac{1}{2} \times$ (Diameter)

$= \left(\dfrac{1}{2} \times 7 \right)$ cm = 3.5 cm.

Hence, the radius of the given circle is 3.5 cm .

Example 3. *Find the circumference of a circle whose radius is 3.5 cm.* $\left(\text{Take } \pi = \dfrac{22}{7} \right)$

Solution : Radius of the circle = 3.5 cm $= \dfrac{7}{2}$ cm.

∴ Circumference of the circle = 2 × π × (Radius)

$= \left(2 \times \dfrac{22}{7} \times \dfrac{7}{2} \right)$ cm = 22 cm.

Hence, the circumference of the given circle is 22 cm.

Example 4. *Find the circumference of a circle whose radius is 5 cm.* [Take π = 3.14]

Solution : Radius of the circle = 5 cm.

∴ Circumference of the circle = 2 × π × (Radius)

= (2 × 3.14 × 5) cm = 31.4 cm.

Hence, the circumference of the given circle is 31.4 cm.

Example 5. *Find the radius of a circle whose circumference is 44 cm.* $\left(\text{Take } \pi = \dfrac{22}{7} \right)$

Solution : Circumference of the circle = 44 cm.

∴ Radius = (Circumference) ÷ 2π

$= \left\{ 44 \div \left(2 \times \dfrac{22}{7} \right) \right\}$ cm $= \left(44 \div \dfrac{44}{7} \right)$ cm

$= \left(44 \times \dfrac{7}{44} \right)$ cm = 7 cm .

Hence, the radius of the circle is 7 cm.

Example 6 . *In the given figure, a circle with centre O and radius 5 cm has been drawn. If M, N and P are three points in the plane of the circle such that OM = 5 cm, ON = 6 cm and OP = 4 cm, find the positions of the points M, N and P with respect to the circle.*

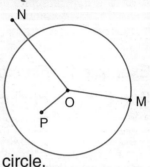

Solution : Since OM = 5 cm = radius of the circle, so M lies on the circle.

Since ON = 6 cm > radius of the circle, so N lies in the exterior of the circle.

Since OP = 4 cm < radius of the circle, so P lies in the interior of the circle.

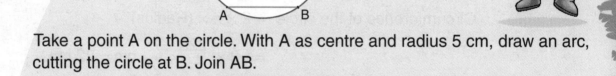

TO DRAW A CHORD OF GIVEN LENGTH IN A GIVEN CIRCLE

Example 7 . *Draw a circle of radius 5.6 cm. In this circle draw a chord of length 5 cm.*

Solution : Take a point O in the plane of the paper. With O as centre and radius 5.6 cm, draw a circle.

Take a point A on the circle. With A as centre and radius 5 cm, draw an arc, cutting the circle at B. Join AB.

Then, AB is the required chord of length 5 cm.

EXERCISE 76

1. In the given figure, O is the centre of a circle. Name the radii and the diameters in the circle.

2. In the figure given here, O is the centre of the circle. Name the chords of the circle.

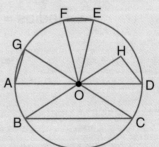

3. *Fill in the blanks:*

   (*a*) If A and B are two points on a circle, then the line segment AB is called a .... of the circle.

   (*b*) A line segment passing through the centre of a circle with its end points on the circle is a .... of the circle.

   (*c*) A diameter is the.................... chord of the circle.

   (*d*) Perimeter of a circle is called its ....

   (*e*) Radius of a circle is .... the length of the diameter of the circle.

   (*f*) Circumference of a circle $= 2 \times \pi \times$ ....

   (*g*) Diameter of a circle $=$ .... $\times$ Radius of the circle.

   (*h*) Any part of a circle is called an ....

   (*i*) .... of a circle is called a semi-circle.

   (*j*) (Circumference of a circle) $\div 2\pi =$ ....

4. *With the help of compass, construct a circle whose radius is :*

   (*a*) 6 cm (*b*) 5.8 cm (*c*) 6.2 cm (*d*) 4 cm 6 mm

5. *Find the diameter of a circle whose radius is:*

   (*a*) 4 cm (*b*) 3.8 cm (*c*) 5.4 cm (*d*) 6.1 cm

6. *Find the radius of a circle whose diameter is:*

   (*a*) 9 cm (*b*) 7.8 cm (*c*) 9.2 cm (*d*) 7 cm

7. *Find the circumference of a circle whose radius is:*

   (*a*) 7 cm (*b*) 6.3 cm (*c*) 5.6 cm (*d*) 4.2 cm

   $\left(\text{Take } \pi = \dfrac{22}{7} \text{ in each case} \right)$

8. *Find the circumference of a circle whose radius is:*

   (*a*) 6 cm (*b*) 8 cm (*c*) 4.5 cm (*d*) 6.5 cm

   [Take $\pi = 3.14$ in each case]

9. *Find the radius of a circle whose circumference is:*

   (*a*) 22 cm (*b*) 17.6 cm (*c*) 30.8 cm (*d*) 79.2 cm

   $\left(\text{Take } \pi = \dfrac{22}{7} \text{ in each case} \right)$

10. *Find the diameter of a circle whose circumference is:*

   (*a*) 66 cm (*b*) 35.2 cm (*c*) 30.8 cm

   $\left(\text{Take } \pi = \dfrac{22}{7} \text{ in each case} \right)$

11. Draw a circle of radius 3.8 cm. In this circle, construct a chord of length 4.2 cm.

12. Draw two concentric circles of radii 4.5 cm and 5.2 cm. Shade the ring formed.

13. *A circle is drawn with centre O and radius 5.5 cm. Write the position of each of the points A, B, C, D and E with respect to the given circle, where*

    (*a*) OA = 6.3 cm   (*b*) OB = 4.8 cm   (*c*) OC = 7 cm

    (*d*) OD = 5.5 cm   (*e*) OE = 5 cm

THINGS TO REMEMBER

1. A **circle** is a simple closed curve all of whose points are at the same distance from a fixed point inside it. This fixed point is called the **centre** of the circle.

2. A line segment joining any point on the circle to its centre is called a **radius** of the circle.

3. A line segment whose end points lie on the circle is called a **chord**.

4. A chord which passes through the centre of the circle is called a **diameter** of the circle.

5. Diameter = 2 × radius.

6. Any part of a circle is called an **arc**.

7. Points A and B on the given circle divide it into two unequal arcs. The shorter arc $\overset{\frown}{ACB}$ is called the **Minor Arc** and the longer arc $\overset{\frown}{BDA}$ is called the **Major Arc**.

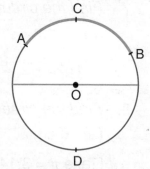

8. Half of a circle is called a **semi-circle**.

9. The perimeter of a circle is called its **circumference**.

10. Circumference of a circle = π × diameter = 2 π × radius.

11. Circles with the same centre are known as **concentric circles**.

ACTIVITY TIME

Activity–1

Take the coins of different denominations and trace out their boundary on a plane sheet. Using a ruler, measure the approximate lengths of their diameters and calculate their radii.

Activity–2

Measuring the circumference of a bangle with a ruler

Take a bangle and put a mark on any point of the bangle. Mark a point P on a plane sheet and draw a straight line starting from P. Hold the bangle upright and match the mark on the

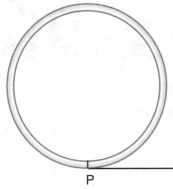

bangle to the point P marked on the paper. Roll the bangle on the paper along the straight line till it takes one full turn and the mark on the bangle again touches the line. Mark this point on the line as Q.

Measure the length PQ. This is the circumference of the bangle.

QUESTION BAG - 1

(OBJECTIVE - TYPE QUESTIONS)

Tick (✓) the correct answer :

1. In the given figure, O is the centre of a circle and P is a given point. The point P lies

   (a) in the exterior of the circle

   (b) on the circle

   (c) in the interior of the circle

2. Which of the following is a true statement?

   (a) A diameter is the smallest chord of a circle.

   (b) Any part of a circle is called a chord.

   (c) The circumference of a circle is called its perimeter.

   (d) Half of a circle with its diameter is called a half circle.

3. The .... of a circle divides it into two equal halves.

   (a) radius (b) chord (c) diameter (d) arc

4. The instrument used to draw circles is

   (a) set square (b) protractor (c) compass (d) None of these

5. If the diameter of a circle is 3.7 cm, its radius is

   (a) 3.7 cm (b) 7.4 cm (c) 1.8 cm (d) None of these

6. In the adjoining figure, O is the centre of the circle. How many chords can you count in the figure?

   (a) 4 (b) 5 (c) 6 (d) 7

7. The radius of a circle is 7 cm. Its circumference is

   (a) 14 cm (b) 21 cm (c) 22 cm (d) 44 cm

8. The circumference of a circle is 88 cm. Its diameter is

   (a) 22 cm (b) 14 cm (c) 28 cm (d) 33 cm

9. The diameter of a circle is 3.5 cm. Its circumference is

   (a) 11 cm (b) 14 cm (c) 22 cm (d) 16.5 cm

10. If the radius of a circle is doubled, then the diameter increases by

    (a) 2 times (b) 3 times (c) 4 times (d) remains the same

11. Which of the following statements is false?

   (a) If we join any two points on a circle we get a diameter of the circle.

   (b) A diameter of a circle contains the centre of the circle.

   (c) A circle has an infinite number of radii.

   (d) The length of a circle is called its circumference.

12. How many chords of a circle can we draw ?

   (a) 1   (b) 2   (c) 4   (d) Any number

QUESTION BAG – 2

1. *Look at the given figure and name the following:*

   (a) Point O   ....

   (b) OX   ....

   (c) AB   ....

   (d) PQ   ....

   (e) PRQ   ....

   (f) OA   ....

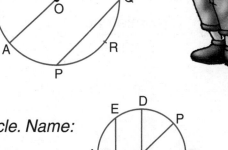

2. *In the adjoining figure, O is the centre of the circle. Name:*

   (a) all the radii

   (b) all the diameters

   (c) all the chords

3. Draw a circle with centre C and radius 4.8 cm. Mark points P, Q and R such that P lies in the interior of the circle, Q lies on the circle and R lies in the exterior of th circle.

4. *Fill in the blanks:*

   (a) An arc is a part of the .... of a circle.

   (b) Diameter is the .... chord of the circle.

   (c) Length of the circular boundary of a circle is called its ....

   (d) Centre of a circle lies in its ....

   (e) The region outside the circumference of a circle is called the .... of the circle.

   (f) Half a circle is called a ....

   (g) A quarter of a circle is called a ....

   (h) The distance between the centre and a point on the circle is called ....

   (i) We name a/an .... by three points.

5. *State whether each of the following statements is true or false:*

(*a*) The centre of a circle bisects each chord of the circle. ....

(*b*) A radius has both end-points on the circle. ....

(*c*) The centre of a circle is at the same distance from any point on the circle .
....

(*d*) Each radius of a circle is also a chord of the circle. ....

(*e*) All the chords of a circle are of the same length. ....

(*f*) A line segment whose end points lie on a circle is called the diameter.
....

(*g*) If the distance of a point from the centre of a circle is more than its radius, the point lies in the interior of the circle. ....

6. *Fill in the blanks for a circle:*

(*a*) Radius = (..........) × (Diameter)

(*b*) Circumference = π × ....

(*c*) $\dfrac{\text{Circumference}}{\text{Radius}}$ = ...

PERIMETERS OF RECTILINEAR FIGURES

RECTILINEAR FIGURES

*A plane figure bounded by line segments is called a **rectilinear figure**.*

Thus, each one of the figures, namely a triangle, a rectangle, a square, a pentagon etc. is a rectilinear figure.

Clearly, a circle is not a rectilinear figure.

PERIMETER OF A RECTILINEAR FIGURE

*The sum of the lengths of all sides of a rectilinear figure is called its **perimeter**.*

PERIMETER OF A TRIANGLE

Perimeter of $\triangle ABC = (\overline{AB} + \overline{BC} + \overline{CA})$

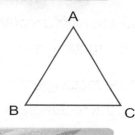

SOLVED EXAMPLES

Example 1. *Find the perimeter of a triangle whose sides are 7 cm, 8.5 cm and 9.3 cm.*

Solution : Perimeter of the given triangle $= (7 + 8.5 + 9.3)$ cm $= 24.8$ cm.

Example 2. *Find the perimeter of an isosceles triangle in which each of the equal sides is 6 cm and the third side is 8 cm.*

Solution : Perimeter of the given triangle $= (6 + 6 + 8)$ cm $= 20$ cm.

Example 3. *Find the perimeter of an equilateral triangle, each of whose sides measures 9 cm.*

Solution : Perimeter of the given triangle
$= (9 + 9 + 9)$ cm $= (3 \times 9)$ cm $= 27$ cm.

PERIMETER OF A RECTANGLE

Perimeter of rectangle ABCD
$$= AB + BC + CD + DA$$
$$= AB + BC + AB + BC$$

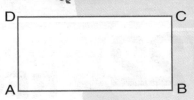

$$[\because CD = AB \text{ and } DA = BC]$$

$$= 2(AB + BC)$$

$$= 2(\text{Length} + \text{Breadth})$$

$\therefore$ **Perimeter of a rectangle = 2 (Length + Breadth)**

And, (Length + Breadth) $= \dfrac{1}{2} \times$ **(Perimeter)**

PERIMETER OF A SQUARE

Clearly,

Perimeter of a square = (4 × side)

$\therefore$ **Side of a square** $= \dfrac{1}{4} \times$ **(its perimeter)**

SOLVED EXAMPLES

Example 1 . *Find the perimeter of a rectangle whose length is 28 cm and the breadth is 17 cm.*

Solution : Length of the rectangle = 28 cm.

Breadth of the rectangle = 17 cm.

Perimeter of the rectangle = 2(Length + Breadth).

= 2 (28 + 17) cm = (2 × 45) cm = 90 cm.

Hence, the perimeter of the rectangle is 90 cm.

Example 2 . *Find the cost of fencing a rectangular park 115 m long and 85 m broad at the rate of Rs 25 per metre.*

Solution : Length of the park = 115 m.

Breadth of the park = 85 m.

Perimeter of the park = 2 (Length + Breadth)

= 2 (115 + 85) m = 400 m.

Thus, the length of the fence = 400 m.

$\therefore$ Cost of fencing = Rs (400 × 25) = Rs 10000.

Hence, the cost of fencing the park is Rs 10000.

Example 3 . *A park is 145 m long and 78 m wide. Reenu jogs around it 5 times. How much distance does she cover?*

Solution : Length of the park = 145 m.

Breadth of the park = 78 m.

Perimeter of the park = 2(Length + Breadth)

$= 2\,(145 + 78)\,m \;=\; (2 \times 223)\,m \;=\; 446\,m.$

Distance covered by Reenu in 1 round $= 446\,m.$

Distance covered by her in 5 rounds $= (446 \times 5)\,m = 2230\,m.$

Hence, Reenu covers 2230 m in 5 rounds.

Example 4. *The perimeter of a rectangle is 66 metres and its length is 18 metres. Find its breadth.*

Solution : Perimeter of the rectangle $= 66\,m.$

$$\therefore \;(\text{Length} + \text{Breadth}) \;=\; \frac{1}{2} \times (\text{Perimeter})$$

$$=\; \left(\frac{1}{2} \times 66\right)\,m = 33\,m.$$

Now, Length $= 18\,m.$

$\therefore$ Breadth $= (33 - 18)\,m = 15\,m.$

Hence, the breadth of the rectangle is 15 m.

Example 5. *Find the perimeter of a square each of whose sides measures 16 cm.*

Solution : Each side of the square $= 16\,cm.$

$\therefore$ Perimeter of the square $= (4 \times \text{side}) = (4 \times 16)\,cm = 64\,cm.$

Hence, the perimeter of the square is 64 cm.

EXERCISE 77

1. Find the perimeter of each of the figures given below:

(a)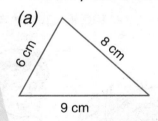

(b)

(c)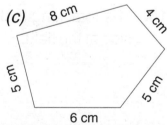

2. Find the perimeter of each of the triangles whose sides are given below :

   (a) 8 cm, 6 cm, 5 cm

   (b) 7.6 cm, 6.4 cm, 5.2 cm

   (c) 4.8 cm, 5.3 cm, 8.2 cm

   (d) 6 cm, 7.3 cm, 8.5 cm

3. Find the perimeter of an isosceles triangle, each of whose equal sides measures 5.8 cm and the length of whose third side is 7.5 cm.

4. Find the perimeter of an equilateral triangle each of whose sides is 8.4 cm.

5. The perimeter of a triangle is 16 cm and two of its sides measure 3.8 cm and 5.6 cm respectively. Find the third side.

6. The perimeter of an equilateral triangle is 17.7 cm. Find the length of each side of the triangle.

7. *Find the perimeter of each of the rectangles with the following dimensions :*
   (*a*) Length = 36 cm, Breadth = 29 cm
   (*b*) Length = 7 m, Breadth = 5 m
   (*c*) Length = 2 m 60 cm, Breadth = 1 m 90 cm
   (*d*) Length = 12.6 m, Breadth = 9.4 m

8. The perimeter of a rectangle is 110 cm and its length is 35 cm. What is the breadth of the rectangle?

9. The perimeter of a rectangular garden is 420 m and its length is 120 m. What is its breadth?

10. *Find the perimeter of the square, each of whose sides measures:*
    (*a*) 45 cm   (*b*) 16 m   (*c*) 2 m 10 cm   (*d*) 3 m 25 cm

11. The sides of a triangular field are 35 m, 60 m and 110 m. Find the length of the wire required to fence the field.

12. A rectangular picture frame is 54 cm long and 36 cm wide. What will be the length of the wooden frame required to make it?

13. A wall is built around a rectangular plot of land of length 63 m and breadth 47 m. Find the cost of constructing the wall at Rs 130 per metre.

14. Tanvy runs 3 times around a square field each of whose sides measures 95 m. How much distance does she run ?

15. The total length of the fence around a square field is 308 m. Find the length of each side of the field.

THINGS TO REMEMBER

1. The perimeter of △ABC   = (AB + BC + CA) units.

2. (i) Perimeter of a rectangle = 2(length + breadth) units
   (ii) (Length + Breadth)   = $\frac{1}{2}$ × (Perimeter).

3. Perimeter of a square   = 4 × (side)

C.C.E. DRILL - 17

QUESTION BAG - 1

(OBJECTIVE - TYPE QUESTIONS)

Tick (✓) the correct answer :

1. Perimeter of a rectilinear figure is

   (a) Sum of all sides   (b) Product of sides

   (c) Both (a) and (b)   (d) None of these

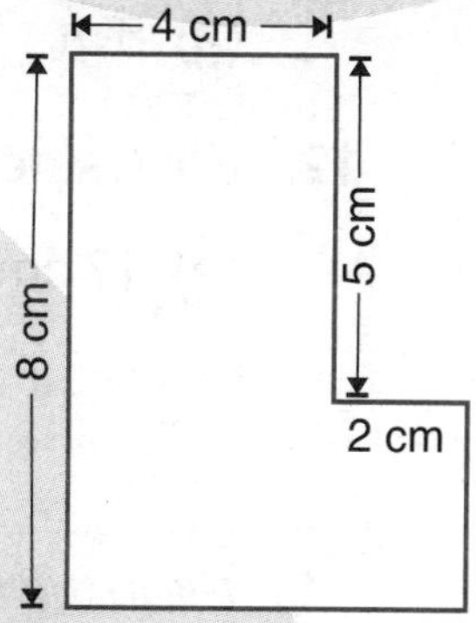

2. The perimeter of the figure shown here is

   (a) 20 cm   (b) 24 cm

   (c) 26 cm   (d) 28 cm

3. Which of the following is not a rectilinear figure?

   (a) Triangle   (b) Rectangle   (c) Circle   (d) Square

4. Amir wants to frame 8 pictures each with length 3 m and breadth 2 m. What length of wood will he need to make the frames?

   (a) 48 m   (b) 80 m   (c) 96 m   (d) 56 m

5. The total length of fence around a square field is 408 m. The length of each side of the field is :

   (a) 204 m   (b) 136 m   (c) 102 m   (d) 68 m

6. Teenu runs 2 times around a square field having each side 85 m long. How much distance does she run?

   (a) 170 m   (b) 255 m   (c) 340 m   (d) 680 m

7. Each side of a square is 8.5 cm long. Its perimeter is

   (a) 17 cm   (b) 34 cm   (c) 25.5 cm   (d) 51 cm

8. Each of the equal sides of an isosceles triangle is 4.7 cm and its third side is 5.6 cm. The perimeter of the triangle is:

   (a) 10.3 cm   (b) 20.6 cm   (c) 15.9 cm   (d) 15 cm

9. The perimeter of a rectangle is 140 cm and its length is 42 cm. The breadth of the rectangle is:

    (a) 35 cm   (b) 24 cm   (c) 28 cm   (d) 26 cm

10. The perimeter of a rectangle is 180 cm and its breadth is 34 cm. The length of the rectangle is :

    (a) 56 cm   (b) 42 cm   (c) 68 cm   (d) 73 cm

11. The cost of fencing a rectangular field at Rs 40 per metre is Rs 3200. If the length of the field is 24 m, then its breadth is

    (a) 8 m   (b) 16 m   (c) 18 m   (d) 24 m

12. Each side of an equilateral triangle is 8.5 cm. Its perimeter is

    (a) 17 cm   (b) 34 cm   (c) 25.5 cm   (d) 42.5 cm

QUESTION BAG - 2

1. *Fill in the blanks :*

    (a) Perimeter of a $\triangle ABC$ = (............+...............+..................) units.

    (b) Perimeter of a rectangle = 2 (...............+...................) units.

    (c) In a rectangle, we have :

    (Length + Breadth) = $\frac{1}{2}$ × (................)

    (d) Perimeter of a square = 4 × (................)

2. How much will it cost to fence a garden 96 m long and 78 m wide at the rate of Rs 12.50 per metre ?

3. Shaloo runs along the sides of a square garden which is 85 m long. If she covers 50 cm in one step, how many steps will she take to run once round the garden ?

4. Rahul jogs 6.5 km everyday. He jogs around a rectangular park 750 m long and 550 m wide. How many rounds of the park does he take ?

23 AREA

INTRODUCTION

If we draw a closed bounded figure on a piece of paper and cut the paper along the boundaries of the figure, then the cut-out gives the amount of surface enclosed by the figure.

The shaded regions shown below in figures (*a*), (*b*) and (*c*) show the amount of surfaces enclosed by a triangle, a rectangle and a circle respectively.

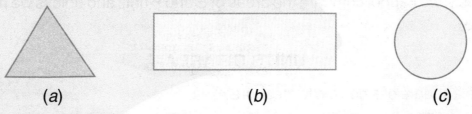

(a)   (b)   (c)

Area : *The measure of the amount of surface enclosed by a closed bounded figure is called its **area.***

COMPARISON OF AREAS

When the given surfaces are of the same shape we compare them by placing one over the other.

Given below are two pentagons A and B.

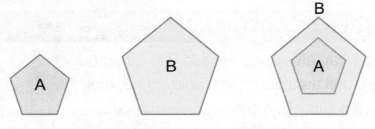

By placing them one over the other, we find that B is larger than A.

Thus, we can say that *area of B is larger than that of A.*

Consider two circles C and D of radii 3 cm and 4 cm respectively.

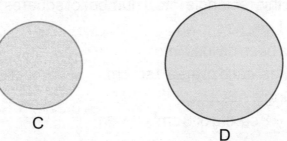

C   D

Obviously, the surface enclosed by circle D is more than enclosed by circle C.

Thus, the area of circle D is more than that of circle C.

Sometimes, it becomes difficult to compare the areas of the two surfaces by simply looking at them, particularly when the figures are of different shapes.

Look at the figures E and F of a rectangle and a triangle respectively.

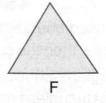

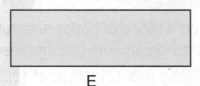

E

F

Obviously, we cannot compare the areas of E and F until and unless we measure them in definite units.

UNITS OF AREA

We use a square of side 1cm to measure Area.

The area of this square is **1 square cm** or **1 cm²** (read as 1 square centimetre)

1 cm²   1 cm

1 cm

Similarly, the area of a square having each side 1 m, is **1 square m** or **1 m²**.

1 m²   1 m

1 m

AREA OF A RECTANGLE AND A SQUARE

A given rectangle can always be divided into a number of squares, each having a unit area, as shown below. And, thus the area of the rectangle is the sum of the areas of these squares.

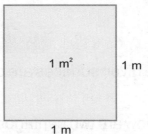

Example : *Find the area of a rectangle of length 4 cm and breadth 2 cm.*

           Verify that : Area of a rectangle = (Length × Breadth)

Solution : Let ABCD be the given rectangle with length 4 cm and breadth 2 cm.

Let us divide this rectangle into a number of squares, each of side 1 cm, as shown.

Clearly, it has been divided into 8 small squares, each of area 1 sq. cm.

Area of rectangle ABCD

           = 8 sq. cm or 8 cm².

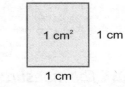

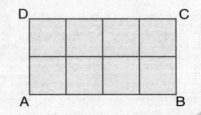

Also, (Length × Breadth) $= (4 × 2)$ cm^2 = 8 cm^2.

Note : (Area of a rectangle) = (Length × Breadth) sq. units.

From the multiplication fact :

Area = Length × Breadth

we get two division facts, namely

Length = $\dfrac{\text{Area}}{\text{Breadth}}$ and Breadth = $\dfrac{\text{Area}}{\text{Length}}$

Since a square is a rectangle whose length and breadth are equal, so

Area of a square = (side × side)

SUMMARY

(i) **Area of a rectangle = (Length × Breadth)**

(ii) **Length = $\dfrac{\text{Area}}{\text{Breadth}}$**   (iii) **Breadth = $\dfrac{\text{Area}}{\text{Length}}$**

(iv) **Area of a square = (Side × Side)**

SOLVED EXAMPLES

Example 1. *Find the area of a rectangle of length 25 cm and breadth 18 cm.*

Solution : Length of the rectangle = 25 cm.

Breadth of the rectangle = 18 cm.

Area of the rectangle = Length × Breadth

$= (25 × 18)$ sq. cm = 450 sq. cm.

Hence, the area of the rectangle is 450 sq. cm.

Example 2. *Find the area of a rectangular plot of land with length 58 metres and breadth 36.5 metres.*

Solution : Length of the plot = 58 m.

Breadth of the plot = 36.5 m.

Area of the plot = Length × Breadth

$= (58 × 36.5)$ sq. m = 2117 sq. m.

Hence, the area of the plot is 2117 sq. metres.

```
      3 6 5
    ×   5 8
    2 9 2 0
  1 8 2 5 0
  2 1 1 7 0
```

Example 3. *The length of a rectangle is 1.6 metres and its breadth is 75 cm. Find the area of the rectangle in sq. cm as well as in sq. metres.*

Solution : Length of the rectangle = 1.6 m = 160 cm.

Breadth of the rectangle = 75 cm.

Area of the rectangle = (Length × Breadth)

$= (160 × 75)$ sq. cm = 12000 sq. cm.

The Other Way (Area in sq. metres) :

Length of the rectangle = 1.6 m.

Breadth of the rectangle = 75 cm = 0.75 m.

Area of the rectangle = (Length × Breadth)

= (1.6 × 0.75) sq. m = 1.2 sq. m.

Hence, the area of the rectangle is 1.2 sq m.

Example 4. *A courtyard 20 m long and 15 m broad is to be paved with bricks of length 25 cm and breadth 12 cm. Find the number of bricks required.*

Solution : Length of the courtyard = 20 m = (20 × 100) cm.

Breadth of the courtyard = 15 m = (15 × 100) cm.

Area of the courtyard = (Length × Breadth)

= (20 × 100 × 15 × 100) sq cm.

Length of a brick = 25 cm.

Breadth of a brick = 12 cm.

Area of a brick = (25 × 12) sq cm.

∴ Required number of bricks = (Area of the courtyard) ÷ (Area of a brick)

$$= \frac{20 \times 100 \times 15 \times 100}{25 \times 12} = 10000.$$

Hence, the number of bricks required is 10000.

Example 5. *Find the length of a rectangular park whose area is 204 sq m and breadth is 12 m.*

Solution : Area of the park = 204 sq. m.

Breadth of the park = 12 m.

∴ Length of the park = $\dfrac{\text{Area}}{\text{Breadth}} = \left(\dfrac{204}{12}\right)$ m = 17 m.

Hence the length of the park is 17 m.

Example 6. *Find the breadth of a rectangle whose area is 285 sq. cm and length is 19 cm.*

Solution : Area of the rectangle = 285 sq cm.

Length of the rectangle = 19 cm.

∴ Breadth of the rectangle = $\dfrac{\text{Area}}{\text{Length}} = \dfrac{285}{19}$ cm = 15 cm.

Hence, the breadth of the rectangle is 15 cm.

Example 7. *Find the area of a square of side 1.6 metres.*

Solution : Side of the square = 1.6 m.

Area of the square = (side × side)

= (1.6 × 1.6) sq m = 2.56 sq. m.

Hence, the area of the square is 2.56 sq. m.

Example 8. *Find the area of a square whose perimeter is 76 cm.*

Solution : Perimeter of the square = 76 cm.

Side of the square = (76 ÷ 4) cm = 19 cm.

Area of the square = (side × side)

= (19 × 19) sq cm

= 361 sq. cm.

Hence, the area of the square is 361 sq. cm.

EXERCISE 78

Find the area of the rectangles having dimensions :

1. Length = 18 cm, Breadth = 12 cm
2. Length = 14 m, Breadth = 9 m
3. Length = 56 cm, Breadth = 8.5 cm
4. Length = 27.5 cm, Breadth =16 cm
5. Length =1.8 m, Breadth = 80 cm
6. Length = 2 m 50 cm, Breadth = 60 cm

Find the area of the square each of whose sides is :

7. 17 cm
8. 23 m
9. 13.5 cm
10. 3 m 40 cm

11. Find the length of the rectangle whose :

(*a*) area = 104 sq cm and breadth = 8 cm

(*b*) area = 378 sq m and breadth = 14 m

(*c*) area = 900 sq cm and breadth = 25 cm

(*d*) area = 102 sq m and breadth = 8.5 m

12. Find the breadth of the rectangle whose :

(*a*) area = 208 sq cm and length = 16 cm

(*b*) area = 391 sq cm and length = 23 cm

(*c*) area = 117 sq m and length = 13 m

(*d*) area = 52 sq m and length = 8 m

13. How many pieces of stone slabs, each 24 cm long and 15 cm broad will be required to lay a path 18 m long and 12 m wide?

14. How many blocks, each 25 cm long and 12 cm wide, will be required to lay a path 12.5 m long and 4.8 m wide?

15. Which carpet is bigger : one measuring 16 m in length and 12.5 m in breadth or another measuring 15 m in length and 13.8 m in breadth?

16. The floor of a hall is completely covered by 26 carpets, each measuring 4 m by 2.5 m. What is the area of the floor of the hall ?

17. *Find the area of each of the following figures :*

(a)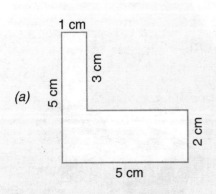

(b)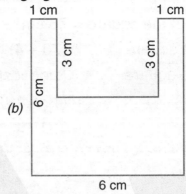

(c)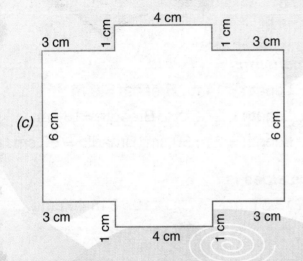

(d)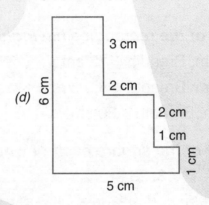

THINGS TO REMEMBER

1. The measure of the amount of surface enclosed by a closed bounded figure is called its area.

2. The area of a square with each side measuring 1 cm is 1 square centimetre, written as 1 sq cm or 1 cm^2.

3. The area of a square with each side measuring 1 m is 1 square metre, written as 1 sq m or 1 m^2.

4. (a) Area of a rectangle = (*Length* × *Breadth*) sq units.

   (b) Length = $\dfrac{\text{Area}}{\text{Breadth}}$ (c) Breadth = $\dfrac{\text{Area}}{\text{Length}}$

5. Area of a square = (side × side) sq units.

ACTIVITY TIME

Activity–1

On a 1 cm × 1 cm square grid, try forming as many English letters as possible, as shown below.

Now compute the area occupied by each letter by counting the number of shaded complete squares and half squares.

For example let us calculate the area of letter A.
'A' occupies 8 complete squares and 2 half - squares.

So, area of letter 'A' $= \left(8 \times 1 + 2 \times \dfrac{1}{2} \right)$ sq. cm = 9 sq . cm.

Similarly, M occupies 8 complete squares and 4 half - squares.

So, area of letter 'M' $= \left(8 \times 1 + 4 \times \dfrac{1}{2} \right)$ sq. cm = 10 sq. cm.

You may repeat the above activity by writing your name on the grid and calculating the area occupied by it by summing up the areas occupied by individual letters.

Activity–2

We may calculate the approximate area of some plane irregular objects also by using the 1 cm × 1 cm square grid.

Let us find the approximate area of a leaf.

Take a leaf. Place it on the grid and trace its outline as shown below.

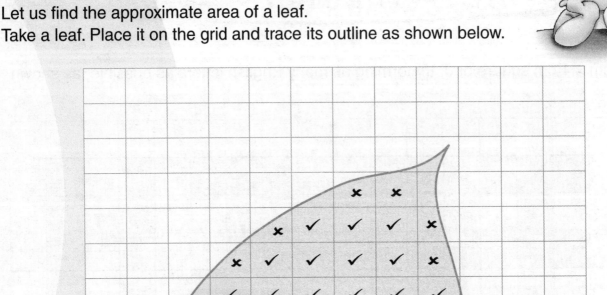

Inside the outline so marked, mark the complete squares with ✓ and the more - than - half squares by ✗.

To calculate the approximate area, we add the number of complete and more-than-half squares occupied by the object on the grid. Note here that half and less-than-half squares are discarded.

For example,

The approximate area of leaf shown above

> = number of complete squares + number of more- than-half squares
>
> = (33 + 11) sq. cm = 44 sq. cm.

C.C.E. DRILL - 18

QUESTION BAG -1

(OBJECTIVE -TYPE QUESTIONS)

Tick (✓) the correct answer :

1. Area of a rectangle is
    (*a*) 2 (length × breadth)   (*b*) length × breadth
    (*c*) 2 (length + breadth)   (*d*) None of these

2. Which of the following has the greatest area ?
    (*a*) A rectangle of length 18 m and breadth 8 m
    (*b*) A square of length 13 m
    (*c*) A rectangle of length 12 m and breadth 14 m
    (*d*) All have the some area

3. The number of squares on a game board of each side 8 cm, if the side of each square is 1 cm, is
    (*a*) 24   (*b*) 32   (*c*) 48   (*d*) 64

4. *In which of the following problems do you need to calculate the area?*
    (*a*) To find the depth of water in a lake
    (*b*) To find the quantity of water in a pool
    (*c*) To find how much paint it will take to cover a wall
    (*d*) To find the length of track traced by an athlete running around a football field

5. The area of the figure shown here is
    (*a*) 10 sq .cm   (*b*) 12 sq. cm   (*c*) 13 sq. cm   (*d*) 15 sq. cm

6. The perimeter and area of a square are numerically equal. The length of a side of the square is
    (*a*) 1 unit   (*b*) 2 units   (*c*) 4 units   (*d*) 8 units

7. Anna is making a rectangular quilt from square pieces of cloth. She fits 8 pieces along the breadth and 15 pieces along the length. How many pieces does she need in all?
    (*a*) 150   (*b*) 120   (*c*) 100   (*d*) 90

8. Each side of the figure shown below, measures 1 cm. The area of the figure is
    (*a*) 9 sq. cm   (*b*) 12 sq. cm
    (*c*) 13 sq. cm   (*d*) Can't say

9. A wooden frame of area 36 sq.m comes in four possible sizes.

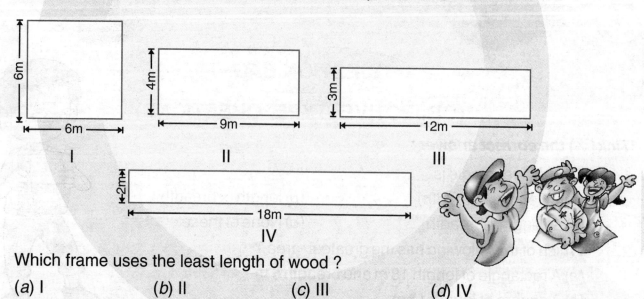

Which frame uses the least length of wood ?

(a) I (b) II (c) III (d) IV

10. Which figure has an area of 24 sq units and a perimeter of 20 units? (Each small square is a unit square).

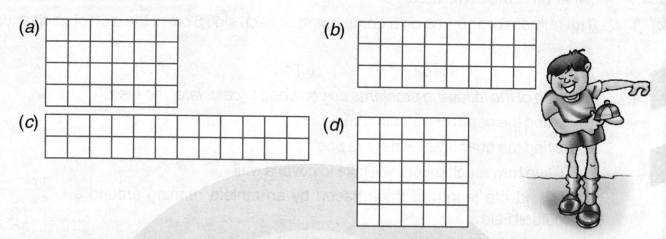

11. The area of a rectangle is 208 sq. cm and its length is 16 cm. Then, its breadth is

(a) 26 cm (b) 13 cm (c) 19.2 cm (d) 19.5 cm

12. A room is 5.4 m long and 4.5 m wide. Its area is

(a) 23.4 sq.m (b) 24.3 sq.m (c) 25 sq.m (d) 19.8 sq.m

13. The perimeter of a square is 84 cm. Its area is

(a) 168 sq.cm (b) 336 sq.cm (c) 441 sq.cm (d) 1764 sq.cm

14. The length of a rectangle is 1.6 m and its breadth is 75 cm. Then, its area is

(a) 1200 sq.cm (b) 12000 sq.cm (c) 6000 sq.cm (d) 9000 sq.cm

1. *Fill in the blanks :*

    (a) 1 sq. m = ☐ sq. cm

    (b) Length of a rectangle = $\dfrac{\text{Area}}{\boxed{}}$

    (c) Breadth of a rectangle = $\dfrac{\text{Area}}{\boxed{}}$

2. Calculate the area and perimeter of a rectangle of length $16\frac{2}{3}$ m and breadth $4\frac{1}{2}$ m.

3. The area of a rectangle is $8\frac{2}{3}$ sq. cm. If its length is $5\frac{7}{9}$ cm, find its perimeter.

4. A rectangular park is 64 m long and 56 m broad. Find the cost of

    (a) levelling the park at Rs 4.50 per sq.m

    (b) fencing the park at Rs 76.50 per metre

5. Find the number of square tiles to be laid in a square path of side 18 cm if the side of each tile is 3 cm.

6. A room is 13.6 m long and 6.4 m wide. It is to be paved with square marble tiles each of side 80 cm. How many marble tiles will be required ?

7. *State whether each of the following statements is true or false :*

    (a) To find the size of carpet required for a room, we need to measure the perimeter ....

    (b) Two figures having the same area also have the same perimeter ....

24 VOLUME

The objects having definite shape and size are called **solids**. *Solid objects occur in different shapes. We are already familiar with the shapes of some solids shown below.*

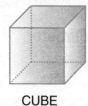 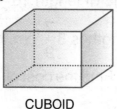   

| CUBE | CUBOID | CONE | CYLINDER | SPHERE |

Each of these solids occupies a certain amount of space, called **volume.**

Let us revive the ideas about a cuboid and a cube.

CUBOID:

A solid bounded by six rectangular faces is called a **cuboid**.

A match box, a chalk box, a brick, a tile, a book, an almirah etc. are all examples of a cuboid.

CUBE:

A cuboid whose length, breadth and height are all equal, is called a **cube**.

Dice, Ice-cubes, Sugar cubes etc. are all examples of a cube.

The measure of the amount of space occupied by a solid is called its **volume**.

In this chapter, we shall learn the method of finding the volume of a cuboid and that of a cube.

(i) CUBIC CENTIMETRE

   The volume of a cube of edge 1 cm, is called **1 cubic centimetre.**
   We denote it by **1 cu. cm** or **1 cm³.**

(ii) CUBIC METRE

   The volume of a cube of edge 1 m, is called **1 cubic metre.**
   We denote it by **1 cu.m** or **1 m³.**

Example   :   *Find the volume of a cuboid of length 4 cm, breadth 3 cm and height 1 cm.*

Solution : We may divide it into a number of cubes, each of edge 1 cm, as shown in the figure given below.

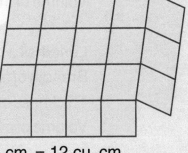

The volume of each such cube is 1 cu.cm.

Clearly, 12 such cubes are formed.

∴ Volume of given cuboid = 12 cu. cm.

Also (Length × Breadth × Height) = (4 × 3 × 1) cu. cm. = 12 cu. cm.

Similarly, we may repeat with some more cuboids.

In each case, we shall find that:

Volume of a Cuboid = (Length × Breadth × Height) cubic units ◎

Since a cube is a cuboid in which length = breadth = height, we have

Volume of a Cube = (Side × Side × Side) cubic units ◎

SOLVED EXAMPLES

Example 1 . *The length, breadth and height of a cuboid are 12 cm, 8 cm and 6.5 cm respectively. Find its volume.*

Solution : Length of the cuboid = 12 cm.

Breadth of the cuboid = 8 cm.

Height of the cuboid = 6.5 cm.

Volume of the cuboid = length × breadth × height

= (12 × 8 × 6.5) cu cm

= 624 cu cm.

Hence, the volume of the cuboid is 624 cu cm.

Example 2 . *Find the volume of a cube whose each edge measures 8 cm.*

Solution : Length of each side of the cube = 8 cm.

Volume of the cube = (Side × Side × Side) cubic units

= (8 × 8 × 8) cu cm

= 512 cu cm.

Hence, the volume of the cube is 512 cu cm.

Example 3 . *How many bricks each 24 cm long, 12.5 cm wide and 8 cm thick will be required to build a wall 18 m long, 2.5 m high and 40 cm thick?*

Solution : Length of the wall = 18 m = 1800 cm.

Height of the wall = 2.5 m = 250 cm.

Thickness of the wall = 40 cm.

Volume of the wall = (length × height × thickness) cubic units
= (1800 × 250 × 40) cu cm

Length of a brick = 24 cm.

Breadth of a brick = 12.5 cm.

Thickness of a brick = 8 cm.

Volume of a brick = (24 × 12.5 × 8) cu cm.

∴ The number of bricks required = $\dfrac{\text{Volume of the wall}}{\text{Volume of 1 brick}}$

$$= \dfrac{(1800 \times 250 \times 40)}{(24 \times 12.5 \times 8)}$$

$$= \dfrac{(1800 \times 250 \times 40 \times 10)}{(24 \times 125 \times 8)} = 7500.$$

Hence, the number of bricks required = 7500.

Example 4 . *How many boxes, each of size 12 cm × 8 cm × 6 cm can be packed in a carton of size 60 cm × 48 cm × 36 cm?*

Solution : Size of each box is (12 cm × 8 cm × 6 cm).

∴ Length of the box = 12 cm, Breadth of the box = 8 cm,

Height of the box = 6 cm.

∴ Volume of 1 box = (12 × 8 × 6) cubic cm.

Size of each carton = (60 cm × 48 cm × 36 cm).

∴ Length of each carton = 60 cm, Breadth of each carton = 48 cm,

Height of each carton = 36 cm.

∴ Volume of each carton = (60 × 48 × 36) cubic cm.

Required number of boxes = $\dfrac{\text{Volume of 1 carton}}{\text{Volume of 1 box}}$

$$= \dfrac{(60 \times 48 \times 36)}{(12 \times 8 \times 6)} = 180.$$

EXERCISE 79

1. *Find the volume of the cuboid whose dimensions are :*
   (a) length = 16 cm, breadth = 12 cm, height = 8 cm
   (b) length = 14 m, breadth = 8 m, height = 2.5 m
   (c) length = 12.5 cm, breadth = 7.8 cm, height = 6 cm
   (d) length = 4.8 m, breadth = 3.5 m, height = 0.75 m

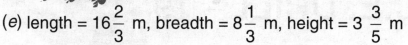

(e) length = $16\frac{2}{3}$ m, breadth = $8\frac{1}{3}$ m, height = $3\frac{3}{5}$ m

2. Find the volume of the cube whose edge is:

    (a) 14 cm   (b) $3\frac{1}{2}$ m   (c) 1.2 m   (d) 6.5 cm

3. Find the volume of the earth dug out from a pit 6.5 m long, 2.4 m wide and 1.5 m deep.

4. Find the volume of the earth dug out from a cubical pit each of whose edges measures 4.1 metres.

5. *A room is 12 m long, 7.8 m broad and 5 m high.*

    (a) How much air does it contain?

    (b) How many boys can sit in the room, if each boy occupies 2.6 cubic metres of air space?

6. How many boxes, each of size 10 cm × 8 cm × 5 cm can be packed in a carton of size 1 m × 72 cm × 50 cm?

7. How many bricks each 25 cm long, 16 cm wide and 7.5 cm thick will be required to build a terrace 5 m long, 3 m broad and 80 cm high?

8. A wooden block measures 24 cm by 18 cm by 15 cm. How many cubical blocks of edge 6 cm can be cut from it?

9. *Fill in the blanks:*

    (a) The measure of the amount of space occupied by a solid is called its ....

    (b) Volume of a cuboid = ... × .... × ....

    (c) Volume of a cube   = ... × .... × ....

THINGS TO REMEMBER

1. Every solid body occupies a certain amount of space.
2. The measure of the amount of space occupied by a solid is called its volume.
3. Volume of a cuboid = (length × breadth × height) cubic units.
4. Volume of a cube = (side × side × side) cubic units.

QUESTION BAG - 1

(OBJECTIVE-TYPE QUESTIONS)

Tick (✓) *the correct answer:*

1. The volume of the adjoining box is

    (*a*) 180 cu. cm   (*b*) 210 cu. cm   (*c*) 225 cu. cm   (*d*) 240 cu. cm

2. How many ice-cubes with 2 cm side can be put in an ice-box whose dimensions are 4 cm × 4 cm × 4 cm?

    (*a*) 2   (*b*) 4   (*c*) 8   (*d*) 16

3. Each edge of a cubical box measures 160 cm. How many cubical packets of edge 8 cm can be packed in it?

    (*a*) 400   (*b*) 800   (*c*) 4000   (*d*) 8000

4. Box A measures 10 cm by 6 cm by 4 cm and Box B measures 6 cm by 6 cm by 7 cm. Which has greater volume?

    (*a*) Box A   (*b*) Box B

    (*c*) Both have the same volume   (*d*) Can't compare

5. The volume of a cube of side 6 cm is

    (*a*) 36 cu. cm   (*b*) 216 cu. cm   (*c*) 240 cu. cm   (*d*) 1296 cu. cm

6. How many small cubes of edge 10 cm can be put in a cubical box of side 80 cm?

    (*a*) 256   (*b*) 480   (*c*) 512   (*d*) 640

7. A cube of side 6 cm is cut into small cubes each of side 2 cm. How many small cubes will be formed?

    (*a*) 6   (*b*) 9   (*c*) 12   (*d*) 27

8. The volume of a cube whose edge measures 12 m is .... times the volume of a cuboid of dimensions 8 m × 6 m × 4 m.

    (*a*) 5   (*b*) 6   (*c*) 7   (*d*) 9

9. A cuboid measures 36 m × 24 m × 18 m. How many cubes of edge 6 m can be cut from the cuboid?

    (*a*) 36   (*b*) 72   (*c*) 144   (*d*) 288

10. Amit has 60 one-cm cubes. Which of these cuboids can he not build?

    (*a*) 5 cm long, 4 cm wide, 3 cm high   (*b*) 2 cm long, 3 cm wide, 10 cm high

    (*c*) 4 cm long, 4 cm wide, 4 cm high   (*d*) 6 cm long, 5 cm wide, 2 cm high

11. Volume of a cuboid is $\frac{1}{8}$ cu. m. What is its volume in cu. cm?

(a) 12500   (b) 25000   (c) 125000   (d) 250000

QUESTION BAG - 2

1. *Fill in the blanks:*

(a) To find the volume of a box, we multiply the area of its base by its ....

(b) Volume of a box of dimensions 9 m × 6 m × 3 m = ... cu. m

(c) Volume of a cube of side 4 cm = ... cu. cm.

(d) A tea pack has a volume of 2500 cu. cm. If its length is 25 cm and breadth is 10 cm, is height is ....

(e) A water tank holds 500 cu.m of water. Its height is 5 m and breadth is 4m. Its length is ....

(f) 1 cu. m = ... cu. cm.

2. Find the volume of a cuboid of length $12\frac{2}{3}$ cm, breadth $8\frac{1}{3}$ cm and height $3\frac{3}{5}$ cm.

3. Find the volume of a brick of dimensions 21.6 cm, 9.8 cm and 7.4 cm.

4. How many bricks will be needed to construct a wall 8 m long, 6 m high and 22 cm thick if each brick measures (25 cm × 11 cm × 6 cm)?

5. How many planks of size 2 m × 25 cm × 8 cm can be made from a wooden block 5 m long, 70 cm wide and 32 cm thick?

25 PICTOGRAPH AND BAR DIAGRAMS

INTRODUCTION

Numerical Data : *The collection of information in the form of numerical figures, is called* ***numerical data****.*

For example, the table below is the numerical data regarding the number of students present in a class during a week.

Monday	Tuesday	Wednesday	Thursday	Friday	Saturday
46	48	45	48	47	42

Pictorial Representation of Numerical Data : *We may represent numerical data through pictures or graphs, called pictorial representation of data.*

PICTOGRAPH

Representing numerical data by picture symbols is called a ***pictograph.***

SOLVED EXAMPLES

Example 1. *The following table shows the daily production of T.V. sets in an industry during a week.*

Day	Monday	Tuesday	Wednesday	Thursday	Friday	Saturday
Production	250	300	150	100	50	200

Represent the above information through a pictograph.

Solution : Scale : Take to represent 50 T.V. sets.

Then, we may draw the pictograph as under :

Day	Production
Monday	
Tuesday	

298

COMPOSITE MATHEMATICS – 5

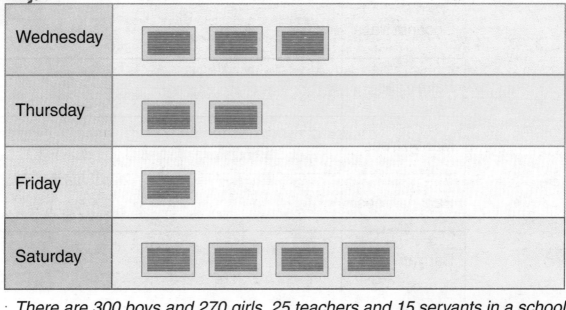

Wednesday	
Thursday	
Friday	
Saturday	

Example 2. There are 300 boys and 270 girls, 25 teachers and 15 servants in a school. Take your own scale and symbols and draw a pictograph to represent the data.

Solution : Let us take the following symbols and scale :

☐ ≡ 30 boys   △ ≡ 30 girls

◯ ≡ 5 teachers   ▭ ≡ 5 servants

Now, we may draw the pictograph as under :

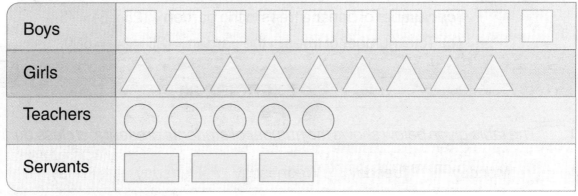

Boys	☐ ☐ ☐ ☐ ☐ ☐ ☐ ☐ ☐ ☐
Girls	△ △ △ △ △ △ △ △ △
Teachers	◯ ◯ ◯ ◯ ◯
Servants	▭ ▭ ▭

Example 3. Look at the symbols given below :

⬭ ≡ 25 coconut trees   ▭ ≡ 25 mango trees

◯ ≡ 25 banana trees   △ ≡ 25 palm trees

☐ ≡ 25 banyan trees   ✡ ≡ 25 neem trees

The following pictograph shows the number of various trees in a garden. Study the pictograph and answer the questions that follow :

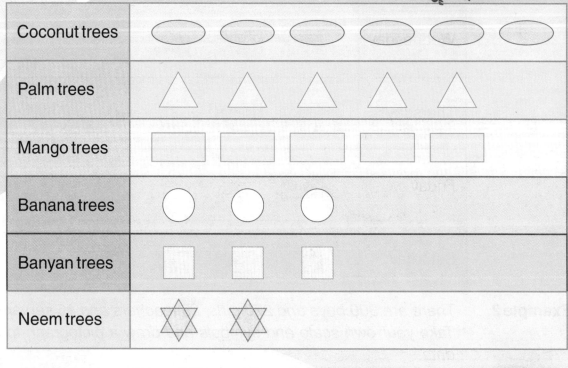

Coconut trees	
Palm trees	
Mango trees	
Banana trees	
Banyan trees	
Neem trees	

(a) How many coconut trees are there in the garden?

(b) How many palm trees are there in the garden?

(c) How many banana trees are there in the garden?

(d) How many trees are there in the garden?

Solution : (a) Number of coconut trees in the garden = (25 × 6) = 150.

(b) Number of palm trees in the garden = (25 × 5) = 125.

(c) Number of banana trees in the garden = (25 × 3) = 75.

(d) Total number of trees in the garden = (25 × 24) = 600.

EXERCISE 80

1. The table given below shows the number of students present in a class during a week.

Monday	Tuesday	Wednesday	Thursday	Friday	Saturday
36	30	33	39	30	27

Take △ to represent 3 students present in the class and draw the pictograph.

2. There are 6500 men, 4500 women and 1500 children in a village.

Taking the scale ▢ ≡ 500 men, ▢ ≡ 500 women and ◯ ≡ 500 children,

draw the pictograph to show the population of the village.

3. The number of various types of vehicles running in a day, on the roads of Meerut city is shown below :

Cycles	Scooters	Cars	Buses
800	500	300	200

Convey the above information through the pictograph.

4. *The following pictograph shows the number of students using various modes of transportation for going to their schools.*

On foot	
On Bicycle	
By Car	
By Bus	

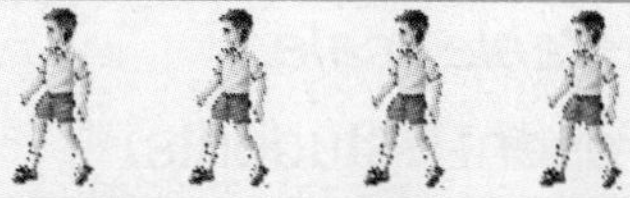

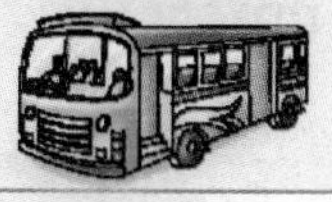

If each picture represents 100 students using that mode, answer the questions given below :

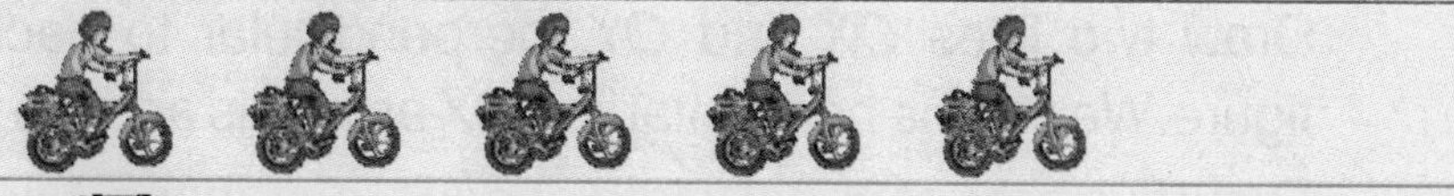

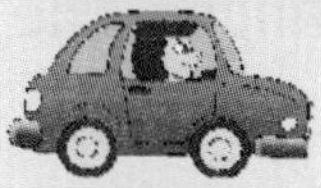

(*a*) How many students go to school on foot?

(*b*) How many students use school bus?

(*c*) How many students use cycles to go to their school?

(*d*) How many students are there in all in the school?

(*e*) What mode is adopted by maximum number of students?

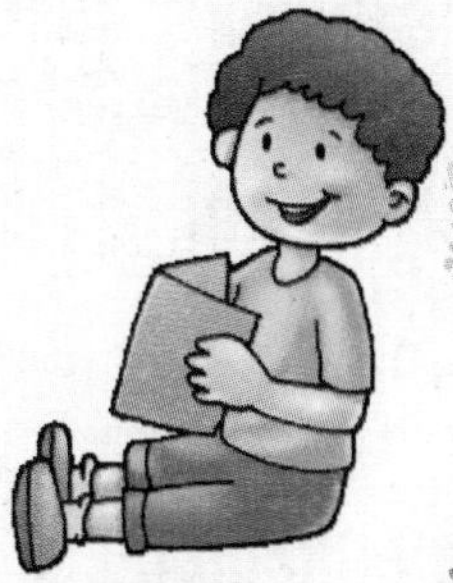

5. There are 1350 persons living in a colony of Delhi. The number of persons knowing various languages is given below :

Hindi	Tamil	Bengali	Malayalam
500	450	250	150

Draw a pictograph which conveys the above information.

BAR GRAPH

In a bar graph, the numerical data is represented by rectangles of equal width with equal space between them.

These rectangles are called ***bars.***

These bars are of various heights, drawn by selecting a particular scale.

SOLVED EXAMPLES

Example 1.   *The table given below shows the number of students in various standards of primary section of a school.*

Standard	I	II	III	IV	V
Number of students	65	50	45	35	25

Draw a bar graph by taking a suitable scale.

Solution :   Choose the scale : 1 cm to represent 5 students.

Step 1 :   Draw two lines *OX* and *OY*, perpendicular to each other, as shown in the figure. We call the horizontal line OX as x-axis and the vertical line OY as y-axis.

Step 2 :   Draw five bars of equal width at equal distances. The heights of these bars are respectively:

$$\frac{65}{5} = 13 \text{ cm for I; } \frac{50}{5} = 10 \text{ cm for II; } \frac{45}{5} = 9 \text{ cm for III;}$$

$$\frac{35}{5} = 7 \text{ cm for IV and } \frac{25}{5} = 5 \text{ cm for V.}$$

Step 3 :   Shade these bars with a fine pencil, as shown below.

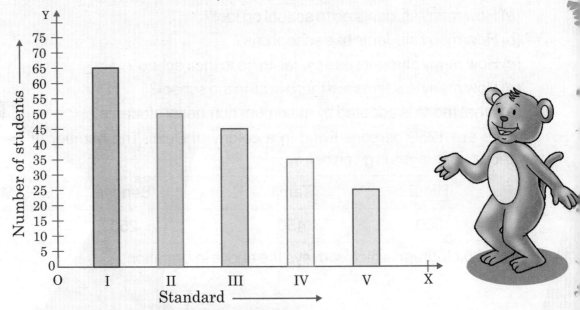

Example 2 .   *The following bar graph shows the number of men, women and children in a village.*

Scale : 1 cm to represent 50 people.

Read the bar graph carefully and answer the following questions :

(a) *What is the scale of the graph?*

(b) *How many men are there in the village?*

(c) *How many women are there in the village?*

(d) *How many children are there in the village?*

(e) *What is the total population of the village?*

Solution :

(a) The scale is : 1 cm represents 50 people.

(b) Clearly, there are 750 men in the village.

(c) Clearly, there are 550 women in the village.

(d) Clearly, there are 200 children in the village.

(e) Total population of the village = 750 + 550 + 200 = 1500.

EXERCISE 81

1. The table given below shows the number of absentees in a school during first five days of a week.

Day	I	II	III	IV	V
Number of absentees	30	45	20	50	15

Draw a bar graph to convey the information.

2. The marks obtained by Amit in five consecutive tests are given below :

Test	I	II	III	IV	V
Marks Obtained	60	80	40	70	90

Draw a bar graph showing the marks obtained by Amit in these tests.

3. There are 300 students in a school. Out of these 125 speak Tamil, 75 speak Telugu, 50 speak Malayalam, 25 speak Hindi and 25 speak Bengali. Draw a bar graph to represent the data.

4. The number of different books in a library are given below :

English	Mathematics	General Knowledge	Science	Tamil
450	600	150	250	200

Draw a bar graph to represent the above data.

5. The following bar graph shows the rainfall (in cm) at a place during 6 months of a year.

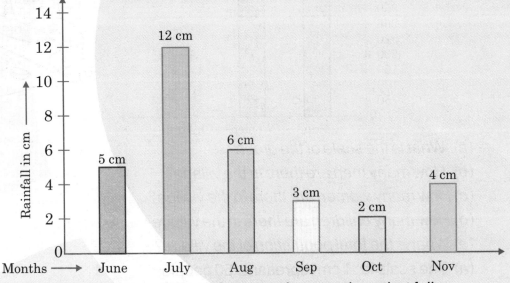

Read the bar graph carefully and answer the questions that follow :

(*a*) In which month the rainfall was maximum?

(*b*) How much was the rainfall in September?

(*c*) Which month was the driest ?

6. Read the bar-graph given below and answer the following questions :

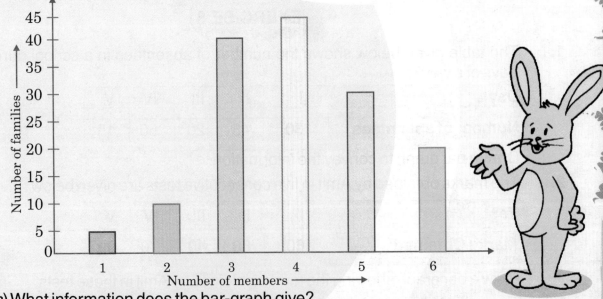

(*a*) What information does the bar-graph give?

(*b*) How many families have 3 members?

(*c*) How many families have 6 members?

ANSWERS

EXERCISE 1

1. (a) XVIII (b) XXVI (c) XXXIII (d) XXXIX (e) XLIV (f) LXV (g) LXXVII (h) LXXXII
   (i) XCI (j) XCIX

2. (a) 66 (b) 31 (c) 45 (d) 68 (e) 90 (f) 97 (g) 73 (h) 81
   (i) 79 (j) 95

3. (a) Five lakh thirty-seven thousand four hundred twelve (b) Eighty-eight thousand eighty-eight
   (c) Six hundred thirty-six thousand nine hundred five (d) One lakh one thousand one
   (e) Forty-nine lakh six thousand ninety (f) Fourteen lakh one hundred forty
   (g) Nine million five hundred thirty-six thousand eighty-seven (h) Eight million eighty thousand eighty

4. (a) 20,022 (b) 5,05,505 (c) 4,40,040 (d) 10,00,030 (e) 206,501 (f) 1,354,015 (g) 2,032,108 (h) 5,000,008

5. (a) 100 (b) 10

6. (a)

Digit	2	8	9	6	7
Place Value	20000	8000	900	60	7

(b)

Digit	5	3	0	1	9	4
Place Value	500000	30000	0	100	90	4

(c)

Digit	5	2	6	7	9	0	8
Place Value	5000000	200000	60000	7000	900	0	8

7. (a) 8991 (b) 940000 (c) 6999300

8. (a) 80000 + 600 + 50 + 6 (b) 400000 + 5000 + 70 + 7 (c) 1000000 + 800000 + 60000 + 5000 + 500 + 40

9. (a) 2,08,006 (b) 10,10,550 (c) 23,04,004

10. (a) < (b) > (c) < (d) < (e) < (f) <

11. (a) 10359 (b) 87520   12. (a) 5056 (b) 9663

13. (a) 174918 (b) 607437 (c) 2176600 (d) 3325948   14. Rs 127153   15. 589289

16. (a) 235755 (b) 267027 (c) 1454506   17. 37406   18. 271613

19. (a) 1685740 (b) 3962300 (c) 9785000 (d) 62100 (e) 4350000 (f) 5265000

20. (a) 2063553 (b) 2295986 (c) 2682090   21. Rs 716002

22. (a) Q = 879, R = 59 (b) Q = 8796, R = 31 (c) Q = 8769, R = 65 (d) Q = 13250, R = 7
    (e) Q = 10465, R = 49 (f) Q = 235, R = 174

23. 907 km   24. 349

25. (a) 1, 2, 3, 4, 6, 8, 12, 16, 24, 48 (b) 1, 2, 3, 4, 5, 6, 8, 10, 12, 15, 20, 24, 30, 40, 60, 120

26. (a) 7, 14, 21, 28, 35 (b) 18, 36, 54, 72

27. (a) 1, 3, 5, 7, 9, 11, 13, 15, 17, 19 (b) 72, 74, 76, 78, 80, 82, 84, 86, 88

28. 2, 5, 13, 17, 31, 37, 43, 49, 71, 73, 83, 97   29. (a) 8 (b) 15

30. (a) 24 (b) 60   31. (a) 48 (b) 30 (c) 33

32. (a) $\dfrac{15}{18}$ (b) $\dfrac{30}{36}$ (c) $\dfrac{35}{42}$ (d) $\dfrac{50}{60}$

33. (a) < (b) > (c) < (d) > (e) < (f) >

34. (a) $\dfrac{2}{7}, \dfrac{3}{7}, \dfrac{5}{7}, \dfrac{6}{7}$ (b) $\dfrac{2}{19}, \dfrac{10}{19}, \dfrac{13}{19}, \dfrac{15}{19}$ (c) $\dfrac{1}{7}, \dfrac{1}{5}, \dfrac{1}{4}, \dfrac{1}{3}, \dfrac{1}{2}$ (d) $\dfrac{5}{11}, \dfrac{5}{10}, \dfrac{5}{9}, \dfrac{5}{8}, \dfrac{5}{6}$

35. (a) $\dfrac{5}{7}$ (b) $\dfrac{7}{9}$ (c) $\dfrac{7}{8}$ (d) $\dfrac{9}{11}$ 36. (a) $\dfrac{2}{5}$ (b) $\dfrac{3}{7}$ (c) $\dfrac{2}{13}$ (d) $\dfrac{4}{15}$

37. (a) $\dfrac{47}{7}$ (b) $\dfrac{75}{8}$ (c) $\dfrac{96}{17}$ 38. (a) $11\dfrac{8}{9}$ (b) $17\dfrac{2}{11}$ (c) $14\dfrac{2}{15}$

39. (a) 0.3 (b) 0.07 (c) 0.23 (d) 0.009 (e) 0.079

40. (a) $\dfrac{6}{10}$ (b) $\dfrac{75}{100}$ (c) $32\dfrac{5}{10}$ (d) $\dfrac{64}{1000}$ (e) $65\dfrac{189}{1000}$

41. (a) $10 + 8 + \dfrac{9}{10} + \dfrac{5}{100} + \dfrac{6}{1000}$ (b) $400 + 2 + \dfrac{5}{100}$ (c) $50 + 9 + \dfrac{3}{1000}$

42. (a) Rs 663.64   (b) Rs 963.52   (c) Rs 186.11   43. (a) Rs 692.93   (b) Rs 57.92   (c) Rs 91.71
44. Rs 137.20   45. Rs 13182.75   46. Rs 9.75
47. (a) 230 m   (b) 8056 mm   (c) 365 kg   (d) 2005 *l*   (e) 15730 *ml*   (f) 12220g
48. (a) 5 m 53 cm   (b) 2 *l* 685 *ml*   (c) 5 quintal 65 kg   (d) 8 kg 760 g
49. (a) 155 kg 724 g   (b) 133 m 54 cm   (c) 111 km 442 m   (d) 134 *l* 350 *ml*
50. (a) 13 m 28 cm   (b) 65 km 625 m   (c) 188 kg 748 g   (d) 26 *l* 576 *ml*
51. 297 m 75 cm   52. 13 kg 825 g   53. 23 *l* 725 *ml*   54. (a), (c), (d) and (f)
55. (a) point   (b) ray   (c) simple closed figure   (d) three   (e) square   (f) Diameter   (g) circumference
56. Sides: EF, FG, GH and EH
    Diagonals : EG, FH
57. 24 cm   58. 8 cm   59. (a) 26 cm   (b) 21 cm   60. (a) 31 m 60 cm   (b) 33 m 40 cm
61. (a) 1 : 10 a.m   (b) 11 : 30 a.m   (c) 1 : 10 p.m   (d) 1 : 00 p.m   62. 1 hour 40 minutes   63. 1 : 45 p.m
64. (a) No   (b) Yes   (c) No   (d) No   65. Friday   66. 11th June, 2010

EXERCISE 2

1. (a) LXXVIII   (b) CLXXXIX   (c) CCXLVII   (d) CXCVI   (e) CCCLXV   (f) CCCXCIX   (g) CDXLIX   (h) CDXCV
   (i) CCCXLIV   (j) CDLXVI
2. (a) 69   (b) 91   (c) 146   (d) 192   (e) 385   (f) 259   (g) 296   (h) 196
   (i) 266   (j) 313
3. (a), (c), (e), (g), (h), (i)
4. (a) <   (b) >   (c) >   (d) <   (e) <   (f) <

C.C.E. DRILL - 1

QUESTION BAG - 1

1. (a)   2. (c)   3. (b)   4. (c)   5. (b)   6. (b)   7. (d)   8. (b)

QUESTION BAG - 2

1. (a) CXCVIII   (b) 296   (c) CCXXIX   (d) CCCL   (e) 349   (f) CCCLXXXIX   (g) CDXXX
   (h) 404   (i) CDXCV   (j) 499
2. (a) V, L, D   (b) I, V   (c) D, M   3. (a), (b), (d), (e), (f), (h)
4. (a) XCIX, CIX, CXIX, CXX, CXXI   (b) CXC, CCXX, CCXL, CCLX, CCXC
   (c) CDXLV, CDLVIII, CDLXIII, CDLXV, CDLXIX
5. (a) LXXVII   (b) LXXXVIII   (c) XXVIII   (d) CCCXXIV   (e) CCLIV   (f) CDLXXXIII

EXERCISE 3

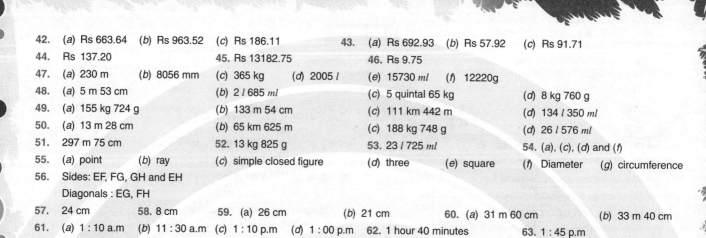

1. (a) 6,23,974   (b) 37,68,954   (c) 5,26,73,894   (d) 43,06,15,029
   (e) 68,10,08,546   (f) 70,50,00,038   (g) 80,08,08,088   (h) 90,00,00,100
   (i) 30,31,00,001
2. (a) Seventy-four lakh ten thousand five hundred seven   (b) Thirty-nine lakh three hundred two
   (c) Two crore forty-one lakh five thousand sixty-three   (d) Ten crore fifty-three thousand one hundred nine
   (e) Twenty-two crore seven lakh eight thousand five hundred eighteen
   (f) Thirty-six crore ten lakh six thousand two hundred eighty-four   (g) Fifty crore nineteen lakh six
   (h) Ten crore one lakh one thousand one hundred   (i) Four crore four lakh four thousand four
3. (a) 92,05,055   (b) 6,65,20,716   (c) 9,19,09,990   (d) 12,10,00,365
   (e) 5,00,42,109   (f) 23,05,07,108   (g) 30,00,15,018   (h) 52,01,00,031
   (i) 13,00,00,570   (j) 10,00,10,011   (k) 1,00,01,001
4.

Digit	6	4	1	9	7	5	2	8
Place Value	600000000	40000000	1000000	900000	70000	500	20	8

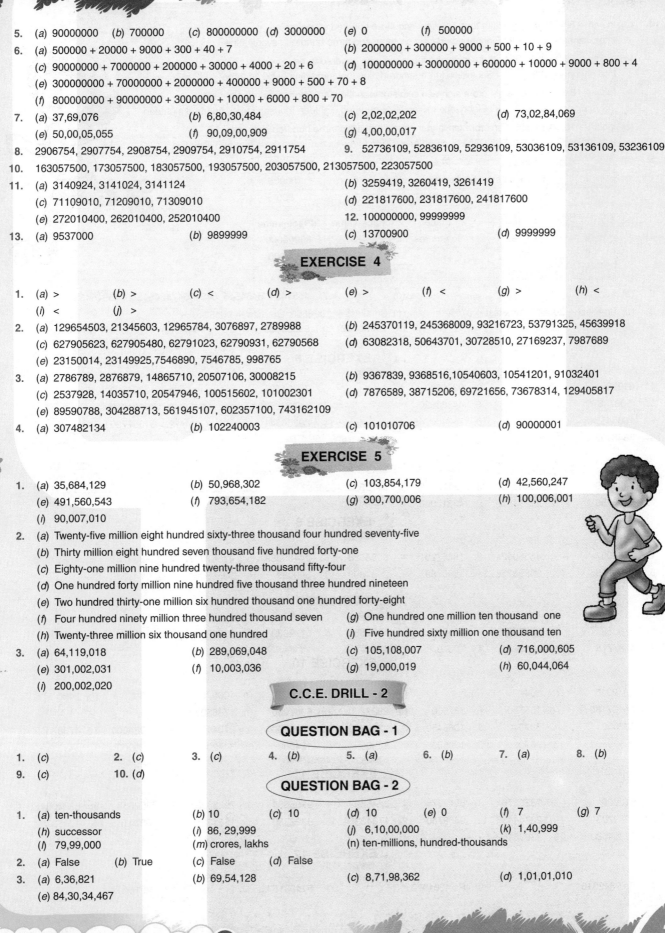

5. (a) 90000000   (b) 700000   (c) 800000000   (d) 3000000   (e) 0   (f) 500000

6. (a) 500000 + 20000 + 9000 + 300 + 40 + 7   (b) 2000000 + 300000 + 9000 + 500 + 10 + 9

   (c) 90000000 + 7000000 + 200000 + 30000 + 4000 + 20 + 6   (d) 100000000 + 30000000 + 600000 + 10000 + 9000 + 800 + 4

   (e) 300000000 + 70000000 + 2000000 + 400000 + 9000 + 500 + 70 + 8

   (f) 800000000 + 90000000 + 3000000 + 10000 + 6000 + 800 + 70

7. (a) 37,69,076   (b) 6,80,30,484   (c) 2,02,02,202   (d) 73,02,84,069

   (e) 50,00,05,055   (f) 90,09,00,909   (g) 4,00,00,017

8. 2906754, 2907754, 2908754, 2909754, 2910754, 2911754   9. 52736109, 52836109, 52936109, 53036109, 53136109, 53236109

10. 163057500, 173057500, 183057500, 193057500, 203057500, 213057500, 223057500

11. (a) 3140924, 3141024, 3141124   (b) 3259419, 3260419, 3261419

   (c) 71109010, 71209010, 71309010   (d) 221817600, 231817600, 241817600

   (e) 272010400, 262010400, 252010400   12. 100000000, 99999999

13. (a) 9537000   (b) 9899999   (c) 13700900   (d) 9999999

EXERCISE 4

1. (a) >   (b) >   (c) <   (d) >   (e) >   (f) <   (g) >   (h) <

   (i) <   (j) >

2. (a) 129654503, 21345603, 12965784, 3076897, 2789988   (b) 245370119, 245368009, 93216723, 53791325, 45639918

   (c) 627905623, 627905480, 62791023, 62790931, 62790568   (d) 63082318, 50643701, 30728510, 27169237, 7987689

   (e) 23150014, 23149925, 7546890, 7546785, 998765

3. (a) 2786789, 2876879, 14865710, 20507106, 30008215   (b) 9367839, 9368516, 10540603, 10541201, 91032401

   (c) 2537928, 14035710, 20547946, 100515602, 101002301   (d) 7876589, 38715206, 69721656, 73678314, 129405817

   (e) 89590788, 304288713, 561945107, 602357100, 743162109

4. (a) 307482134   (b) 102240003   (c) 101010706   (d) 90000001

EXERCISE 5

1. (a) 35,684,129   (b) 50,968,302   (c) 103,854,179   (d) 42,560,247

   (e) 491,560,543   (f) 793,654,182   (g) 300,700,006   (h) 100,006,001

   (i) 90,007,010

2. (a) Twenty-five million eight hundred sixty-three thousand four hundred seventy-five

   (b) Thirty million eight hundred seven thousand five hundred forty-one

   (c) Eighty-one million nine hundred twenty-three thousand fifty-four

   (d) One hundred forty million nine hundred five thousand three hundred nineteen

   (e) Two hundred thirty-one million six hundred thousand one hundred forty-eight

   (f) Four hundred ninety million three hundred thousand seven   (g) One hundred one million ten thousand one

   (h) Twenty-three million six thousand one hundred   (i) Five hundred sixty million one thousand ten

3. (a) 64,119,018   (b) 289,069,048   (c) 105,108,007   (d) 716,000,605

   (e) 301,002,031   (f) 10,003,036   (g) 19,000,019   (h) 60,044,064

   (i) 200,002,020

C.C.E. DRILL - 2

QUESTION BAG - 1

1. (c)   2. (c)   3. (c)   4. (b)   5. (a)   6. (b)   7. (a)   8. (b)

9. (c)   10. (d)

QUESTION BAG - 2

1. (a) ten-thousands   (b) 10   (c) 10   (d) 10   (e) 0   (f) 7   (g) 7

   (h) successor   (i) 86, 29,999   (j) 6,10,00,000   (k) 1,40,999

   (l) 79,99,000   (m) crores, lakhs   (n) ten-millions, hundred-thousands

2. (a) False   (b) True   (c) False   (d) False

3. (a) 6,36,821   (b) 69,54,128   (c) 8,71,98,362   (d) 1,01,01,010

   (e) 84,30,34,467

4. (a) Indian→ 8,46,379 ; Eight lakh forty-six thousand three hundred seventy-nine
   International→ 846,379 ; Eight hundred forty-six thousand three hundred seventy-nine

   (b) Indian→ 63,09,903 ; Sixty-three lakh nine thousand nine hundred three
   International→ 6,309,903 ; Six million three hundred nine thousand nine hundred three

   (c) Indian→ 8,18,18,818 ; Eight crore eighteen lakh eighteen thousand eight hundred eighteen
   International→ 81,818,818 ; Eighty-one million eight hundred eighteen thousand eight hundred eighteen

   (d) Indian→ 10,10,36,365 ; Ten crore ten lakh thirty-six thousand three hundred sixty-five
   International→ 101,036,365 ; One hundred one million thirty-six thousand three hundred sixty-five

5. (a)

Digit	Period	Place	Face-value	Place-value
1	Thousands	Hundred-thousands	1	100000
5	ones	Hundreds	5	500

   (b)

Digit	Period	Place	Face-value	Place-value
8	Crores	Ten-crores	8	800000000
6	Lakhs	Lakhs	6	600000
0	Ones	Tens	0	0

6. (a) >   (b) <   (c) >   (d) >   7. 4554454, 5454545, 5454554, 45454545, 45545455

8. (a) Smallest→ 205678, Greatest→ 875620   (b) Smallest→ 1023569, Greatest→ 9653210

9. (a) 102345   (b) 987654   10. (a) 10000002   (b) 99999987   11. (a) 1113569   (b) 1000478

EXERCISE 6

1. 6192891   2. 9330603   3. 78221184   4. 42224203
5. 50379875   6. 44533620   7. 447492576   8. 780919386
9. 188545548   10. 733466245   11. 20256341   12. 513977901
13. 784800815

EXERCISE 7

1. 14243996   2. 52498608   3. 12182462   4. 9172999, 15986674   5. 21021220, 34068766   6. 14847119
7. 1300796   8. 21211579   9. 43312000

EXERCISE 8

1. 2862067   2. 4158062   3. 1885728   4. 5385888   5. 24485889   6. 41567877   7. 38889758   8. 46687946
9. 29897596   10. 98898768   11. 1898889   12. 2987898   13. 590089   14. 3958806

EXERCISE 9

1. 578559   2. 277768   3. 485855   4. 1098866   5. 5779689   6. 218889   7. 644887   8. 5888887
9. 4687775   10. 2419636   11. 70070

EXERCISE 10

1. (a) 2346   (b) 2947   (c) 1   (d) 0   (e) 37   (f) 1000, 48   (g) 903   (h) 2460
2. (a) 27180   (b) 168750   (c) 387500   (d) 2927200   (e) 6087000   (f) 47385000
3. 327000   4. 587040   5. 1066450   6. 2367600   7. 6290200   8. 21044000   9. 11924000   10. 47382000
11. 199998000   12. 4670   13. 198600   14. 82900   15. 124000   16. 3472000   17. 5726000

EXERCISE 11

1. 610006   2. 1826276   3. 8949375   4. 3245393   5. 9765504   6. 7025838   7. 3352653   8. 8323084
9. 9289708   10. 22744436   11. 9089760   12. 17843364   13. 9322250   14. 15513855   15. 16074165   16. 10363782
17. 33264880   18. 23633162

EXERCISE 12

1. Rs 9842310   2. Rs 4301970   3. 5149815 kg   4. 160164 kg

5. 1071356 metres   6. 4600152   7. 1297116 metres   8. Rs 51677850
9. 607104   10. 32374656   11. 30576168

EXERCISE 13

1. Q = 1435, R = 24   2. Q = 5647, R = 43   3. Q = 7836, R = 4   4. Q = 2435, R = 29
5. Q = 2463, R = 104   6. Q = 5036, R = 92   7. Q = 4730, R = 67   8. Q = 13685, R = 47
9. Q = 15456, R = 47   10. Q = 15761, R = 562   11. Q = 10798, R = 254   12. Q = 10390, R = 785
13. Q = 10279, R = 373   14. Q = 17089, R = 67   15. Q = 12709, R = 121   16. 575682
17. 2246921   18. Q = 10010, R = 9   19. Q = 101010, R = 10

EXERCISE 14

1. 16095   2. 8709   3. Rs 4796   4. Rs 1650   5. 6875 kg   6. 7075 litres   7. 879   8. 1785
9. 2907   10. 8975, 50 metres   11. 1809

C.C.E. DRILL - 3

QUESTION BAG - 1

1. (a)   2. (c)   3. (d)   4. (d)   5. (d)   6. (c)   7. (d)   8. (c)
9. (d)   10. (b)

QUESTION BAG - 2

1. (a)
```
    6 3 [6] 7 8
  + [2][8] 9 [5] 4
    9 2 6 3 [2]
```
(b)
```
    [2] 8 7 5 [9] 6
  + 3 5 [9] 4 7 [8]
    6 [4] 7 [0] 7 4
```
(c)
```
    5 1 9 6 [4] 5
  −   [2] 7 [8][8] 2
    4 9 [1] 7 6 3
```
(d)
```
    7 0 [7] 2 8 6
  −   [3] 5 6 [5][9]
    6 7 1 [6] 2 7
```

2. (a) 1344216   (b) 7465165
3. (a) 63500   (b) 10000   (c) 850000   (d) 650000   (e) 2000   (f) 72000   (g) 1200000   (h) 0
    (i) 1   (j) 52000   (k) 12000000 (l) 1   (m) 0   (n) 2657
4. 9989001   5. 3444066   6. 1710465   7. 529134   8. 745   9. 238   10. 266 kg, 15694 kg
11. 31757818   12. Rs 6590400   13. 99975   14. 269, 36   15. 635580   16. 317584

EXERCISE 15

1. 15   2. 32   3. 7   4. 26   5. 103   6. 32   7. 34   8. 45
9. 11   10. 78   11. 215   12. 7

EXERCISE 16

1. 17   2. 12   3. 18   4. 16   5. 60   6. 8   7. 4   8. 3

C.C.E. DRILL - 4

QUESTION BAG - 1

1. (d)   2. (c)   3. (c)   4. (a)   5. (d)   6. (c)   7. (c)   8. (a)

QUESTION BAG - 2

1. (a) 2   (b) 6   (c) 6   (d) 13   (e) 200   (f) 180   (g) 71   (h) 12
    (i) 4   (j) 306
2. (a) 146   (b) 10102 (c) 3848   (d) 440   (e) 28   (f) 105
3. (a) True   (b) True   (c) True   (d) False   (e) True

EXERCISE 17

1. (a) 6, 12, 18, 24, 30, 36 (b) 11, 22, 33, 44, 55, 66 (c) 19, 38, 57, 76, 95, 114 (d) 21, 42, 63, 84, 105, 126
   (e) 25, 50, 75, 100, 125, 150
2. (a) 1, 2, 3, 6, 9, 18 (b) 1, 2, 4, 7, 14, 28 (c) 1, 2, 4, 8, 16, 32 (d) 1, 3, 5, 9, 15, 45
   (e) 1, 2, 3, 4, 5, 10, 12, 15, 20, 30, 60
3. (a), (b), (d), (e), (f) 4. (a), (c), (d), (f), (g) 5. (b), (c), (f), (h) 6. (a), (b), (d), (e), (g)
7. (a), (c), (e), (g) 8. (a), (b), (d), (f), (g) 9. (b), (d), (e), (f), (h) 10. (a), (b), (e), (f), (h)
11. (b), (c) 12. (a), (b), (e), (f), (h)
13. (a) Odd (b) Even (c) Odd (d) Odd (e) Even (f) Even (g) Even (h) Odd
14. (a) 74, 76, 78, 80, 82, 84, 86 (b) 520, 522, 524, 526, 528, 530
15. (a) 65, 67, 69, 71, 73, 75, 77, 79 (b) 625, 627, 629, 631, 633, 635, 637, 639

EXERCISE 18

1. 11, 67, 19, 83, 89 2. 51, 87, 81, 78, 93 3. 2, 3, 5, 7, 11, 13, 17, 19, 23, 29, 31, 37, 41, 43, 47
4. 53, 57, 61, 67, 71,73, 79, 83, 89, 97 5. (3, 5), (5, 7), (11, 13), (17, 19), (29, 31), (41, 43)
6. 93, 94, 95, 96, 98, 99 7. (5, 7), (5, 9), (7, 11), (21, 25)
8. (a) 2 × 2 × 3 × 5 (b) 2 × 2 × 3 × 7 (c) 2 × 2 × 3 × 3 × 5 (d) 2 × 3 × 5 × 7 (e) 2 × 2 × 2 × 7 × 13
9. (a) 2 × 3 × 3 × 5 (b) 2 × 2 × 2 × 3 × 3 × 3 (c) 2 × 2 × 3 × 5 × 5 (d) 3 × 3 × 5 × 7 (e) 2 × 3 × 3 × 5 × 5
10. (3, 5), (5, 7), (11, 13), (17, 19)
11. (a) 1 (b) 2 (c) 4 (d) 2 (e) 1 (f) 2 (g) 97

EXERCISE 19

1. (a) 8 (b) 9 (c) 8 (d) 4 (e) 7 (f) 4
2. (a) 15 (b) 18 (c) 12 (d) 15 (e) 26 (f) 36 (g) 14 (h) 6 (i) 24
3. (a) 8 (b) 12 (c) 21 (d) 28 (e) 36 (f) 7
4. (a) 8 (b) 6 (c) 55 (d) 16 (e) 14 (f) 12
5. (a) 24 (b) 27 (c) 24 (d) 36 (e) 115 (f) 55
6. (a) 6 (b) 5 (c) 15 (d) 41

EXERCISE 20

1. (a) 72 (b) 180 (c) 315 (d) 168 (e) 324 (f) 270
2. (a) 150 (b) 96 (c) 210 (d) 168 (e) 300 (f) 576 (g) 540 (h) 2040
   (i) 1728

EXERCISE 21

1. (a) H.C.F = 29, L.C.M. = 435 (b) H.C.F. = 23, L.C.M. = 1449 (c) H.C.F. = 90, L.C.M. = 1350
2. 60 3. 330 4. 195 5. 25 6. 55 7. 8 m 8. 9 litres 9. 48
10. 60 11. 120 seconds or 2 minutes

C.C.E. DRILL - 5

QUESTION BAG - 1

1. (c) 2. (b) 3. (b) 4. (a) 5. (b) 6. (d) 7. (c) 8. (d)
9. (d) 10. (c) 11. (c) 12. (b) 13. (d) 14. (a)

QUESTION BAG - 2

1. 19, 71, 59, 73, 67, 83, 97, 43
2.

	Number	2	3	4	5	6	8	9	10	11
(a)	99880	✓	x	✓	✓	x	✓	x	✓	✓
(b)	46632	✓	✓	✓	x	✓	✓	x	x	x
(c)	67968	✓	✓	✓	x	✓	✓	✓	x	x
(d)	726354	✓	✓	x	x	✓	x	x	x	x
(e)	50505	x	✓	x	✓	x	x	x	✓	x

3. (a) H.C.F = 2, L.C.M = 630　(b) H.C.F = 15, L.C.M = 90　(c) H.C.F = 6, L.C.M = 1386　(d) H.C.F = 15, L.C.M = 6930
　(e) H.C.F = 30, L.C.M = 180　(f) H.C.F = 14, L.C.M = 84

4. (a) 6　(b) 90　(c) 12　　5. (a) 23　(b) 11　(c) 32　(d) 34

6. (a) 360　(b) 3720　(c) 1680　(d) 7260　　7. 180 minutes or 3 hours

8. (a) False　(b) False　(c) True　(d) True　(e) True　(f) False　(g) True　(h) True
　(i) False　(j) True　(k) True　(l) True　(m) False　(n) False

EXERCISE 22

1. (a) Shaded = $\frac{2}{3}$, Unshaded = $\frac{1}{3}$　(b) Shaded = $\frac{1}{6}$, Unshaded = $\frac{5}{6}$　(c) Shaded = $\frac{4}{9}$, Unshaded = $\frac{5}{9}$

2. $\frac{1}{4}, \frac{1}{7}, \frac{1}{10}, \frac{1}{11}$　　3. (a) and (c)　　4. (a) and (b)　　5. (b) and (d)

6. (b), (c), (d) and (e)　　7. (a) $\frac{18}{5}$　(b) $\frac{19}{7}$　(c) $\frac{20}{3}$　(d) $\frac{29}{6}$　(e) $\frac{50}{7}$

8. (a) $2\frac{3}{4}$　(b) $2\frac{1}{8}$　(c) $3\frac{5}{6}$　(d) $3\frac{4}{5}$　(e) $2\frac{1}{7}$

9. (a) $\frac{4}{6}, \frac{6}{9}, \frac{8}{12}, \frac{10}{15}$　(b) $\frac{10}{12}, \frac{15}{18}, \frac{20}{24}, \frac{25}{30}$　(c) $\frac{8}{14}, \frac{12}{21}, \frac{16}{28}, \frac{20}{35}$　(d) $\frac{6}{10}, \frac{9}{15}, \frac{12}{20}, \frac{15}{25}$
　(e) $\frac{16}{22}, \frac{24}{33}, \frac{32}{44}, \frac{40}{55}$

10. (a) 20　(b) 24　(c) 35　(d) 81

11. $\frac{21}{33}$　　12. $\frac{35}{42}$　　13. $\frac{5}{6}$　　14. $\frac{7}{8}$

15. (a) Yes　(b) No　(c) Yes　(d) Yes　(e) Yes　(f) No

EXERCISE 23

1. Yes　2. Yes　3. No　4. No　5. No　6. Yes　7. $\frac{1}{3}$　8. $\frac{2}{3}$

9. $\frac{7}{8}$　10. $\frac{5}{6}$　11. $\frac{5}{9}$　12. $\frac{2}{5}$　13. $\frac{5}{9}$　14. $\frac{4}{5}$　15. $\frac{4}{5}$　16. $\frac{2}{3}$

17. $\frac{9}{10}$　18. $\frac{3}{4}$

EXERCISE 24

1. (a) $\frac{3}{4}$　(b) $\frac{6}{7}$　(c) $\frac{7}{9}$　(d) $\frac{11}{13}$　(e) $\frac{20}{21}$　(f) $\frac{23}{27}$

2. (a) $\frac{1}{5}$　(b) $\frac{5}{7}$　(c) $\frac{4}{9}$　(d) $\frac{7}{13}$　(e) $\frac{8}{11}$　(f) $\frac{6}{7}$

3. (a) $\frac{3}{11}, \frac{6}{11}, \frac{7}{11}, \frac{9}{11}, \frac{10}{11}$　(b) $\frac{2}{15}, \frac{7}{15}, \frac{8}{15}, \frac{11}{15}, \frac{13}{15}$
　(c) $\frac{3}{19}, \frac{5}{19}, \frac{7}{19}, \frac{11}{19}, \frac{13}{19}$　(d) $\frac{9}{25}, \frac{11}{25}, \frac{12}{25}, \frac{13}{25}, \frac{23}{25}$

4. (a) $\frac{3}{5}, \frac{3}{7}, \frac{3}{8}, \frac{3}{11}, \frac{3}{14}$　(b) $\frac{8}{9}, \frac{8}{11}, \frac{8}{13}, \frac{8}{15}, \frac{8}{17}$
　(c) $\frac{5}{6}, \frac{5}{8}, \frac{5}{11}, \frac{5}{12}, \frac{5}{14}$　(d) $\frac{10}{11}, \frac{10}{17}, \frac{10}{19}, \frac{10}{21}, \frac{10}{23}$

EXERCISE 25

1. (a) <　(b) >　(c) <　(d) >　(e) =　(f) <　(g) >　(h) >
　(i) >

2. (a) <　(b) >　(c) >　(d) <　(e) <　(f) <

3. (a) $\frac{2}{3}, \frac{7}{9}, \frac{5}{6}, \frac{11}{12}$　(b) $\frac{1}{2}, \frac{8}{15}, \frac{7}{10}, \frac{4}{5}$　(c) $\frac{3}{10}, \frac{1}{3}, \frac{2}{5}, \frac{5}{6}$　(d) $\frac{5}{12}, \frac{17}{24}, \frac{7}{8}, \frac{15}{16}$

4. (a) $\frac{3}{4}, \frac{5}{8}, \frac{9}{16}, \frac{1}{2}$　(b) $\frac{9}{14}, \frac{13}{28}, \frac{11}{35}, \frac{2}{7}$　(c) $\frac{7}{8}, \frac{3}{4}, \frac{17}{24}, \frac{7}{12}$　(d) $\frac{1}{2}, \frac{7}{15}, \frac{2}{5}, \frac{3}{10}$

(e) $\dfrac{5}{9}$, $\dfrac{1}{3}$, $\dfrac{4}{15}$, $\dfrac{3}{12}$　　　(f) $\dfrac{5}{6}$, $\dfrac{2}{3}$, $\dfrac{3}{8}$, $\dfrac{1}{2}$

C.C.E. DRILL - 6

QUESTION BAG - 1

1. (b)　　2. (c)　　3. (d)　　4. (b)　　5. (a)　　6. (a)　　7. (c)　　8. (d)
9. (a)　　10. (d)

QUESTION BAG - 2

1. (a) $\dfrac{15}{18}$　　(b) $\dfrac{35}{42}$　　(c) $\dfrac{225}{270}$　　(d) $\dfrac{300}{360}$

2.

Improper fraction	$\dfrac{41}{7}$	$\dfrac{86}{9}$	$\dfrac{115}{13}$	$\dfrac{227}{15}$	$\dfrac{395}{54}$	$\dfrac{120}{21}$
Mixed Numeral	$5\dfrac{6}{7}$	$9\dfrac{5}{9}$	$8\dfrac{11}{13}$	$15\dfrac{2}{15}$	$7\dfrac{17}{54}$	$5\dfrac{15}{21}$

3. (a) <　　(b) <　　(c) >　　(d) <

4. (a) $\dfrac{8}{9}$, $\dfrac{6}{7}$, $\dfrac{3}{4}$, $\dfrac{5}{8}$, $\dfrac{2}{5}$, $\dfrac{1}{3}$　　(b) $\dfrac{4}{7}$, $\dfrac{2}{9}$, $\dfrac{11}{63}$, $\dfrac{1}{21}$

5. (a) True　(b) False　(c) False　(d) True　(e) False　(f) False　(g) False　(h) False

6. (a) $3\dfrac{5}{6}$　(b) $\dfrac{52}{7}$　(c) $\dfrac{7}{13}$　(d) improper　(e) decreases　(f) $\dfrac{4}{9}$

EXERCISE 26

1. 1　　2. $\dfrac{7}{9}$　　3. $1\dfrac{1}{11}$　　4. $1\dfrac{2}{7}$　　5. $1\dfrac{1}{4}$　　6. $1\dfrac{1}{3}$　　7. $1\dfrac{1}{4}$　　8. $1\dfrac{4}{15}$
9. $1\dfrac{1}{10}$　　10. $1\dfrac{3}{16}$　　11. 1　　12. $1\dfrac{7}{19}$

EXERCISE 27

1. $\dfrac{7}{10}$　2. $1\dfrac{5}{21}$　3. $1\dfrac{5}{18}$　4. $1\dfrac{2}{3}$　5. $\dfrac{41}{48}$　6. $1\dfrac{5}{24}$　7. $\dfrac{13}{15}$　8. $\dfrac{59}{60}$
9. $1\dfrac{23}{36}$　10. $1\dfrac{11}{12}$　11. $3\dfrac{13}{24}$　12. $1\dfrac{6}{7}$　13. $1\dfrac{17}{36}$　14. $1\dfrac{23}{24}$　15. $1\dfrac{11}{48}$　16. $2\dfrac{1}{36}$
17. $1\dfrac{1}{4}$　18. $3\dfrac{1}{24}$

EXERCISE 28

1. $7\dfrac{3}{5}$　2. $8\dfrac{6}{7}$　3. $9\dfrac{5}{8}$　4. $9\dfrac{3}{4}$　5. $3\dfrac{1}{14}$　6. $3\dfrac{1}{9}$　7. $7\dfrac{7}{12}$　8. $6\dfrac{3}{5}$
9. $7\dfrac{13}{18}$　10. $4\dfrac{23}{30}$　11. $11\dfrac{3}{10}$　12. $8\dfrac{13}{18}$

EXERCISE 29

1. 2　2. $\dfrac{1}{4}$　3. $\dfrac{2}{5}$　4. $\dfrac{1}{5}$　5. $\dfrac{1}{5}$　6. $\dfrac{2}{3}$　7. 1　8. $\dfrac{2}{9}$　9. $\dfrac{1}{7}$

EXERCISE 30

1. $\dfrac{1}{6}$　2. $\dfrac{1}{2}$　3. $\dfrac{1}{12}$　4. $\dfrac{1}{24}$　5. $\dfrac{1}{6}$　6. $\dfrac{11}{12}$　7. $\dfrac{1}{2}$　8. $5\dfrac{2}{5}$
9. $\dfrac{29}{48}$　10. $\dfrac{7}{15}$　11. $4\dfrac{3}{8}$　12. $1\dfrac{5}{6}$　13. $1\dfrac{1}{4}$　14. $2\dfrac{5}{9}$　15. $2\dfrac{11}{12}$　16. $1\dfrac{1}{4}$
17. $2\dfrac{1}{24}$　18. $1\dfrac{5}{6}$　19. $4\dfrac{1}{36}$　20. $3\dfrac{7}{15}$　21. $\dfrac{7}{8}$　22. $3\dfrac{1}{7}$　23. $3\dfrac{1}{20}$　24. $\dfrac{7}{12}$

312

COMPOSITE MATHEMATICS – 5

EXERCISE 31

1. $\dfrac{5}{8}$ 2. $1\dfrac{1}{8}$ 3. $\dfrac{5}{18}$ 4. $\dfrac{4}{5}$ 5. $\dfrac{1}{6}$ 6. $\dfrac{5}{18}$ 7. $4\dfrac{1}{12}$ 8. $5\dfrac{5}{24}$

9. $\dfrac{1}{18}$ 10. $1\dfrac{1}{2}$ 11. $2\dfrac{3}{8}$ 12. $\dfrac{1}{6}$

EXERCISE 32

1. $2\dfrac{1}{20}$ m 2. $4\dfrac{1}{12}$ hours 3. $9\dfrac{5}{8}$ kg 4. $3\dfrac{9}{20}$ m 5. $11\dfrac{2}{5}$ litres 6. $26\dfrac{5}{12}$ kg 7. Vikas, $4\dfrac{11}{12}$ cm

8. $4\dfrac{1}{10}$ 9. $1\dfrac{17}{18}$ 10. $9\dfrac{1}{3}$ km 11. $8\dfrac{1}{18}$ kg 12. $2\dfrac{5}{12}$ m 13. The sum of $1\dfrac{3}{12}$ and $1\dfrac{1}{3}$

C.C.E. DRILL - 7

QUESTION BAG - 1

1. (c) 2. (d) 3. (d) 4. (b) 5. (c) 6. (b) 7. (d) 8. (c) 9. (b)

QUESTION BAG - 2

1. False 2. $\dfrac{1}{15}$ cup 3. (a) $1\dfrac{17}{30}$ (b) $5\dfrac{1}{18}$ (c) $8\dfrac{5}{12}$

4. (a) $5\dfrac{21}{40}$ (b) $2\dfrac{11}{12}$ (c) $\dfrac{1}{42}$ (d) $1\dfrac{7}{24}$ (e) $1\dfrac{65}{168}$

5. (a) $\dfrac{19}{24}$ (b) $4\dfrac{7}{12}$ (c) $2\dfrac{13}{24}$ 6. $1\dfrac{5}{6}$ metres 7. $6\dfrac{9}{20}$ 8. $6\dfrac{65}{66}$ 9. $10\dfrac{77}{120}$ m

EXERCISE 33

1. $2\dfrac{1}{2}$ 2. $2\dfrac{2}{3}$ 3. $4\dfrac{2}{3}$ 4. $3\dfrac{3}{5}$ 5. $6\dfrac{2}{3}$ 6. $10\dfrac{1}{2}$ 7. $5\dfrac{4}{7}$ 8. $13\dfrac{2}{9}$

9. $8\dfrac{2}{5}$ 10. 15 11. $29\dfrac{1}{3}$ 12. $87\dfrac{1}{2}$ 13. $107\dfrac{1}{2}$ 14. $86\dfrac{2}{3}$ 15. 274 16. $69\dfrac{1}{3}$

EXERCISE 34

1. $\dfrac{15}{28}$ 2. $\dfrac{3}{4}$ 3. $\dfrac{8}{45}$ 4. $1\dfrac{2}{5}$ 5. $3\dfrac{1}{2}$ 6. $2\dfrac{4}{7}$ 7. $1\dfrac{1}{2}$ 8. $69\dfrac{1}{3}$

9. $13\dfrac{1}{3}$ 10. $47\dfrac{1}{4}$ 11. $19\dfrac{4}{5}$ 12. $15\dfrac{3}{4}$ 13. $7\dfrac{1}{2}$ 14. $63\dfrac{3}{4}$ 15. $7\dfrac{1}{2}$ 16. 36

17. 60 18. 117 19. $\dfrac{1}{15}$ 20. 9

EXERCISE 35

1. Rs $43\dfrac{4}{5}$ 2. 978 kg 3. Rs 52 4. Rs $236\dfrac{1}{2}$ 5. 54 m 6. Rs 868 7. $13\dfrac{1}{8}$ km 8. 415 litres

9. $22\dfrac{1}{2}$ litres 10. 4250 km 11. 26 m 12. $160\dfrac{1}{2}$ meters

EXERCISE 36

1. $\dfrac{1}{6}$ 2. $\dfrac{1}{63}$ 3. $\dfrac{4}{7}$ 4. $\dfrac{2}{5}$ 5. $\dfrac{2}{5}$ 6. $\dfrac{5}{8}$ 7. $1\dfrac{3}{5}$ 8. 42

9. 16 10. 32 11. 54 12. 36 13. 60 kg 14. 6 15. 35 16. 2 km

17. 21 18. $\dfrac{1}{4}$

COMPOSITE MATHEMATICS – 5

313

EXERCISE 37

1. (a) $\dfrac{5}{3}$ (b) $\dfrac{16}{9}$ (c) 8   (d) $\dfrac{19}{10}$ (e) $\dfrac{1}{15}$ (f) $\dfrac{7}{12}$ (g) $\dfrac{13}{24}$ (h) $\dfrac{7}{20}$

(i) $\dfrac{14}{51}$ (j) $\dfrac{8}{53}$ (k) 1   (l) does not exist

2. $\dfrac{2}{7}$ 3. $\dfrac{1}{36}$ 4. $\dfrac{2}{3}$ 5. $\dfrac{8}{15}$ 6. $1\dfrac{1}{6}$ 7. $\dfrac{7}{10}$ 8. $\dfrac{1}{12}$ 9. $1\dfrac{3}{4}$

10. 6   11. 3   12. 28   13. $10\dfrac{2}{3}$ 14. $4\dfrac{1}{3}$ 15. $7\dfrac{1}{2}$ 16. $1\dfrac{4}{5}$ 17. $\dfrac{5}{12}$

18. $\dfrac{7}{20}$ 19. $\dfrac{13}{40}$ 20. $\dfrac{13}{20}$ 21. $\dfrac{1}{8}$

EXERCISE 38

1. Rs $32\dfrac{4}{5}$ 2. Rs $52\dfrac{4}{5}$ 3. 18   4. $12\dfrac{3}{4}$ litres   5. $60\dfrac{3}{4}$ km   6. $10\dfrac{1}{2}$ kg   7. 16   8. $2\dfrac{1}{8}$ m

9. $5\dfrac{3}{5}$ cm   10. $\dfrac{7}{19}$

C.C.E. DRILL - 8

QUESTION BAG - 1

1. (a)   2. (b)   3. (a)   4. (b)   5. (c)   6. (b)   7. (d)

QUESTION BAG - 2

1. (a) 25   (b) 8   (c) 20   (d) 375   (e) 440   (f) 28

2. (a) 0   (b) $\dfrac{6}{7}$ (c) 1   (d) $\dfrac{3}{11}$ (e) 0   (f) $\dfrac{3}{2}$ (g) 0   (h) 3

(i) 25   (j) 121   (k) 5   (l) 4   (m) $\dfrac{5}{3}$ (n) $\dfrac{25}{36}$ (o) not possible   (p) 63

3. (a) 6   (b) 2   (c) 9   (d) 5

4. (a) $6\dfrac{2}{9}$ (b) $6\dfrac{1}{8}$ (c) $84\dfrac{3}{20}$ (d) $7\dfrac{2}{3}$ (e) $11\dfrac{9}{10}$

5. (a) $\dfrac{11}{103}$ (b) $\dfrac{8}{21}$ (c) $\dfrac{10}{153}$ 6. (a) $7\dfrac{7}{8}$ (b) 5   (c) $2\dfrac{1}{2}$

7. 96 m   8. $81\dfrac{3}{5}$ km   9. $31\dfrac{1}{2}$ 10. $2\dfrac{3}{5}$ 11. $\dfrac{3}{4}$ 12. $10\dfrac{1}{2}$ km   13. $\dfrac{5}{8}$ m   14. $14\dfrac{122}{183}$

15. (a) $\dfrac{3}{5}$ (b) 18   (c) 25   (d) 1   (e) proper   (f) 1   (g) 5   (h) reciprocal

16. (a) True   (b) False   (c) False   (d) False   (e) True   (f) True   (g) False   (h) False

EXERCISE 39

1. (a) sixteen point two three
   (c) eighty-six point zero four seven
   (e) one point zero one
   (g) thirty point one zero eight
   (b) decimal eight seven one
   (d) one hundred three point zero zero five
   (f) two thousand three hundred five point six one
   (h) one hundred forty point zero six two

2. (a) 35.65   (b) 108.07   (c) 6.932   (d) 0.503   (e) 340.9   (f) 416.106   (g) 3006.009   (h) 200.12

3. (a)

Digit	2	3	7	6	4	1
Place Value	200	30	7	$\frac{6}{10}$	$\frac{4}{100}$	$\frac{1}{1000}$

(b)

Digit	2	9	0	5	3
Place Value	20	9	0	$\frac{5}{100}$	$\frac{3}{1000}$

(c)

Digit	8	2	0	4
Place Value	8	$\frac{2}{10}$	0	$\frac{4}{100}$

(d)

Digit	2	0	3	5	6	4	7
Place Value	2000	0	30	5	$\frac{6}{10}$	$\frac{4}{100}$	$\frac{7}{1000}$

4. (a) $19.35 = 10 + 9 + \frac{3}{10} + \frac{5}{100}$

(b) $23.04 = 20 + 3 + \frac{4}{100}$

(c) $137.506 = 100 + 30 + 7 + \frac{5}{10} + \frac{6}{1000}$

(d) $0.613 = \frac{6}{10} + \frac{1}{100} + \frac{3}{1000}$

(e) $8.137 = 8 + \frac{1}{10} + \frac{3}{100} + \frac{7}{1000}$

(f) $2605.034 = 2000 + 600 + 5 + \frac{3}{100} + \frac{4}{1000}$

(f) $0.008 = \frac{8}{1000}$

(g) $407.65 = 400 + 7 + \frac{6}{10} + \frac{5}{100}$

5. (a) 27. 36   (b) 436. 135   (c) 40.834   (d) 507.023   (e) 3201.607   (f) 609.706

EXERCISE 40

1. (a) 9.50, 102.86   (b) 4.80, 6.06   (c) 0.300, 1.457   (d) 48.001, 7.140, 3.900
   (e) 101.010, 19.708, 10.600   (f) 0.500, 5.700, 17.716

2. (a) <   (b) <   (c) <   (d) >   (e) >   (f) <   (g) =   (h) <
   (i) <   (j) >   (k) >   (l) <

3. (a) 0.01, 0.06, 0.1, 0.34, 0.61   (b) 2.109, 2.901, 2.91, 3.005, 3.05, 4.03   (c) 0.78, 0.82, 1.28, 1.8, 2.08, 2.8
   (d) 1.001, 1.01, 1.1, 10.001, 10.01, 10.1   (e) 77.9, 78.8, 78.89, 87.88, 87.9, 87.98   (f) 0.003, 0.03, 0.3, 3.03, 30.03, 30.3
   (g) 3.4, 3.47, 3.74, 4.37, 4.7, 4.73

4. (a) 1.1, 1.01, 0.1, 0.01, 0.001   (b) 3.1, 3.01, 2.3, 2.03, 0.75, 0.57   (c) 2.13, 2.1, 2.01, 1.93, 1.9, 1.87
   (d) 55.55, 55.5, 55.05, 5.55, 5.5, 5.05   (e) 6.6, 6.06, 6.006, 0.66, 0.6, 0.06   (f) 2.22, 2.2, 2.021, 2.02, 2.012, 2.002
   (g) 2.6, 2.06, 2.006, 1.9, 1.09, 1.009

EXERCISE 41

1. (a) 12.21   (b) 52.12   (c) 50.05   (d) 310.19   (e) 508.94   (f) 175.407
2. (a) 131.255   (b) 282.36   (c) 1051.179   (d) 3612.56   (e) 470.446   (f) 103.477
3. (a) 515.296   (b) 217.092   (c) 273.079   (d) 339.021   (e) 1634.976
4. (a) 3.17   (b) 5.85   (c) 47.77   (d) 2.776   (e) 87.239   (f) 177.549
5. (a) 13.87   (b) 38.4   (c) 46.64   (d) 9.56   (e) 57.906   (f) 79.86   (g) 64.916   (h) 17.995
6. (a) 8.44   (b) 428.52   (c) 263.4   (d) 863.675   (e) 556.087   (f) 158.567
7. (a) 40.491   (b) 112.82   (c) 56.961   (d) 325.97
8. 14.16   9. 18.54   10. 81.2   11. 6.214   12. 24.544   13. Rs 20.85   14. 35.75 litres

EXERCISE 42

1. $\frac{3}{10}$ 2. $\frac{3}{5}$ 3. $\frac{7}{20}$ 4. $\frac{69}{200}$ 5. $4\frac{4}{5}$ 6. $7\frac{3}{100}$ 7. $2\frac{3}{4}$ 8. $8\frac{1}{100}$

9. $6\frac{1}{20}$ 10. $8\frac{3}{25}$ 11. $16\frac{1}{4}$ 12. $9\frac{1}{200}$ 13. $4\frac{11}{25}$ 14. $4\frac{111}{250}$ 15. $70\frac{5}{8}$ 16. $92\frac{17}{20}$

17. $65\frac{3}{4}$ 18. $12\frac{3}{8}$ 19. $24\frac{3}{200}$ 20. $45\frac{27}{50}$ 21. 1.9   22. 3.47   23. 1.057   24. 30.18

25. 19.035   26. 0.25   27. 0.4   28. 0.875   29. 0.9375   30. 3.75   31. 4.625   32. 6.15

33. 8.04   34. 9.24   35. 0.064   36. 7.152   37. 0.492   38. 6.34   39. 0.925

40. 2.475   41. 0.694   42. 18.6   43. 16.375   44. 26.95

EXERCISE 43

1. 293.6 2. 1129.23 3. 2130.75 4. 3945.68 5. 771.282 6. 586.95 7. 1190.508 8. 287.946
9. 2006.22 10. 37.881 11. 16716.7 12. 28427.5 13. 175.4 14. 476.53 15. 895 16. 0.7
17. 0.08 18. 1032.4 19. 4975.2 20. 7212 21. 850 22. 1 23. 7450 24. 3910
25. 7935 26. 79360 27. 145800 28. 16030 29. 3 30. 600

EXERCISE 44

1. 1.35 2. 0.24 3. 0.078 4. 4.626 5. 129.086 6. 417.095 7. 336.7553 8. 555.1232
9. 63.65748 10. 220.5522 11. 66.26064 12. 114.21042 13. 14.93625 14. 318.0288 15. 1.028415 16. 0.18018
17. 0.22757 18. 0.002925 19. 0.030015 20. 0.02925 21. 0.00001 22. 0.168 23. 0.3519 24. 0.008
25. 84.456 26. 8.5116 27. 0.3243 28. (a) 953.42 (b) 9.5342 (c) 0.95342 (d) 0.095342

EXERCISE 45

1. Rs 221.60 2. Rs 905.25 3. Rs 387.45 4. 546 kg 5. 775.2 kg 6. 97800 kg 7. 610.2 litres 8. 11.83 kg
9. Rs 45206.50 10. Rs 105.60 11. 2.814 kg 12. 1062.5 km 13. 469.2 km 14. Rs 34425 15. 76.26 kg

EXERCISE 46

1. 8.3 2. 6.1 3. 3.4 4. 5.06 5. 7.368 6. 7.163 7. 61.247 8. 16.95
9. 12.08 10. 5.76 11. 0.48 12. 0.43 13. 0.008 14. 0.0002 15. 0.07 16. 0.032
17. 0.142 18. 0.545 19. 0.345 20. 0.0176 21. 0.0715 22. 0.0265 23. 0.075 24. 0.008

EXERCISE 47

1. 2.364 2. 0.576 3. 0.0347 4. 0.005 5. 3.173 6. 0.9587 7. 0.08923 8. 0.00769
9. 0.0008 10. 1.3428 11. 0.47635 12. 0.0389 13. 0.0069342 14. 10.12 15. 13.46 16. 7.921
17. 0.24 18. 1.178 19. 0.0256 20. 0.0452 21. 0.0052 22. 0.0015 23. 0.0929 24. 0.0365

EXERCISE 48

1. 5.4 2. 0.37 3. 0.056 4. 1.45 5. 16.93 6. 11.38 7. 17.56 8. 0.6
9. 2.31 10. 13.4 11. 61.2 12. 0.08 13. 0.0546 14. 9 15. 6.9 16. 12
17. 0.9 18. 0.004 19. 0.006 20. 0.008 21. 7060, 70.6
22. (a) 140 (b) 0.19 (c) 0.274 (d) 0.15

EXERCISE 49

1. 60 2. 1100 3. 500 4. 30 5. 1.2 6. 1680 7. 15 8. 8
9. 0.2 10. 0.375 11. 1.75 12. 0.0625 13. 0.4375 14. 0.875 15. 2.375 16. 0.525
17. 0.85 18. 3.35 19. 16.32 20. 8.225 21. 9.45 22. 0.46875

EXERCISE 50

1. Rs 15.65 2. Rs 14.85 per kg 3. Rs 68.60 4. 98.5 kg 5. 29 6. 8.5 litres 7. Rs 68.50
8. Rs 48 9. 25 10. 2.25 m 11. 40 12. 26 13. 89.45 km 14. 14.85

C.C.E. DRILL - 9

QUESTION BAG - 1

1. (a) 2. (c) 3. (c) 4. (a) 5. (b) 6. (c) 7. (b) 8. (a)
9. (b) 10. (c) 11. (a) 12. (d) 13. (a) 14. (d) 15. (d) 16. (a)
17. (b)

QUESTION BAG - 2

1. (a) 2.67   (b) 1.94   (c) 2.54

2. (a) 1.9, 2.0, 2.1   (b) 9.010, 9.011, 9.012   (c) 6.998, 6.999, 7.000

3. (a) Decimal expansion : $5.729 = 5 + 0.7 + 0.02 + 0.009$
   Fractional expansion : $5.729 = 5 + \dfrac{7}{10} + \dfrac{2}{100} + \dfrac{9}{1000}$

   (b) Decimal expansion : $67.054 = 60 + 7 + 0.05 + 0.004$
   Fractional expansion : $67.054 = 60 + 7 + \dfrac{5}{100} + \dfrac{4}{1000}$

   (c) Decimal expansion : $875.99 = 800 + 70 + 5 + 0.9 + 0.09$
   Fractional expansion : $875.99 = 800 + 70 + 5 + \dfrac{9}{10} + \dfrac{9}{100}$

   (d) Decimal expansion : $48.03 = 40 + 8 + 0.03$
   Fractional expansion : $48.03 = 40 + 8 + \dfrac{3}{100}$

4. (a) <   (b) >   (c) <   (d) <   (e) <   (f) >

5. (a) 0.06, 0.066, 0.6, 0.606, 0.66, 0.666
   (b) 6.023, 6.032, 6.203, 6.23, 6.302, 6.32
   (c) 60.88, 66.08, 66.8, 66.88, 68.06, 68.66

6. (a) >   (b) >   (c) >   (d) <

7. 54.13

8. (a) hundredths   (b) $\dfrac{7}{10}$ (c) two   (d) 10,100,1000   (e) three   (f) 0.5   (g) three   (h) $\dfrac{3}{4}$
   (i) 0.75   (j) $1\dfrac{16}{25}$ (k) 0.001

9. (a) False   (b) False   (c) False   (d) True   (e) False   (f) True   (g) False   (h) True
   (i) False

10. (a) 45.5   (b) 1.856   (c) 0.054   (d) 82.575

11. (a) 10   (b) 1000   (c) 100   (d) 100   (e) 1000   (f) 1000   (g) 0   (h) 3.874
    (i) 0.093   (j) 6.37   (k) 0.000069   (l) 0.000707

12. (a) 0.06   (b) 0.2   (c) 0.007   (d) 0.0048   (e) 0.9   (f) 1   (g) 0.45   (h) 0.0001

13. (a) 0.12   (b) 1.65   (c) 0.586   (d) 0.5212   (e) 112   (f) 1586

14. (a) 1.375   (b) 0.48   (c) 2.4

15. (a) 2.5   (b) 0.5   (c) 0.75   (d) 1.25   (e) 1.5   (f) 0.95   (g) 5.5   (h) 4
    (i) 10   (j) 4   (k) 2   (l) 4   (m) 4   (n) 3.3

16. (a) 100   (b) 10   (c) 100   (d) 1000   (e) 414.7   (f) 0.000101

EXERCISE 51

1. (a) 80   (b) 480   (c) 880   (d) 4230   (e) 20310   (f) 34900   (g) 105410   (h) 208980

2. (a) 400   (b) 900   (c) 5700   (d) 7100   (e) 16300   (f) 48800   (g) 110100   (h) 218700

3. (a) 6000   (b) 9000   (c) 13000   (d) 27000   (e) 219000   (f) 576000   (g) 1036000   (h) 1867000

4. (a) 10000   (b) 20000   (c) 20000   (d) 20000   (e) 350000   (f) 150000   (g) 460000   (h) 1570000

5. (a) 100000   (b) 300000   (c) 500000   (d) 800000   (e) 1100000   (f) 1400000   (g) 17000000   (h) 21400000

6. (a) 2000000   (b) 2000000   (c) 7000000   (d) 7000000   (e) 3000000   (f) 16000000   (g) 37000000   (h) 54000000

7. (a) 60000000   (b) 40000000   (c) 100000000   (d) 70000000   (e) 80000000   (f) 110000000

8. (a) 136472510   (b) 136472500   (c) 136473000   (d) 136470000   (e) 136500000   (f) 140000000

9. (a) 90000000   (b) 85600000   (c) 85643000   10. (a) 65 to 74   (b) 135 to 144   (c) 985 to 994   (d) 2345 to 2354

11. (a) 850 to 949   (b) 1550 to 1649   (c) 5250 to 5349   (d) 32450 to 32549

12. (a) 8500 to 9499   (b) 17500 to 18499   (c) 26500 to 27499

EXERCISE 52

1. (a) 6   (b) 3   (c) 5   (d) 17   (e) 14   (f) 38   (g) 10   (h) 77

2. (a) 3.7   (b) 8.4   (c) 9.7   (d) 10.3   (e) 24.8   (f) 32.3   (g) 86.8   (h) 102.4

3. (a) 0.71   (b) 5.24   (c) 11.42   (d) 17.89   (e) 26.68   (f) 47.85   (g) 53.15   (h) 103.77

4. (a) 0.789   (b) 2.164   (c) 78.473   (d) 19.015   (e) 32.404   (f) 123.004

5. (a) 0.26   (b) 1.36   (c) 0.22   (d) 0.38   (e) 1.10   (f) 5.07

6. (a) 0.385   (b) 0.857   (c) 0.455   (d) 0.462   (e) 0.867   (f) 3.364   (g) 2.706   (h) 10.667

7. (a) Numbers greater than or equal to 10.5 but less than 11.5
   (b) Numbers greater than or equal to 16.5 but less than 17.5
   (c) Numbers greater than or equal to 19.5 but less than 20.5
   (d) Numbers greater than or equal to 45.5 but less than 46.5

C.C.E. DRILL - 10

QUESTION BAG - 1

1. (c)   2. (d)   3. (b)   4. (d)   5. (c)   6. (c)   7. (b)   8. (a)
9. (c)   10. (a)   11. (c)   12. (c)   13. (b)   14. (c)   15. (b)

QUESTION BAG - 2

1. (a) 10 (b) 60 (c) 600 (d) 6300 (e) 44000 (f) 82000 (g) 360000 (h) 1800000
2. (a) True (b) True (c) False (d) True (e) False (f) True (g) True (h) True
(i) False (j) True (k) False

EXERCISE 53

1. (a) 8000 m (b) 9400 m (c) 3750 m (d) 16024 m 2. (a) 7564 m (b) 3840 m (c) 6600 m (d) 456 m
3. (a) 900 cm (b) 760 cm (c) 236 cm (d) 8000 cm 4. (a) 60 hm (b) 530 dam (c) 463 dam (d) 250 dm
5. (a) 234 mm (b) 4100 mm (c) 5630 mm (d) 3428 mm 6. (a) 3042 m (b) 806 cm (c) 66 mm (d) 4040 mm
7. (a) 5 km 30 m (b) 6 hm 4 dam (c) 16 m 40 cm (d) 80 m 5 dm 8. (a) 12034 m (b) 50009 m (c) 625 mm (d) 708 cm

EXERCISE 54

1. (a) 0.8 cm (b) 0.65 m (c) 1.6 m (d) 0.08 m 2. (a) 0.864 km (b) 2.375 km (c) 0.058 km (d) 0.009 km
3. (a) 5.6 cm (b) 26.8 cm 4. (a) 6.65 m (b) 35.28 m (c) 8.05 m (d) 60.06 m
5. (a) 8.275 km (b) 24.065 km (c) 36.01 km (d) 6.00504 km
6. (a) 0.015 hm (b) 0.48 m 7. 90.08 m 8. 800.8 m 9. 4000.095 m

EXERCISE 55

1. 50 km 418 m 2. 22 km 8 m 3. 15 km 660 m 4. 93 m 62 cm
5. 41 m 79 cm 6. 16 m 7. 7 km 2 hm 8. 6 km 412 m
9. 7 km 964 m 10. 5 km 998 m 11. 3 m 15 cm 12. 8 m 82 cm
13. 25 km 303 m 14. 2 m 65 cm 15. 21 m 16. 21 km 400 m
17. 3.4 m 18. 42.5 km per hour

EXERCISE 56

1. (a) 4000 g (b) 8500 g (c) 2840 g (d) 3560 g
2. (a) 13235 g (b) 9085 g (c) 5300 g (d) 850 g
3. (a) 6345 g (b) 7690 g (c) 5600 g (d) 856 g
4. (a) 90 hg (b) 650 dag (c) 591 dag (d) 420 dg
5. (a) 2036 g (b) 6008 g (c) 5000005 mg (d) 5050 mg
6. (a) 6 kg 250 g (b) 7 hg 5 dag (c) 50 g 8 dg (d) 18 g 30 cg
7. (a) 6.34 kg (b) 5.46 kg (c) 0.536 g (d) 0.023 g
8. (a) 4.075 kg (b) 7.95 kg (c) 9.005 kg (d) 16.065 g (e) 6.635 g (f) 53.008 g

EXERCISE 57

1. 23 kg 465 g 2. 18 kg 375 g 3. 27 kg 780 g 4. 134 g 650 mg
5. 108 g 108 mg 6. 1 kg 888 g 7. 8 kg 125 g 8. 1 kg 994 g
9. 1 kg 985 g 10. 23 kg 670 g 11. Nisha, 3 kg 585 g 12. 34 kg 575 g
13. 205 kg 200 g 14. 8 kg 750 g

EXERCISE 58

1. (a) 8000 ml (b) 3360 ml (c) 6250 l (d) 56 l 2. (a) 65345 l (b) 5035 l (c) 36005 l
3. (a) 8375 ml (b) 37065 ml (c) 15006 ml 4. (a) 2800 l (b) 6375 (c) 8050 ml
5. (a) 6.125 l (b) 18.046 l (c) 120.00 6. (a) 8.625 kl (b) 50.06 kl (c) 30.005 kl
7. (a) 3.56 l (b) 0.068 l (c) 0.009 l

EXERCISE 59

1. 54 l 763 ml 2. 128 l 166 ml 3. 183 l 21 ml 4. 183 kl 412 ml
5. 151 kl 613 ml 6. 17 kl 110 ml 7. 36 l 735 ml 8. 37 l 375 ml
9. 33 l 185 ml 10. 23 kl 704 l 11. 62 kl 918 ml 12. 4 kl 733 l
13. 17 l 14. 10 l 15. 46 l 250 ml 16. 15 l 635 ml
17. 75 kg 340 g; 17 kg 390 g 18. 10.5 l 19. 19 l 400 ml 20. 1.5 litres 21. 40

C.C.E. DRILL - 11

QUESTION BAG - 1

1. (c) 2. (b) 3. (c) 4. (c) 5. (d) 6. (c) 7. (a) 8. (d)

9. (c) 10. (c) 11. (d) 12. (a) 13. (c)

QUESTION BAG - 2

1. (a) 100 (b) 100 (c) 10 (d) 10 (e) 10 (f) 100 (g) 1000000 (h) 10000
   (i) 10 (j) 1000

2. (a) 0.001 (b) 0.01 (c) 0.1 (d) 0.01 (e) 100 (f) 0.01 (g) 0.1 (h) 0.1
   (i) 0.001 (j) 0.001 (k) 0.01 (l) 0.01

3. (a) 686000 (b) 37.5 (c) 0.063 (d) 0.79 (e) 93780 (f) 0.0001 (g) 3330 (h) 6050
   (i) 0.038 (j) 0.00096 (k) 8.6 (l) 0.0356 (m) 5550 (n) 0.0037

4. (a) 5.7 (b) 9.05 (c) 10.084 (d) 20.02 (e) 7.096 (f) 15.064 (g) 460 (h) 968
   (i) 160.016

5. (a) 9 mm (b) 4 km 544 m (c) 7 m 64 cm (d) 5 g 375 mg (e) 8 kg 864 g (f) 23 l 275 ml

6. (a) False (b) False (c) True (d) True (e) False

7. (a) 0.23004 km (b) 48.3 km (c) 0.000396 km (d) 0.00063 km (e) 0.070359 km

8. (a) 3.84 g (b) 0.345 g (c) 46.6 g   9. 158

EXERCISE 60

1. 132. 2. 7.9 3. $5\frac{9}{10}$ 4. 5 5. 55 6. 12 7. 30 8. 10.5 9. 122 runs

10. Rs 735 11. 66 km per hour 12. 15 years 4 months 13. 15 m 14. Rs 9000

EXERCISE 61

1. (a) $\frac{7}{20}$ (b) $\frac{12}{25}$ (c) $\frac{18}{25}$ (d) $\frac{21}{25}$ (e) $\frac{3}{40}$ (f) $\frac{1}{12}$ (g) $\frac{1}{6}$ (h) $\frac{3}{8}$
   (i) $\frac{27}{20}$ (j) $\frac{9}{4}$ (k) $\frac{1}{50}$ (l) $\frac{12}{125}$

2. (a) 0.23 (b) 0.72 (c) 0.06 (d) 0.1 (e) 0.356 (f) 1.04 (g) 1.8 (h) 2.35
   (i) 0.045 (j) 0.0625 (k) 0.003 (l) 0.0025

3. (a) 23% (b) 9% (c) 70% (d) 25% (e) $12\frac{1}{2}$% (f) 40 % (g) 15% (h) 45%
   (i) 72% (j) 54% (k) $56\frac{1}{4}$% (l) $92\frac{1}{2}$% (m) $66\frac{2}{3}$% (n) 220% (o) 325% (p) 270%

4. (a) 80% (b) 25% (c) 76% (d) 6% (e) 32.5% (f) 0.4% (g) 105% (h) 420%

5. (a) 42 (b) 18 (c) 56 (d) 54 (e) 88 (f) 48 (g) $6\frac{3}{10}$ (h) $\frac{63}{100}$
   (i) $2\frac{1}{4}$

6. (a) Rs 14 (b) 28 kg (c) 105 g (d) Rs 7.50 (e) $7\frac{1}{5}$ months or 219 days (f) 5 cm (g) 80 ml
   (h) 160 g (i) 100 ml

7. (a) 25% (b) 20% (c) 80% (d) $62\frac{1}{2}$% (e) 70% (f) 50%

8. (a) 45% (b) 20% (c) 40% (d) 15% (e) 30% (f) 9%

9. 175 10. 135 11. 28 12. Rs 125 13. 150 cm 14. 1250 g 15. 14, 21 16. Rs 2700

17. 48% 18. Zinc = 117g, Copper = 208 g

EXERCISE 62

1. (a) 6 : 40 a.m. (b) 1 : 30 p.m. (c) 0 : 20 a.m. (d) 12 : 06 p.m. (e) 12 : 56 p.m. (f) 2 : 38 p.m. (g) 4 : 24 p.m. (h) 0 : 00 a.m.
   (i) 11 : 47 p.m. (j) 9 : 39 p.m. (k) 1 : 54 p.m. (l) 8 : 00 p.m.

2. (a) 0405 hours (b) 2332 hours (c) 0008 hours (d) 0046 hours (e) 1215 hours (f) 1418 hours (g) 2200 hours (h) 0058 hours
   (i) 1258 hours (j) 0110 hours (k) 0230 hours (l) 2130 hours

3. (a) 12 : 10 p.m (b) 0 : 45 a.m (c) 8 : 00 p.m 4. (a) 4 : 10 p.m. (b) 0 : 46 a.m. (c) 12 : 05 p.m. (d) 11:05 p.m.

1. (a) 192 hours   (b) 408 hours   (c) 163 hours   (d) 342 hours   (e) 275 hours
2. (a) 600 minutes   (b) 536 minutes   (c) 1003 minutes   (d) 5065 minutes
   (e) 2880 minutes
3. (a) 540 seconds   (b) 414 seconds   (c) 816 seconds   (d) 12316 seconds
   (e) 18305 seconds
4. (a) 48 months   (b) 70 months   (c) 176 months
5. (a) 41 days   (b) 60 days   (c) 302 days   (d) 730 days   (e) 1215 days
6. (a) 2 hours 17 minutes   (b) 6 hours 25 minutes   (c) 17 hours 3 minutes   (d) 33 hours 26 minutes
7. (a) 22 minutes 34 seconds   (b) 35 minutes 5 seconds   (c) 54 minutes 28 seconds
8. (a) 3 days 1 hour   (b) 8 days 8 hours   (c) 22 days 1 hour   (d) 42 days 8 hours
9. (a) 32 weeks 6 days   (b) 48 weeks 5 days   (c) 57 weeks 1 day

EXERCISE 64

1. (a) 6 days 6 hours   (b) 21 days   (c) 10 weeks 2 days
2. (a) 9 hours 50 minutes   (b) 15 hours 40 minutes   (c) 25 hours   (d) 13 hours
3. (a) 14 minutes 45 seconds   (b) 22 minutes 25 seconds   (c) 36 minutes   (d) 24 minutes 25 seconds
4. (a) 2 days 8 hours   (b) 3 days 16 hours   (c) 2 days 18 hours   (d) 1 week 4 days
5. (a) 2 hours 15 minutes   (b) 2 hours 44 minutes   (c) 6 hours 52 minutes   (d) 14 hours 20 minutes
6. (a) 4 minutes 8 seconds   (b) 11 minutes 29 seconds   (c) 12 minutes 48 seconds   (d) 2 minutes 12 seconds
7. 5 years 3 months   8. 11 : 20 p.m.   9. 4 : 10 a.m   10. 10 : 30 a.m   11. 9 : 50 a.m   12. 7 hours 45 minutes

EXERCISE 65

1. 7 hours 25 minutes   2. 10 hours 30 minutes   3. 11 hours 40 minutes   4. 2 days 18 hours 50 minutes
5. 4 years 4 months 26 days   6. 70 days   7. 27 years 7 months   8. Amit, 4 years 10 months 23 days

C.C.E. DRILL - 12

QUESTION BAG - 1

1. (c)   2. (c)   3. (c)   4. (d)   5. (b)   6. (c)   7. (a)   8. (c)
9. (c)   10. (c)   11. (d)

QUESTION BAG - 2

1. (a) 1 : 10 p.m   (b) 3 : 35 a.m   (c) 4 : 05 a.m   (d) 1 : 25 p.m   (e) 9 : 40 p.m   (f) 4 : 50 a.m
2. (a) 1822 hours   (b) 1310 hours   (c) 0 : 52 a.m   (d) 11 : 16 p.m   (e) 1905 hours   (f) 1233 hours   (g) 9:25 p.m   (h) 6 : 18 p.m
3. 12th January   4. 7 : 10 p.m   5. 19 hours 15 minutes
6. (a) 17 hr 42 min   (b) 25 hr 11 min 40 sec   (c) 13 hr 24 min 27 sec   (d) 3 hr 57 min 44 sec
7. (a) 16 years 5 months   (b) 51 days 13 hours
8. (a) 7 min 46 sec   (b) 9 days 16 hours   (c) 26 years 8 months
9. (a) 19 days 12 hours   (b) 14 weeks 3 days   (c) 47 years 3 months   (d) 12 hours 15 minutes
   (e) 14 minutes 27 seconds   (f) 205 minutes   (g) 569 seconds   (h) 23760 seconds
   (i) 135 hours   (j) 91 months   (k) 39 days

EXERCISE 66

1. (a) 856 paise   (b) 9267 paise   (c) 12305 paise   (d) 7070 paise
   (e) 84 paise   (f) 3 paise   (g) 10 paise   (h) 9 paise
2. (a) 3685 paise   (b) 606 paise   (c) 3750 paise   (d) 1925 paise
   (e) 2375 paise
3. (a) Rs 83.65   (b) Rs 70.00   (c) Rs 8.74   (d) Rs 7.08
   (e) Rs 1.04   (f) Re 0.92   (g) Re 0.16   (h) Re 0.09
   (i) Re 0.02

EXERCISE 67

1. Rs 82.50　　2. Rs 113.60　3. Rs 109.45　4. Rs 422.10　5. Rs 579.10　6. Rs 16.68　7. Rs 26.06　8. Rs 7.18
9. Rs 55.15　　10. Rs 197　　11. Rs 294.15　12. Rs 41.75　13. Rs 314.35

EXERCISE 68

1. Rs 115.60　2. Rs 1295.70　3. Rs 1655.52　4. Rs 4880.80　5. Rs 4833.72　6. Rs 3207.40　7. Rs 12.70　8. Rs 25.75
9. Rs 47.05　10. Rs 16.25　11. Rs 381.60　12. Rs 3714　13. Rs 644.40　14. Rs 16.50　15. Rs 53.05　16. Rs 38.50

EXERCISE 69

1. (c)　　2. (b)　　3. (a)　　4. (b)　　5. (b)　　7. 1 - (C), 2 -(B), 3 - (F) , 4 - (A), 5 - (D), 6 - (E)
8. (a) one　　(b) no　　(c) cannot　　(d) definite　　(e) definite
9. (a) Line segments: $\overline{BC}$; Rays : $\overrightarrow{BA}$, $\overrightarrow{CD}$　　(b) Line segments : $\overline{DE}$, $\overline{EF}$, $\overline{DF}$; Rays : $\overrightarrow{DG}$, $\overrightarrow{EH}$, $\overrightarrow{FI}$
   (c) Line segments : $\overline{ON}$, $\overline{OP}$; Rays : $\overrightarrow{NM}$, $\overrightarrow{PQ}$

EXERCISE 70

1. (a), (c)
2. (a) ∠PRQ ; Vertex: R; Arms: $\overrightarrow{RP}$, $\overrightarrow{RQ}$　　　　(b) ∠DCE; Vertex : C; Arms: $\overrightarrow{CD}$, $\overrightarrow{CE}$
   (c) ∠PQR; Vertex: Q; Arms: $\overrightarrow{QP}$, $\overrightarrow{QR}$　　　(d) ∠LMN; Vertex: M; Arms: $\overrightarrow{ML}$, $\overrightarrow{MN}$
3. (a) 3; ∠OAB, ∠BAC, ∠OAC　　　　　　　　(b) 6; ∠DEF, ∠FEG, ∠GEH, ∠DEG, ∠FEH, ∠DEH
4. (a) ∠BAC, ∠ABC, ∠BCA, ∠DCA, ∠DAC, ∠ADC, ∠DAB, ∠DCB　　(b) ∠XYZ, ∠YZX, ∠YXZ
   (c) ∠PQR, ∠QRS, ∠RST, ∠STV, ∠TVP, ∠VPQ　　5. (a) M, P, O, D, Q　　　(b) X, Y, A, N　　(c) Z, T

EXERCISE 71

2. (a) Obtuse	(b) Acute	(c) Right	(d) Acute	(e) Obtuse	(f) Right		
3. (a) Acute	(b) Right	(c) Obtuse	(d) Acute	(e) Obtuse	(f) Obtuse	(g) Obtuse	(h) Acute
4. (a) No	(b) Yes	(c) No	(d) Yes	(e) No	(f) No	(g) Yes	(h) Yes
5. (a) No	(b) Yes	(c) No	(d) No	(e) Yes	(f) No	(g) Yes	(h) Yes
6. (a) 47°	(b) 34°	(c) 18°	(d) 71°	(e) 63°	(f) 10°	(g) 45°	(h) 5°
7. (a) 150°	(b) 133°	(c) 110°	(d) 165°	(e) 90°	(f) 77°	(g) 96°	(h) 43°
8. (a) vertex	(b) degrees	(c) protractor	(d) 90°	(e) straight			

C.C.E. DRILL - 13

QUESTION BAG - 1

1. (d)　　2. (c)　　3. (c)　　4. (d)　　5. (b)　　6. (c)　　7. (b)　　8. (b)
9. (c)　　10. (c)　　11. (a)　　12. (c)　　13. (c)　　14. (b)

QUESTION BAG - 2

1. (a) common　(b) vertex　(c) degrees　(d) two　(e) acute　(f) reflex　(g) complete　(h) 360°
2. (a) True　(b) False　(c) True　(d) False　(e) True　(f) True
3. (a) No　(b) Yes　(c) Yes　　4. d, c, e, a, b
5. (a) Acute　(b) Right　(c) Acute　(d) Straight　(e) Obtuse　(f) Complementary　(g) Supplementary
6. ∠DOC　　7. ∠DOE　　8. (a) 285°　(b) 200°　(c) 325°　(d) 270°　(e) 215°
9. (a) 40°　(b) 15°　(c) 45°　(d) 115°

EXERCISE 73

1. (a) 12; (AB,CD), (CD, GH), (GH, EF), (EF, AB), (BF, CG), (CG, DH), (DH, AE), (AE, BF), (BC, FG), (FG, EH), (EH, AD), (AD, BC)
   (b) 24
2. (a) intersect　(b) right angle　(c) remains constant

C.C.E. DRILL - 14

QUESTION BAG - 1

1. (d)   2. (c)   3. (c)   4. (a)   5. (c)   6. (a)   7. (b)

QUESTION BAG - 2

1. (a) perpendicular   (b) perpendicular   (c) parallel   (d) parallel   (e) perpendicular
2. (a) True   (b) True   (c) True   3. (a) CD and AB   (b) CD and EF, AC and BD, AD and BC

EXERCISE 74

1. (a) L,M,N   (b) LM, MN, LN   (c) ∠L, ∠M, ∠N
2. (a) Isosceles   (b) Scalene   (c) Scalene   (d) Equilateral   (e) Isosceles   (f) Isosceles
4. (a) No   (b) No   (c) Yes   (d) No   (e) Yes   (f) Yes
5. (a) different   (b) two, equal   (c) equilateral   (d) greater   (e) 60°   (f) different   (g) equal
6. (a) False   (b) True   (c) True   (d) False   (e) True

EXERCISE 75

1. (a) Obtuse-angled   (b) Right-angled   (c) Obtuse-angled   (d) Acute-angled
   (e) Right-angled   (f) Acute-angled
2. (a) 50°   (b) 115°   (c) 83°   (d) 33°   (e) 80°   (f) 35°
3. 80°   4. 83°   5. 40°   6. 55°   7. 60°   8. 64°, 64°, 52°   9. 45°   10. 50°
11. (a) scalene   (b) isosceles   (c) equilateral
12. (a) acute-angled   (b) obtuse-angled   (c) right-angled   (d) obtuse-angled
13. (a) 3   (b) 1   (c) 1
14. (a) No   (b) Yes   (c) Yes   (d) No

C.C.E. DRILL - 15

QUESTION BAG - 1

1. (b)   2. (c)   3. (d)   4. (c)   5. (b)   6. (c)   7. (b)   8. (c)
9. (d)   10. (c)   11. (b)   12. (d)   13. (b)   14. (c)   15. (a)   16. (b)
17. (c)

QUESTION BAG - 2

1. (a) No   (b) No   (c) Yes   2. (a) No   (b) No   (c) Yes
3. (a) non-collinear   (b) 3, 3   (c) different   (d) greater   (e) 180°   (f) 90°   (g) obtuse-angled
4. (a) True   (b) True   (c) True   (d) True   (e) False   (f) True   (g) True
5. (a) 55°   (b) 80°   (c) less than   (d) ∠C   6. (a) No   (b) No   (c) No   (d) Yes
7. 45°   8. (a) 70°   (b) 88°   (c) 80°   (d) 27°
9. (a) No   (b) Yes   (c) No   (d) No   (e) No   (f) Yes
10 (a) Acute-angled   (b) Right-angled   (c) Acute-angled   (d) Obtuse-angled
   (e) Right-angled   (f) Obtuse-angled

EXERCISE 76

1. Radii : OA, OB, OC, OD, OE   Diameters : AB, CD   2. AD, BC, GC, EF, AG
3. (a) chord   (b) diameter   (c) longest   (d) circumference   (e) half   (f) radius   (g) 2   (h) arc
   (i) Half   (j) Radius
5. (a) 8 cm   (b) 7.6 cm   (c) 10.8 cm   (d) 12.2 cm
6. (a) 4.5 cm   (b) 3.9 cm   (c) 4.6 cm   (d) 3.5 cm   7. (a) 44 cm   (b) 39.6 cm   (c) 35.2 cm   (d) 26.4 cm
8. (a) 37.68 cm   (b) 50.24 cm   (c) 28.26 cm   (d) 40.82 cm   9. (a) 3.5 cm   (b) 2.8 cm   (c) 4.9 cm   (d) 12.6 cm
10. (a) 21 cm   (b) 11.2 cm   (c) 9.8 cm
11. (a) exterior of the circle   (b) interior of the circle   (c) exterior of the circle   (d) on the circle
    (e) interior of the circle

QUESTION BAG - 1

1. (c)   2. (c)   3. (c)   4. (c)   5. (d)   6. (b)   7. (d)   8. (c)
9. (a)   10. (a)   11. (a)   12. (d)

QUESTION BAG - 2

1. (a) Centre   (b) Radius   (c) Diameter   (d) Chord   (e) Arc   (f) Radius
2. (a) OA, OB, OC, OD, OP   (b) AB, CD   (c) AB, CD, EF, BC
4. (a) circumference   (b) longest   (c) circumference   (d) interior   (e) exterior   (f) semi-circle
   (g) quadrant   (h) radius   (i) arc
5. (a) False   (b) False   (c) True   (d) False   (e) False   (f) False   (g) False
6. (a) $\frac{1}{2}$ (b) d   (c) 2π

EXERCISE 77

1. (a) 23 cm   (b) 27 cm   (c) 28 cm   2. (a) 19 cm   (b) 19.2 cm   (c) 18.3 cm   (d) 21.8 cm
3. 19.1 cm   4. 25.2 cm   5. 6.6 cm   6. 5.9 cm
7. (a) 1 m 30 cm   (b) 24 m   (c) 9 m   (d) 44 m   8. 20 cm   9. 90 m
10. (a) 180 cm   (b) 64 m   (c) 8 m 40 cm   (d) 13 m   11. 205 m   12. 1 m 80 cm   13. Rs 28600   14. 1140 m
15. 77 m

QUESTION BAG - 1

1 (a)   2. (d)   3. (c)   4. (b)   5. (c)   6. (d)   7. (b)   8. (d)
9. (c)   10. (a)   11. (b)   12. (c)

QUESTION BAG - 2

1. (a) $\vec{AB}, \vec{BC}, \vec{CA}$ (b) length, breadth   (c) perimeter   (d) side   2. Rs 4350   3. 680   4. 5

EXERCISE 78

1. 216 sq. cm   2. 126 sq.m   3. 476 sq. cm   4. 440 sq. cm   5. 1.44 sq. m   6. 1.5 sq. m or 15000 sq. cm   7. 289 sq. cm
8. 529 sq. m   9. 182.25 sq. cm   10. 11.56 sq. m   11. (a) 13 cm   (b) 27 m   (c) 36 cm   (d) 12 m
12. (a) 13 cm   (b) 17 cm   (c) 9 m   (d) 6.5 m   13. 6000   14. 2000   15. 15 m by 13.8 m   16. 260 sq.m
17. (a) 13 sq. cm   (b) 42 sq. cm   (c) 68 sq. cm   (d) 19 sq. cm

QUESTION BAG - 1

1. (b)   2. (b)   3. (d)   4. (c)   5. (c)   6. (c)   7. (b)   8. (c)
9. (a)   10. (a)   11. (b)   12. (b)   13. (c)   14. (b)

QUESTION BAG - 2

1. (a) 10000   (b) Breadth   (c) Length   2. area = 75 sq. m, perimeter = $42\frac{1}{3}$ m   3. $14\frac{5}{9}$ cm
4. (a) Rs 16128   (b) Rs 18360   5. 36   6. 136   7. (a) False   (b) False

EXERCISE 79

1. (a) 1536 cu. cm   (b) 280 cu. m   (c) 585 cu. cm   (d) 12.6 cu. m   (e) 500 cu. m
2. (a) 2744 cu. cm   (b) 42.875 cu. m   (c) 1.728 cu. m   (d) 274.625 cu. cm   3. 23.4 cu. m   4. 68.921 cu. m   5. (a) 468 cu.m   (b) 180
6. 900   7. 4000   8. 30
9. (a) volume   (b) length, breadth, height   (c) side, side, side

C.C.E. DRILL - 19

QUESTION BAG - 1

1. (*d*)　　2. (*c*)　　3. (*d*)　　4. (*b*)　　5. (*b*)　　6. (*c*)　　7. (*d*)　　8. (*d*)
9. (*b*)　　10. (*c*)　　11. (*c*)

QUESTION BAG - 2

1. (*a*) height　　(*b*) 162　　(*c*) 64　　(*d*) 10 cm　　(*e*) 25 m　　(*f*) 1000000 cu. cm
2. 380 cu. cm　　3. 1566.432 cu. cm　　4. 6400　　5. 28

EXERCISE 81

5. (*a*) July　　(*b*) 3 cm　　(*c*) October
6. (*a*) Number of families having a particular number of members　　(*b*) 40　　(*c*) 20